THE BOTTOM LINE BOOK OF FREEBIES

Bottom Line
Books

ISBN 0-88723-249-3

Bottom Line® Books publishes the opinions of expert authorities in
many fields. The use of a book is not a substitute for legal,
accounting or other professional services. Consult competent
professionals for answers to your specific questions.

All information herein was accurate at the time of printing.
Specific offers and prices can and will change frequently.

Bottom Line® Books is a registered trademark of Boardroom® Inc.
55 Railroad Ave., Greenwich, CT 06830

Printed in the United States of America
10 9 8 7 6 5 4 3 2 1

Contents

Contents

Contents

Contents

Contents

Contents

Contents

An Ocean
Of
Free Things

Help for Seniors Is Just a Phone Call Away

Did you know that you can get dozens of services delivered right to your front door? Eldercare Locator will connect you to a wide range of services for seniors no matter where you live in the US. Services include Meals-on-Wheels (for home-delivered meals), legal assistance, help with housing problems, recreation, adult day care, home health care, nursing home ombudsman (to help you get the treatment you deserve) and a whole lot more. Through Eldercare Locator you can tap into a nationwide network of organizations for seniors in all areas of the country.

Getting the right help at the right time is worth a fortune, but will cost you nothing. If you are calling for someone else, be sure to have the name, address and zip code of the person needing assistance, plus a description of the type of service needed.

Call between 9 a.m. and 5 p.m., Monday through Friday. The toll-free number is 800-677-1116. *Or write to:*

> Eldercare Locator
> National Association of
> Area Agencies on Aging
> 927 15 St. NW, 6th fl.
> Washington, DC 20005
> 202-296-8130
> *On the Web at:*
> www.aoa.dhhs.gov

Free for the Asking Right in Your Backyard

In your search for the best that life has to offer for free or practically free, the first thing to remember is that there are lots of things all around you that are free for the asking which you might never have thought of. All you have to do is be aware of them and ask. *Here are just a few examples:*

Free Long-Distance Calls

Because of all the intense competition between phone companies, if you are willing to switch companies, you will be offered all kinds of deals—from $100 checks to several hours of free calls. In most cases, there is no obligation to stay with the company after you have used up your free long-distance calls. Helpful: Be sure you know all the details before signing up with anyone.

All Long-Distance Calls For 5¢ a Minute

Shop around for the best deal before you sign up with any phone company. Some companies now offer long distance service for as little as 5¢ a minute, 24 hours a day, 7 days a week. Companies like IDT Corporation, for example, are resellers, which means they buy time from other long distance companies and resell it to their customers at low prices. For more information on IDT's 5¢-a-minute plan, (for a low monthly fee of $3.95) call 800-CALL-IDT (or 800-225-5438). Online at www.idt.net/ld/index.htm.

Free for Using Your Credit Card

The credit card war is heating up...and you stand to benefit. Today more

You Make the Call! A Consumer Guide to Understanding Your Phone Bill.
Source: National Consumers League, 1701 K St. NW, Ste. 1200, Washington, DC 20006. Or phone 202-835-3323, or online at www.nclnet.org.

3

Is Your Family Really Safe? Candle safety…Christmas tree fires…fire extinguishers…and more. NFPA Fact Sheets, available from 617-770-3000. Or write to:

National Fire Protection Association, One Batterymarch Park, Quincy, MA 02269. Online at www.nfpa.org

and more banks and companies are offering credit cards with added bonuses for using them. For example, some credit cards give you one frequent flyer mile for each dollar charged on the card. You can use the accumulated miles to get free airline tickets.

Also, many larger chain stores offer free dollars to spend in their store just for opening a charge account with the store. There is no obligation to use the card once you have it. If you don't plan to use it, just cut it up and throw it away.

Remember, you can negotiate with your credit card company to lower the interest you are being charged and to waive the annual fee. Be careful of the "low introductory rate" offered by many banks. They may offer a finance charge of 4.9% for the first six months, but then the rate will jump up to 15% or 20%. If you shop around you will find rates of 10% or less year-round (not just for a limited time).

Free Haircuts

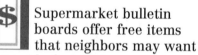

Did you know that free haircuts are available through many local beauty and barber schools? Check your phone book and give them a call. Some may ask for a small fee or a tip for the trainee. Some of the better known hair designers may offer free style and cuts during certain months or certain times of the year. Call your favorite salon and find out when they are training their students. You will benefit by getting the designer for free, while in his or her own salon you might be charged anywhere from $50 and up.

Often companies like Clairol offer free hair coloring when new products are being tested.

Don't hesitate to give any of them a call. Remember, if you don't ask, you'll never know.

Department Store Freebies

Have you ever wanted to try free perfume or have a makeover? Just go to one of the larger department stores in your area. You are never obligated to buy, and some of the companies give out free product samples. You could stock up by going from store to store. So next time you need a new look, try your local department store.

Free for Consumers

Supermarket bulletin boards offer free items that neighbors may want to get rid of or trade.

Credit card companies offer free month trials on discount shopping clubs, travel clubs, insurance promotions and other types of specials. But remember to cancel after the free month has transpired if you don't want to continue the particular service.

Get free magazine subscriptions, audiotapes and CDS. How? Look in your local newspaper for offers at the supermarkets: "buy one item, get one free." It's a good way to stock up on nonperishable items that you will use, such as paper towels, soft drinks and canned soup.

Grand Magnet for Grandparents

"My Grandchild Did This" refrigerator magnet is a perfect addition to include when sending along a child's art work to a grandparent. This will really show off the grandchild's delightful creations. Enclose $1 with a business-sized SASE with two stamps on it, *and send to:*

Practical Parenting
Dept I
15245 Minnetonka Blvd.
Minnetonka, MN 55345
Or call:
1-800-255-3379
for the Practical Parenting catalog.
On the Web at:
www.practicalparenting.com

Free Topsoil and Firewood

Contractors frequently have a problem disposing of the dirt they remove when excavating a building site. Often they will offer free landfill and free top soil to anyone who wants it. Typically you will have to remove it yourself or pay a nominal delivery charge.

Similar opportunities for free firewood can be found when land is being cleared.

Free Birthday Dinner

There are quite a few restaurants that offer free birthday dinners. You only have to show a driver's license or some proof of birth date. Check with your favorite restaurants to see if they offer this courtesy.

Also check local restaurant ads for coupons for "buy one dinner, and get another one free."

Enjoy a Free Concert

Don't overlook all the free outdoor concerts and theater productions in community parks, especially during the summer months. Check the local parks and recreation department or the local newspaper.

Many movie theaters have special prices on slow nights. For example, some theaters offer a Tuesday night special of two tickets for the price of one.

If you like concerts and drama, consider being a volunteer usher. Some theater and opera companies give volunteers free tickets in exchange for usher work.

Life Advice

MetLife has a series of educational brochures called "Life Advice." There are more than 70 topics, ranging from taxes to starting a business to planning for retirement. Each brochure is filled with valuable advice.

For a specific brochure or for a list of the topics available, call MetLife at 800-638-5433. Or visit their Web site at www.lifeadvice.com. There is also a free weekly newsletter available.

Trace Your Family Tree

Many diseases run in families. One of the first things a doctor might ask you for is a family tree to see if you may have a predisposition for a particular disease. If you are interested in tracing your family history, the first place to start is to ask relatives for family details. Next, see if your local library has a family history center where you can track your lineage. The family history library of the Church of Latter-day Saints

Crash Course: Simple Tips that Could Help Save Lives. How to respond quickly and correctly immediately after witnessing a car accident. *Source:* Shell Oil Co. 800-376-0200. On the Web at www.countonshell.com, then go to "Products & Services" for free booklets.

Best Genealogy Site. Preeminent site for Internet ancestor searches. Links to military, birth and death records, more. On the Web at www.familysearch.org.

has the largest collection of genealogical records in the world. For the free booklet "Discovering Your Family Tree," call 800-346-6044—or *write to:*

Family History Library
35 North West Temple St.
Salt Lake City, UT 84150-3400
www.familysearch.org

Free Miracle Polishing Cloth

If you are looking for a business you can start or a product you can sell, check out the Miracle Polishing Cloth. It cleans and polishes any surface—metal, wood, glass or tile—and restores jewelry and silverware. For a free sample ($3.98 value), plus information on how to make money selling this miracle cloth, *write to:*

R & S Industries Corp.
8255-IN Brentwood Industrial Dr.
St. Louis, MO 63144-2814
314-781-5400
Or on the Web at:
www.miraclepolishingcloth.com

Consumer Complaints

Have you had this happen to you? You bought a product that turned out to be of inferior quality, and when you returned it to the store, they refused to give you a refund or exchange. Be prepared for the next time this might happen to you. For help in resolving a complaint, get a copy of *The Consumer Action Handbook.* It includes a directory of government, nonprofit and corporate consumer-complaint assistance sources and much more. No

household should be without this resource. For a free copy, *write to:*

Consumer Action Handbook
Federal Consumer Information Center
Dept. WWW
Pueblo, CO 81009
888-878-3256
Or order online at:
www.pueblo.gsa.gov

Local Help for Consumers

The listing of consumer protection agencies at the back of this book will serve you time and again. It includes the phone numbers of local consumer protection agencies. If you have a problem with a company or a service, call the office nearest you and explain your complaint.

Go Right to the Top

Whenever you have a complaint with a larger company, get the phone number and call the company directly. If the person you speak to tries to give you the brush-off, ask to speak to a supervisor. If you still don't get satisfaction, ask to speak to the supervisor's supervisor—all the way up to the top. If you still are not satisfied, ask for the name and mailing address of the president of the company, and write a polite letter to that person explaining your complaint in detail. Nine times out of 10 the president will hand the matter over to someone who will contact you with an offer to resolve the complaint to your satisfaction. Try it...it works!

Book Bargains

"Catalog of Book Bargains" is for all book lovers who want to save up to 90% or more off original book prices. Recent best-sellers are sold in this 50-page catalog at very sharp discounts. The catalog is free from Daedalus Books at 800-395-2665 or on the Web at www.salebooks.com. *Or write to:*

> **Daedalus Books, Inc.**
> 9645 Gerwig Ln.
> Columbia, MD 21046

Get Rich at Home

Have you ever dreamed of starting your own business from home? If so, send for this special report, "Mail Order Success Secrets." Learn how to start your own successful business in your spare time with little money and grow rich in the most exciting business in the world. *Send an SASE to:*

> **Roblin-BSR**
> 405 Tarrytown Rd., Ste. 414
> White Plains, NY 10607
> 888-229-FREE
> www.roblinpress.com

A Great Cigar Catalog

If you are a cigar smoker or know someone who is, this catalog is a must. Not only will you find every cigar available, but also all the cigar accessories imaginable. You will even learn about the Cigar Hall of Fame as well as some unusual and interesting gifts for people who don't smoke. *Send a postcard to:*

> **Thompson Cigar Company**
> 5401 Hangar Ct.
> PO Box 30303
> Tampa, FL 33630
> *Or call:*
> 800-216-7107
> *Or go online to:*
> www.thompsoncigar.com

Surprise Gift Club

We have all faced the problem of what to give someone as a gift. Finally, here is help. The Surprise Gift of the Month Club has developed an innovative solution. They offer you a broad selection of items from kites, iron-ons, coasters, stickers and records to crewel and needlepoint kits, plus many more items to select from. Anyone young or old will be delighted to receive a surprise gift each month. It's a beautiful way to say, "I'm thinking of you" to someone special. For a sample of the assorted crewel and needlepoint kits, *send $1 for postage and handling to:*

> **Surprise Gift of the Month Club**
> PO Box 11
> Garnerville, NY 10923
> *Or go online to:*
> www.myfree.com
> *for a multitude of related offers.*

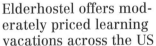

Terrific Travel Opportunities

Elderhostel offers moderately priced learning vacations across the US and Canada, as well as to 70 nations abroad. These are terrific opportunities for senior citizens who enjoy adventure and travel, but who have a limited amount of money to spend. The subjects taught on these vacations range from astronomy to zoology.

For a catalog of courses and travel itineraries, call toll-free 877-426-8056.

To be added to the mailing list, call, or go to the Web site at www.elderhostel.org.

When Your Children Leave the Nest. Keeping in touch…taking care of yourself…taking stock of your life.
Source: MetLife Consumer Education Center, 800-638-5433.

Plug into Electrical Safety. How to spot and correct hazards in the home. Free.

Source: National Electrical Safety Foundation, 1300 N. 17 St., Ste. 1847, Rosslyn, VA 22209, 703-841-3229. Include a business-sized SASE with two stamps. www.nesf.org

A Gem of a Gift

If you like gems and gemstones, whether in the rough or finished into fine jewelry or artifacts, this catalog is for you. You will find some fabulous closeout buys on fantastic gemstones, geodes, even Mexican onyx and malachite carvings. Whether you are a collector or someone in need of a gift, send for this catalog. Call 800-844-3100. *Or write to:*

> **House of Onyx, Inc.**
> 120 North Main St.
> Greenville, KY 42345-1504
> www.houseofonyx.com

What to Look For in a Gem

Buying a valuable gem can be a tricky affair unless you are prepared. Have you ever wondered what makes one diamond more valuable than another when they both look the same to the naked eye? Before buying any gemstone it is essential to learn exactly what to look for. For example, do you know the four Cs that determine a diamond's value? They are Cut, Color, Clarity and Carat (weight). To learn more about what to look for when buying a diamond, send for a free consumer kit from the American Gem Society. *Send a business-sized SASE to:*

> **American Gem Society**
> 8881 W. Sahara Ave.
> Las Vegas, NV 89117
> 702-255-6500
> www.ags.org

Sleep Tight

A healthful good night's sleep makes for a productive, pleasant person.

Learn all the facts on how to get a healthful sleep by selecting the right bedding, pillows and sleep positions. The makers of Simmons will send you free "Consumer Guide to Better Sleep," plus several others, including "It's Never Too Early to Start Caring for Your Back" and tips for shopping for the right bed. They will offer you an online sleep analysis. To get a copy, *send a business-sized SASE to:*

> **Simmons Beautyrest**
> One Concourse Center, Ste. 600
> Box C-93
> Atlanta, GA 30328
> www.simmonsco.com

A Home-Buying Must

Are you considering buying a house? If so, this is a must. You will receive "The American Home Owners Foundation's Top 10 Home Buyer's Tips." They will also include the "Top 10 Remodeling Tips." Call the American Homeowner's Foundation at 800-489-7776 or on the Web at www.american homeowners.org.

Money-Saving Tips

All sorts of money savers and money makers. Dollar stretchers, holiday tips, daily poems and more. Includes an assortment of quick and easy recipe ideas, and the *Frugal Mom Weekly Newsletter.* Online at www. thefamilycorner.com.

Overflowing with Love

Love guru Greg Godek, author of the best-selling book *1001 Ways to Be*

Romantic, would like to give you a free one-year subscription to *LoveLetter Newsletter.* The newsletter is overflowing with great romantic ideas. Put the spark back in your love life. Call Casablanca Press at 800-43-BRIGHT, or online at www.sourcebooks.com.

Easy Reading

For adults whose reading levels are at grades 4 and above, here is a great way to help improve reading skills. Each issue of the *News for You* newsletter contains articles on important international news, as well as features on education, health, leisure, law and more. The newsletter is in a format that is easy to read and understand. To get one free, ask for a sample copy of *News for You* by calling 800-448-8878, or *write to:*

New Readers Press
PO Box 35888
Syracuse, NY 13235
800-448-8878
Or on the Web at:
www.newreaderspress.com

Shop Easy

Do you like to relax and shop at home? If so, get a copy of Lillian Vernon's free catalog. It is always full of affordable treasures from around the world. Call 800-545-5426. On the Web at www.lillianvernon.com.

Classic Gifts

Harriet Carter has provided distinctive gifts since 1958. For one of her fun-filled catalogs with plenty of unique gifts, call 800-377-7878. *Or write to:*

Harriet Carter Gifts
425 Stump Rd.
North Wales, PA 19454
www.harrietcarter.com

Get That Bug

The makers of Raid bug sprays would like you to have a highly informative chart, "Raid Insecticides—What to Use for Effective Control." Learn how to deal with crawling, flying and biting pests, both inside and outside your home (including plant pests). You will also receive a money-saving coupon. *Send a business-sized SASE to:*

Insect Control
SC Johnson
1525 Howe St.
Racine, WI 53403-5011
800-494-4855
www.johnsonwax.com

Free Art Films

To help bring art appreciation to a wider audience, the National Gallery of Art has a free videotape loan program. Choose from dozens of videos and slide programs, available to individuals, community groups and schools. Your only obligation is to pay the postage when returning the video. For a complete catalog and reservation card, *write to:*

National Gallery of Art
Department of Education Resources
Extension Programs
Washington, DC 20565
Online at:
www.nga.gov/education/
Then click on "Loan Programs."

This Old House? Tips for buying a good older home. Free.
Source: National Inspection Services, 1136 E. Stuart St., Ste. 4204, Fort Collins, CO 80525. Include a business-sized SASE. Or online at www.nationalinspection.net. Or call 800-248-1976 for additional services.

The Inside Story: A Guide to Indoor Air Quality. Free.

Source: Indoor Air Quality Hotline, 800-438-4318. Booklet also available online at www.epa.gov

TV Show Tickets Free!

The TV networks provide free tickets to all of their shows that have live audiences. If you plan to be in Los Angeles or New York and would like to see a TV show, before your trip, write to the ticket department of the network you are interested in. Generally, you will be sent a letter which can be exchanged for tickets for any show that is open at the time of your visit. *Write to:*

ABC
320 West 66 St.
New York, NY 10023
In Los Angeles:
Call Audiences Unlimited
818-753-3470 Ext.14
Paramount Guest Relations
323-956-1777
www.paramount.com

NBC
30 Rockefeller Plaza
New York, NY 10112
In Los Angeles:
3000 W. Alameda Ave.
Burbank, CA 91523

CBS
524 W. 57 St.
New York, NY 10019
In Los Angeles:
7800 Beverly Blvd.
Los Angeles, CA 90036-2188

Oprah
In Chicago:
Call 312-591-9222
www.oprah.com

Useful Web Sites
www.abc.go.com
www.nbci.com
www.cbs.com
www.nytix.com

For Sea Lovers

Do you love the sea? You can send for this 50-page catalog, full of decorative nautical ideas for the home. If you are looking for a ship model, marine painting or ship's wheel, you will find it here. Call 631-477-1990. *Or send a postcard to:*

S.T. Preston & Son, Inc.
Main Street Wharf
Greenport, NY 11944
www.prestons.com

No More Chapped Lips

If you suffer from dry, chapped lips or mouth sores, this is especially for you.
www.blistex.com

For Larger or Taller Women

Lane Bryant offers a stunning collection of dresses, coats, jeans, sportswear, lingerie and shoes for the woman who wears half-size or large-size apparel. You will find name brands and designer fashions in their free catalogs, "Woman Within" and more. Call 800-677-0216, or online at www.lbcatalog.com.

Need Help with Infant Feeding?

Breast milk storage bottles, gel packs for diaper packs and more in this catalog. *Available from:*
Ross Products
625 Cleveland Ave.
Columbus, OH 43215
800-986-8510
www.similac.com

Your Own Flag from Capitol Hill

Did you know that your Congressperson will provide a unique service for you free of charge? If you would like to have your own flag sent to you from the US Capitol Building, write to your congressperson. Prices range from $16 to $31, depending on size and material, plus shipping and handling. This also makes a unique gift for someone special. *Write to your Congressperson at:*
>**US House of Representatives**
>Washington, DC 20515
Or:
>**US Senate**
>Washington, DC 20510

Save on Scents

If you love all those expensive perfumes and colognes advertised on TV and radio and in magazines, but are not as enamored with the high prices, then this is a must for you. Essential Products makes an affordable line of perfumes and colognes, which are almost identical to brands costing 10 times as much. For a free list and scented cards, *send a business-sized SASE to:*
>**Essential Products Co., Inc.**
>90 Water St.
>New York, NY 10005
>212-344-4288

Soft and Warm

You know how terrific it feels to have something super soft gently touching your body? Well, The Company Store offers comforters, pillows and outerwear made from a superior blend of hand-selected, white-goose and duck-down feathers. Get a free catalog by calling 800-285-DOWN, or *send a postcard to:*
>**The Company Store**
>500 Company Store Rd.
>LaCrosse, WI 54601
Or shop online at:
>www.thecompanystore.com

Preserve Our History

If you would like to participate in the preservation of sites, buildings and objects that are important to American history and culture, there is something you can do. *Send a card asking for the* "Historic Preservation" *package to:*
>**National Trust for Historic Preservation**
>1785 Massachusetts Ave. NW
>Washington, DC 20036
>202-588-6000
>www.nthp.org

Mail-Order Rights

When you purchase an item by mail, do you know your rights? Here is a practical and informative guide detailing the protection you have under the FTC's Mail Order Merchandise Rule. A free copy of "Shopping by Phone and Mail" is yours *by writing to:*
>**Consumer Response Center**
>Federal Trade Commission
>600 Penn. Ave. NW, Room H-130
>Washington, DC 20580
>www.ftc.org

Flags of All Kinds

If you are looking for flags of any kind— custom designs, states, nations, historic and sports—

Pet Catalog. Products for dogs and cats— devices to help with behavior and training…collars…furniture…grooming accessories…health care…tags… treats…etc.
Source: Drs. Foster & Smith Inc., 800-381-7179. Online at www.drsfostersmith.com

11

About Protecting Your Child. Safety rules for children and parents...dealing with strangers...cyberspace precautions...when a child is missing.
Source: MetLife Consumer Education Ctr., 800-638-5433.

plus poles and countless accessories, there is a free catalog that has them all. Go on the Web to www.qualityflags.com.

Free Gift from the President

Can you imagine the excitement of getting a letter from the President of the United States? The President will send a signed card embossed with the Presidential seal to any couple celebrating their 50th anniversary (or beyond), and to any citizen celebrating an 80th (or subsequent) birthday. Special greetings will be sent to individuals 100 years or older. At the other end of the spectrum, the President will also send a congratulatory card to any newborn child. You can also have the card sent to you so you can frame it and give it as a special one-of-a-kind gift. *Send your requests at least four weeks in advance to:*

White House Greeting Office
1600 Pennsylvania Ave. NW
Washington, DC 20500

Or request by fax at 202-456-2461.

Free Presidential Photo

How would you like a full-color, autographed photo of the President and First Lady? To get one, request it by fax at 202-456-2461. *Or write to:*

White House Greeting Office
1600 Pennsylvania Ave. NW
Washington, DC 20500

Free from the White House

The President would like you to have a beautiful full-color book, *The White House—The House of the People.* It features a room-by-room photo tour and history of the White House. *For a free copy, write to:*

The White House
1600 Pennsylvania Ave. NW
Washington, DC 20500
or request by fax at 202-456-2461.

Let the President Know

Yes, your opinion really does count. Whether you agree or disagree with his policies, the President would like to hear what you have to say. With this phone number, you will be connected right to the White House where you will be able to express your opinion on the subject that concerns you most. Call 202-456-1414.

More Money for Moving

The Interstate Moving Guide" is a useful pamphlet that can help make your interstate move run smoothly. It tells you how to prepare for moving day, how moving costs are calculated, a glossary of moving terms and lots more. *It's free from:*

Atlas Van Lines
1212 St. George Rd.
Evansville, IN 47711
www.atlasvanlines.com
800-252-8885

A Moving Experience

To help you with your next move, United Van Lines has set up a toll-free number you can call. They will provide you with the phone number of the United Van Lines office nearest you, which is set up to answer any specific questions you may have. For example, they can answer your questions about employment, educational facilities, housing and more in 7,000 cities and towns throughout the 50 states (and foreign countries too). Your local United Van Lines office can also provide you with guides that make preplanning a lot easier. Call 636-343-3900, or go online to www.unitedvanlines.com

Free Moving Kit

Mayflower has a packet of useful moving materials, free for the asking. It includes labels for marking boxes, plus tips to make your move run smoother and faster. Ask for a "Moving Kit" from a local Mayflower mover, *or send a postcard to:*

> **Mayflower Transit**
> One Mayflower Dr.
> Fenton, MO 63026
> www.mayflowertransit.com

Get Rid of Facial Hair

If you are bothered by unsightly facial hair, call the Nudit Hotline. You can discuss with experts the sensitive issue of hair removal treatments. The hotline number is 800-62-NUDIT.

Free Classes and Lots More

You may not be aware of it, but your local cooperative extension office offers an amazing range of free information and services to all who request them. Free cooking classes, home and garden seminars, soil analysis, 4-H information, home economics classes and money-management workshops are just a few of the services available. To find your local Cooperative Extension Service or Agricultural Extension Office, check the blue pages of the local phone book. Call the one in your state to find out which services they offer. They will give you the address and phone number of the office nearest you.

Legal Encyclopedia

Plain-English articles on legal topics that affect you most. Visit www.nolo.com for the categories of topics.

Financial Calculators

Want to know how much you'll need to sock away for retirement, or for that new car? Maybe you're considering taking out a loan or mortgage, and want to figure just how much you'll pay in interest. Whatever number-crunching you need, visit www.nolo.com for their online calculators.

Free Help Writing a Will

A little known service offered by many Cooperative Extension Service offices is free help in writing a will. Often the office will have will forms and pamphlets as well as an instructor to help you. Check the blue pages in the phone book for the nearest Extension office.

Custom CDs: Pick songs and sequence from thousands...give the CD a personalized title, too.
Source: www.backintheday.com

Twelve Ways to Lower Your Homeowners Insurance Costs.
Free.
Source: Insurance Information Institute, 110 William St., New York, NY 10038, 212-346-5500. Include a business-sized SASE. Or access it online at www.iii.org. Click on "Home."

Free Samples

Quality Healthcare enhances your well-being by giving you the highest-quality samples, offers and insights from brands you know and trust. Visit www.mtso.com/aolqh/home.jsp

Free Make-up

Dermablend Corrective Cosmetics provides the most natural-looking coverage for face and body. Visit their website www.skinstore.com for a free sample.

Free Soup

Aliments E.D. Foods offers a giant free sample of a variety of soups. There is a $2.98 shipping and handling fee. Visit their website at www.ed-foods.com.

Free Medical Care And Health Information

No-cost Prescription Drugs

Did you know that there are free prescription drugs available to those who cannot afford to pay for them? Many drug manufacturers have programs that provide drugs to those who do not have the money or insurance coverage to pay for them.

You may be suffering from cancer, a heart ailment or some other disease that requires a medication as an essential part of your treatment, but one you cannot afford. Through special indigent programs, drug companies will supply the medication free of charge directly to your pharmacy or to your doctor (if the doctor must administer the drug).

The first step is to tell your doctor that you are not able to afford the needed medicines. Next, see if your doctor has any information on the "indigent patient drug program" for the medication you need.

Surprisingly, many doctors don't even know these programs exist. For that reason, in the back of this book there is a Directory of Free Prescription-Drug Programs, with full information on the drugs covered, the eligibility requirements and how to contact the pharmaceutical company.

Also, many states have programs that provide prescription drugs for as little as $1, or sometimes even free. Check the section on "State Pharmaceutical Programs" in the back of this book.

Another place to check is the Pharmaceutical Manufacturers Association (PMA). It has up-to-date information on the patient programs sponsored by various drug manufacturers. You can access this information on the Web at www.phrma.org.

Striking Back at Stroke

There is some terrific news in the battle against stroke. In the past 25 years, modern medical treatments have reduced the death rate from stroke by 50%. Many doctors now feel that the health threat from stroke can be reduced even more by taking a small dose of aspirin daily, controlling high blood pressure, practicing healthy nutrition and participating in exercise programs. To find out what you can do to avoid a stroke, get a free copy of "Stroke: Hope Through Research." *Contact:*

Brain Resource and Information Network
National Institute of Neurological Disorders & Stroke
PO Box 5801
Bethesda, MD 20824

You can also call toll-free at 800-352-9424, or visit the Web site at www.ninds.nih.gov.

Free Hospital Care

If you don't have insurance coverage, even a very brief hospital stay can easily cost you tens of thousands of dollars and put you on the edge of bankruptcy. Fortunately, now there is something you can do. If you need hospital care but cannot afford it and have no insurance or if you have already been in the hospital and can't afford to pay the bill, try calling the Hill-Burton Hotline. Through this program, more

Taking Part in Clinical Trials: What Cancer Patients Need to Know. What happens in a clinical trial...the difference between phase I, II and III trials.
Source: Cancer Information Service, National Cancer Institute, 800-4-CANCER. www.nci.nih.gov

Your Baby's Eyes.
Vision development and what to expect during different stages. When you should seek professional care.
Source: American Optometric Association, Communications Center, 243 N. Lindbergh Blvd., St. Louis, MO 63141. Include a business-sized SASE. Or call 314-991-4100. www.aoa.org

than a thousand participating hospitals and other health facilities provide free or low-cost medical care to patients who are unable to pay for medical services.

You can qualify for this program even if your income is double the poverty-level income guidelines and even if a medical bill has already been turned over to a collection agency. For more information, call the Hill-Burton Hotline at 800-492-0359. www.aoa.org

Controlling Chronic Headaches

If you suffer from migraine or chronic headaches, the "Headache Information Package" is for you. In it, you will learn about the latest research, new drug treatments, biofeedback and lots more. You will find articles, reports and resources for headache suffers. To get your free package, *contact:*

National Institute of Neurological Disorders and Stroke
PO Box 5801
Bethesda, MD 20824

You can also call toll-free at 800-352-9424, or visit the Web site at www.ninds.nih.gov.

Free Medical Care

How would you like to have the finest medical care money can buy... and not spend a cent for it? That is exactly what thousands of people are doing every year thanks to the National Institutes of Health (NIH) Clinical Center. The NIH is funded by the federal government and is one of the nation's leading medical research centers.

At any one time there are as many as 900 programs underway in dozens of hospitals throughout the country, where researchers are studying the newest procedures in the treatment of every imaginable disease, including all types of cancer, heart disease and Alzheimer's, to mention just a few.

If your condition is one that is being studied, you may qualify for free medical care at the NIH's 540-bed hospital in Bethesda, Maryland. To find out about their ongoing research projects and clinical trials and whether you qualify for treatment, call the NIH toll-free hotline at 800-411-1222. *Or contact:*

National Institutes of Health Clinical Center
6100 Executive Blvd., Suite 3C01, MSC 7511
Bethesda, MD 20892-7511
www.cc.nih.gov

Free Eye Care

One of the key ingredients to enjoying a good quality of life is having good eyesight. This means taking care of such eye problems as cataracts and glaucoma before your eyesight is damaged.

The first step is to find out what you can do to keep your eyes healthy. The National Eye Institute has a number of informative publications that describe various eye diseases and what can be done about them. For a complete list of booklets available, contact the Institute at 301-496-5248. *Or write:*

National Eye Institute
Information Office
2020 Vision Pl.
Bethesda, MD 20892-3655
www.nei.nih.gov

Local Eye Care for Free

The community service pages of your local newspaper occasionally will run announcements by organizations such as the Kiwanis or Lions Clubs. They offer free eyeglasses and eye exams to elderly people who otherwise could not afford them.

Also, check with the local Office of the Aging (see the listing of these offices in the back of this book). There is a wide variety of eye-care programs offered, and many include free eye exams and free eyeglasses.

How to Choose the Right Nursing Home

What should you do if a loved one needs the kind of continuing care that can only be gotten in a nursing home? What can you do to ensure proper care? How do you know how good a particular nursing home is? The first step is to get "A Guide to Choosing a Nursing Home." This handy guide provides a step-by-step approach to evaluating and choosing the right nursing home. It's available free from the Medicare Hotline at 800-MEDICARE, or online at www.medicare.gov.

Free Health Care for You and Your Pet

Remember, if you live near a university that has a medical, dental or even veterinary school, typically, these schools will offer all kinds of medical, dental or veterinary services for free or for a nominal fee. Call the schools in your area and ask which services are provided to the community.

Extend Your Life

The Life Extension Foundation is committed to helping people who are well live longer and healthier lives. The foundation publishes an excellent magazine, *Life Extension,* which will keep you informed and up-to-date on all the new advances in how particular vitamins and nutrients keep our minds alert and our bodies healthy and strong.

Life Extension carries "insider" reports on revolutionary research projects which one day might extend the healthy human lifespan to 150 years and beyond. The foundation will send a copy of the magazine, along with information on how to become a member. *Write:*

> **Life Extension Foundation**
> 1100 West Commercial Blvd.
> Fort Lauderdale, FL 33309
> 800-544-4440
> www.lef.org

Healthy Golden Years

Being a senior can sometimes bring with it special problems that can be easily solved if you have the right kind of information. The National Institute on Aging can help bring this important information to you in several ways. First, it acts as a referral agency, which means that if you have a problem the institute doesn't handle, you will be referred to an agency that can provide the help you need. (Most agencies have toll-free phone numbers.)

Exercise: A Guide from the National Institute on Aging. Stretching, strength, balance and endurance exercises...how to eat a balanced diet... progress charts.
Source: National Institute on Aging, Building 31, Room SC27, 31 Center Drive, MSC 2292, Bethesda, MD 20892. 800-222-2225. Or online at www.nih.gov/nia.

Understanding Managed Care.
Choosing a health plan that is right for you... getting the most out of your plan...what to do if you have problems or complaints...managed care and Medicare and Medicaid.

Source: Kaiser Family Foundation, Publication #1331, 800-656-4533. Publications are also available online at www.kff.org.

Next, the institute's "Age Pages" on the World Wide Web offers valuable information on diseases, disorders and conditions. The institute also puts out a series of extremely useful booklets. Some of the most popular ones are "Aging and Alcohol Abuse," "Dealing with Diabetes," "Forgetfulness: It's Not What You Think," "Osteoporosis: The Silent Bone Thinner," "Stroke: Prevention and Treatment" and "Urinary Incontinence." These brochures can help you with questions on medical care, medications, safety, even health promotion and disease prevention—in short, all of the topics important to every senior. A complete list of free booklets is available either in print or online.

Here is a partial list of the booklets and reports that can be ordered:

- "Aging and Alcohol Abuse"
- "Aging and Your Eyes"
- "Arthritis Advice"
- "Constipation"
- "Crime and the Elderly"
- "Exercise: Feeling Fit for Life"
- "Foot Care"
- "Health Quackery"
- "Hearing and Older People"
- "High Blood Pressure: A Common but Controllable Disease"
- "Life Extension: Science or Science Fiction?"
- "Medicines: Use Them Safely"
- "Hormone Replacement Therapy"
- "Sexuality in Later Life"
- "Shots for Safety"
- "Skin Care and Aging"
- "Taking Care of Your Teeth and Mouth"
- "What to Do About Flu"

To get a copy of a booklet that interests you, contact:
National Institute on Aging
Building 31, Room 5C27
31 Center Dr., MSC 2292
Bethesda, MD 20892

You can also call the toll-free order line at 301-496-1752. Or visit the Web site at www.nih.gov/nia, then click on "Health information."

Alzheimer's Disease Helpline

If someone you love has been diagnosed with Alzheimer's disease, there is a toll-free information hotline you can call. The Alzheimer's Disease Education and Referral Center, which sponsors the hotline, will be happy to send you several helpful publications, such as the "Forgetfulness" booklet and the "Alzheimer's Disease Fact Sheet." Call 800-438-4380. Or visit the Web site at www.alzheimers.org/adear.

Healthy Smiles

Colgate Total wants you to have shiny, healthy teeth and healthy gums. The company would like to send you information on how its formula works even after you stop brushing to fight plaque, gingivitis and cavities. Call toll-free 800-763-0246. Also visit Colgate's World of Healthy Smiles Web site at www.colgate.com.

No Fraud!

Most health care providers are honest and ethical, but a small percentage engage in fraud against you, the consumer. More than $100 billion is lost each year on health care fraud. Cigna Health Care provides detailed examples of the types of fraud, plus ways to avoid and prevent fraud from happening to you. This important information is available free on the Cigna Web site at www.cigna.com.

Check for Thyroid Disease

The American Association of Clinical Endocrinologists has developed a new self-test for thyroid diseases, including cancer. It's as easy as drinking a glass of water, if you know what to look for. If you should notice a bulge or lumpiness below your Adam's apple as you swallow, that's a warning sign to see your doctor. Be sure not to confuse your Adam's apple with a bulge. For a free copy of "The Thyroid Neck Check," *send an SASE to:*

> **American Association of Clinical Endocrinologists**
> 1000 Riverside Ave., Ste. 205
> Jacksonville, FL 32204
> www.aace.com

Medicare Supplemental Insurance

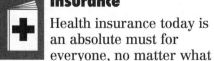

Health insurance today is an absolute must for everyone, no matter what age. It becomes more confusing when dealing with all the questions involved with HMOs and their coverage. Also, it is important to remember that Medicare does not cover all your needs. To be fully covered you must supplement your Medicare insurance, and sometimes considering the options can be overwhelming. Every company has a different idea about how you should supplement your health plan. To help you decide what is best for you, get the informative booklet which answers all of your questions on Medicare supplemental insurance. The booklet even includes an extensive list of where to find more information in your area. Ask for the free "Medicare Supplemental Insurance Guide." Call 800-MEDICARE.

Having Trouble Sleeping?

Did you know that 88% of all Americans suffer from some form of sleep disruption? To learn more about sleep, sleep disorders and drowsy driving, visit the National Sleep Foundation's Web site at www.sleepfoundation.org. *Or send a business-sized SASE with two stamps on it to:*

> **National Sleep Foundation**
> 1522 K St. NW, Ste. 500
> Washington, DC 20005

Dry-Mouth Relief

If you suffer from dry mouth due to radiation therapy or age-related problems, try Salivart. Salivart is an easy spray application of synthetic saliva which will quickly add moisture to your mouth. For a discounted spray can of Salivart, *order online at www.gebauerco.com.*

Caffeine and Women's Health. The latest research on caffeine and pregnancy, fibrocystic breast disease, osteoporosis and heart disease.

Source: International Food Information Council Foundation, 1100 Connecticut Ave. NW, Suite 430, Washington, DC 20036. Include a business-sized SASE. Or online at www.ific.org, then click on "Publications."

Everything You Need to Know About Sucralose and Acesulfame Potassium. How to use these low-calorie sweeteners.

Source: International Food Information Council Foundation, 1100 Connecticut Ave. NW, Washington, DC 20036...or on the Web at www.ific.org.

Gebauer Company
9410 St. Catherine Ave.
Cleveland, OH 44104-5526
800-321-9348,
www.gebauerco.com

Nasal Rescue

Do you suffer from dry, crusted, inflamed nasal membranes? Do you have trouble breathing freely every day and every night? Now there may be a solution to your discomfort: Nasal Moist Gel from Blairex. For samples of this gel, *send $1 postage and handling to:*

Blairex Laboratories, Inc.
PO Box 2127
Columbus, IN 47202-2127
800-252-4739
www.blairex.com

Lowering "Bad" Cholesterol

Cholesterol is a natural, fatlike substance needed by the body to function properly. Unfortunately, some people's bodies produce too much of the wrong type of cholesterol. This can lead to clogging of the arteries and put a person at risk of a heart attack. To find out what you can do to bring "bad" cholesterol to more moderate levels, send for the booklet, "High Blood Cholesterol." *It is free from:*

National Cholesterol Education Program
NHLBI Information Center
PO Box 30105
Bethesda, MD 20824
www.nhlbi.nih.gov

Put Your Best Foot Forward

When your feet ache and you are looking for some kind of relief, what can you do? For answers to that question and for help with your aching feet, the American Podiatric Medical Association has a toll-free number to call for assistance. Call 800-FOOT-CARE.

Don't Skip Foot Care

How many times have you ignored an ingrown toenail until you couldn't stand the pain anymore? Did you ever stub or injure a toe and see it swell up like a balloon? Do you wear the wrong kind of shoes just because they look good? The American Orthopaedic Foot & Ankle Society has some valuable information that can turn sore feet into dancing feet. To get a free copy of "The Adult Foot," just *send a business-sized SASE to:*

American Orthopaedic Foot & Ankle Society
2517 Eastlake Ave. E.
Seattle, WA 98102
www.aofas.org

Free Health Guide

If you are concerned about nonprescription drugs and what effect they may be having on you, get a copy of "Nonprescription Medicines: What's Right for You?" *It's free from:*

Consumer Information
Dept. 556D
Pueblo, CO 81009
800-688-9889
www.pueblo.gsa.gov

Nasal Congestion Help

Do you ever wonder why all those professional football players wear

Band-Aids across their noses? They're not—they're Breathe Right nasal strips. These strips are great for anyone who snores or has nasal congestion and stuffiness, or needs relief from breathing difficulties associated with a deviated septum. Each strip is lined with a special backbone consisting of two parallel strips. When the strips are properly placed across the bridge of the nose, they lift and open the nasal passages, providing immediate and continual relief without drugs. The strips even come in a clear version so they can be worn during the day. Call for information and ask about any promotions, free samples or coupons they may have. Call 800-858-NOSE (858-6673) www.breatheright.com.

Floss Your Troubles Away

How many times have you started to floss your teeth and gotten the floss stuck between your teeth only to have it shred and get even more stuck? The makers of *Glide Floss* have made flossing easier with their newly-patented fiber technology. It is simple to use, slides easily between teeth without shredding and is clinically proven to remove plaque.

For a free sample, call 800-645-4337. Or check the Web site at www.glidefloss.com.

Keeping Lungs Healthy

Do you know what the warning signs of lung disease are? Do you know what to do if you have

emphysema? Are you aware of the common hazards around us every day in our environment that affect our lungs? Would you like helpful hints on quitting smoking? For answers to these questions and lots more, the American Lung Association has a number of useful booklets. To find out more about lung-related problems and solutions, call the American Lung Association at 800-LUNG-USA, or go online at www.lungusa.org.

Help for Stutterers

If you stutter or know anyone who has a stuttering problem, you are not alone. There are some excellent sites to check out on the Internet. The National Stuttering Association's Web site includes essays about stuttering, contacts for local support groups, information on upcoming workshops and links to related sites. Visit the Web site at www.nsastutter.org.

The Stuttering Foundation of America is at www.stuttersfa.org. There you will find helpful information on stuttering, lists of upcoming workshops and referrals to speech pathologists and clinics. The nonprofit group can also be reached at 800-992-9392.

Keep Yourself Cancer Free

The American Institute for Cancer Research has tons of valuable information available for people suffering from cancer and for those who want to keep themselves cancer-free. The institute will send you

Medicines for Epilepsy. Dosages and side effects of 23 drugs used to treat epilepsy.
Source: Epilepsy Foundation, 4351 Garden City Dr., Landover, MD 20785-7223. 800-332-1000. www.epilepsyfoundation.org

How to Do Breast Self-Examination. Illustrated guide to the whys, whens and how-to's of breast examination.

Source: American Cancer Society, 800-227-2345. www.cancer.org

information on how to prevent certain cancers by living a healthy lifestyle, by exercising and by following a well-balanced diet. If you already have cancer, you will want to learn more about how to maintain a healthy diet while fighting the illness. The booklets are free, but if you want to help further research and education on the link between diet and cancer, a small donation would be greatly appreciated.

The Institute also has a variety of free publications designed to help you live a healthier lifestyle. For a small contribution you can also receive a very informative newsletter. Some of the booklets you can get include: "Hints for a Healthy Weight," on how to lose weight sensibly; "Facts on Preventing Cancer: Pesticides," to learn the role supplements play in reducing cancer risk; "The Facts About Fiber," about the importance of eating enough fiber to lower cancer risk; and "Diet, Nutrition and Prostate Cancer," to learn about steps you can take that may reduce your risk of getting one of the most common cancers in the US. Also ask for "Simple Steps to Prevent Cancer," which will alleviate many of the concerns you may have about what causes cancer. You can ask for one or all of these booklets. Call 800-843-8114, or *write to:*

> **American Institute for Cancer Research**
> 1759 R St. NW
> Washington, DC 20009
> www.aicr.org

Breast Cancer Support

The Y-ME Breast Cancer Support Program was created in 1978 by Ann Marcou and Mimi Kaplan, who turned their own difficult experiences into a positive network of volunteers that provides counseling and information to thousands of women suffering from breast cancer. For a free copy of the *Y-ME* newsletter, *write to:*

> **Y-ME**
> 212 W. Van Buren, Ste. 500
> Chicago, IL 60607

The 24-hour support hotline is 800-221-2141. Or visit the Web site at www.y-me.org.

Free Dental Care for Seniors

You know just how expensive dental care can be, especially if you need dentures, tooth implants or gum surgery. Fortunately, if you need expensive dental work but cannot afford it, help is close at hand. Top-quality dental care is available at little or no cost at local dental clinics and at dental colleges nationwide. Also, the dental society in each state has a list of dentists who volunteer their services to help people who cannot afford proper dental care. (For contact information, see the section on "Free and Low-Cost Dental Programs" in the back of this book.)

Kick That Fungus

If you suffer from discomfort or embarrassment stemming from a fungal growth under your fingernails or toenails, there is something you can do to get rid of the problem. The first step is to get the "Kick-It Kit," free from Sporanox. Call toll-free 800-JANSSEN www.janssen.com.

Free Help for Men and for Women

For men:

Call Men's Health Consulting for information on men's health reform and what you can do to help. Call 800-Well-Men.

Published by the founders of *National Men's Health Week* and the Association of American Family Physicians, the "Men's Maintenance Manual" is a free booklet that deals with stress management, sexual health and weight control. It lists the health hotlines of 23 helpful organizations that will provide information on topics ranging from aging to allergies, from sports medicine to stress. Call 800-955-2002, or *write to:*

> **Men's Maintenance Manual**
> 154-182 E. Minor St.
> Emmaus, PA 18098
> www.nmhw.org

For women:

Call the National Women's Health Network Information Clearinghouse. They can provide you with information perspectives on women's health issues, including osteoporosis, breast biopsy and tamoxifen for healthy women. Call 202-628-7814. Or go to www.womenshealthnetwork.org on the Web.

Also, the Office of Research on Women's Health, National Institutes of Health, has a list of useful publications. Call 301-402-1770. Or go to www4.od.nih.gov/orwh/index.html.

Know Your Pension Rights

If you have questions about your pension and your rights, the Pension and Welfare Benefits Administration has a toll-free number to call to order free publications about pensions and health coverage. There are more than 35 free booklets available, including:

- "What You Should Know About Your Pension Rights"
- "Protect Your Pension—A Quick Reference Guide"
- "Women and Retirement Savings"
- "How to File a Claim for Your Benefits"
- "Health Benefits Under COBRA"
- "Pension and Welfare Brief: Can the Retiree Health Benefits Provided by Your Employer Be Cut?"

There are also free guides for small business owners that outline Simplified Employee Pensions (SEP) and Savings Incentive Match Plans for Employees of Small Employers (SIMPLE). For free information, call between 9 a.m. and 8 p.m., Monday through Friday, toll-free at 800-998-7542. Or go online to www.dol.gov/dol/pwba.

Know How to Control Cholesterol and Blood Pressure

We all know how critically important it is to keep our cholesterol and blood pressure at safe levels. To find out what you can do, call the National Heart, Lung and Blood Institute for recorded information on cholesterol and high blood pressure. When you call, you can also leave your name and address for information packets. Call 800-575-WELL, or go to www.nhlbi.nih.gov on the Web.

Understanding Gastroesophageal Reflux Disease (GERD). Prevention and treatment of this condition, in which acid from the stomach backs up into the esophagus, causing heartburn.
Source: American College of Gastroenterology, 4900B S. 31 St., Arlington, VA 22206. 703-820-7400. Also available on the Web at www.acg.gi.org.

Controlling High Blood Pressure: A Guide for Older Women. Lifestyle changes you can make …form to fill out with your doctor that will help you take your medications safely and correctly. English/Spanish.

Source: Alliance for Aging Research, 2021 K St. NW, Ste. 305, Washington, DC 20006. Web site: www.aging research.org.

Take Care of Your Heart

When you call the American Heart Association's toll-free hotline, your call will be routed to your local AHA office for the latest information on heart disease, stroke, high blood pressure and diet. Many offices can tell you about local support groups in your area and low-cost or even free screenings for blood pressure and cholesterol. Call 800-AHA-USA-1 or visit www.americanheart.org.

Stay Young at Heart

The National Institute on Aging would like you to have a copy of "For Hearts and Arteries: What Scientists Are Learning About Age and the Cardiovascular System." Learn how the latest research can help keep your heart running younger, no matter what your age. Call toll-free 800-222-2225. *Or write to:*

NIA Information Center
PO Box 8057
Gaithersburg, MD 20898-8057
www.nih.gov/nia

Discover the World of Natural Medicine

If you are interested in learning about natural remedies and natural products and their effects on your body, send for this catalog of homeopathic remedies. Enzymatic Therapy and Learning offers natural methods to help you feel better. They will include a coupon worth $3 to try any product. To get a free product guide and a list of stores in your area, call the consumer information line at 800-783-2286. www.enzymatictherapy.com

Cold Sore Tip

If you are prone to cold sores, ask your doctor about Denavir. It is a prescription medication. Research shows that applying the cream immediately after a cold sore first appears and then reapplying it every two hours helps cold sores disappear a full day earlier. www.denavir.com

Use Biofeedback to Stay Healthy

Do you ever wonder how the process of reward gratification works? Well, the same principle applies in the use of biofeedback therapy. Biofeedback is an alternative method of treatment where your body learns to detect and control various functions. Learn more about these techniques and how they can contribute to making you healthier and happier. For information about certified biofeedback professionals, *send a business-sized SASE to:*

Biofeedback Certification Institute of America
10200 W. 44 Ave., Ste. 310
Wheat Ridge, CO 80033
303-420-2902
www.bcia.org

Help for Back Troubles

The BackSaver catalog has a wonderful assortment of all types of products for your back, including

chairs, seat and back support cushions, sleeping supports, reading tables and more. The catalog is free. Call 800-222-5728, or *write to:*

BackSaver Products Co.
53 Jeffrey Ave.
Holliston, MA 01746
www.backsavercorp.com

Conquer Bladder Problems

Did you know that nearly half a million people suffer from interstitial cystitis, an often misdiagnosed chronic bladder disorder. The National Institutes of Health has published a booklet that gives basic information on this disease in easy-to-understand layman's terms. Ask for the Interstitial Cystitis booklet. *It is free when you contact:*

IC Booklet
National Kidney and Urologic Diseases Information Clearinghouse
3 Information Way
Bethesda, MD 20892
301-496-4000
www.nih.gov

Curbing Teen Smoking

If you have a teenager, you know that one of the most harmful things peer pressure may cause teens to do is to start smoking. Without the proper guidance, teens may begin a lifelong battle with this dangerous habit. The Centers for Disease Control's Offices on Smoking and Health will help you tackle questions on what you can do to curb teen smoking. For specific advice, call them at 800-CDC-1311 or visit www.cdc.gov/tobacco.

Secrets to a Healthy Heart

The American Heart Association has a valuable toll-free helpline. By calling it, you can receive free copies of a host of booklets dealing with heart-related topics. Topics include blood pressure, CPR, cholesterol, diet, exercise, heart disease and stroke, to mention just a few. Learn the best ways to eat smart and healthy by reducing fat in your diet. You can also learn how to read the new food labels so that you will be purchasing healthier foods. Ask for "ShopSmart with Heart" and "Eating Plan for Healthy Americans."

You can also ask for any other heart-related topics you are interested in. Call toll-free 800-AHA-USA-1, or go online at www.americanheart.org. *Or write to:*

American Heart Association
National Center
7272 Greenville Ave.
Dallas, TX 75231

Before Having a Joint Replacement

If you or anyone you know ever needs a joint replacement, you will want to read the valuable information in this booklet. You will learn why and when a replacement is necessary, how it is performed, the benefits versus the risks and lots more. Ask for "Total Joint Replacement."

American Academy of Orthopaedic Surgeons
6300 N. River Rd.
Rosemont, IL 60018
800-346-AAOS
www.aaos.org

Fast Facts About Arthritis. Information on signs and types and treatment options.
Source: Arthritis Foundation National Office, 1330 W. Peachtree St., Atlanta, GA 30309. 800-283-7800. www.arthritis.org

Dairy Lover's Dream. Test your knowledge, take nutrition quiz, free product information sheets. All on the Web site of the National Dairy Council... www.nationaldairy council.org, then click on "Myths/Facts, Quizzes and Tips."

Sleep Hotline

The American Society of Travel Agents and Searle are happy to provide you with tips on how to feel your best while traveling. Request a free booklet called "Sleep Well...Stay Fit—Tips for Travelers." Call toll-free 800-SHUTEYE. www.astanet.com

Now Hear This

If you are experiencing hearing loss and your doctor has recommended a hearing aid, you may need help in determining what kind of device you need. The American Speech-Language-Hearing Association offers general information about hearing aids and their costs, insurance coverage, proper fit and care. For a free copy of "Audiologist's Hearing Services," call toll-free 800-638-8255. Or online at www.asha.org.

The Latest on Cancer

To help you keep informed about the most up-to-date information about cancer, the National Cancer Institute has a toll-free number. When you call, ask for free publications, for help locating FDA-approved mammography facilities or to speak with cancer specialists. Call 800-4-CANCER. Or visit the Web site at www.nci.nih.gov.

What to Do About Prostate Cancer

Did you know that next to lung cancer, prostate cancer is the #2 cancer killer of men? Almost every man will have some type of prostate problem if he lives long enough. Fortunately, with the modern advances in medicine and drug therapies, help is close at hand. The first step is to inform yourself about this problem and the newest treatments for it. To get a copy of the free "Prostate Information" package or for answers to specific questions, *contact:*

National Kidney and Urologic Diseases Information Clearinghouse
Three Information Way
Bethesda, MD 20892-3580
You can also call 301-654-4415, or visit the Web site at www.niddk.nih.gov.

The Facts About Prostate Cancer

Publications by the National Cancer Institute answer the most often asked questions about prostate cancer. They also include information on problems that might indicate prostate cancer, although the disease can often exist without symptoms. While this cancer is of prime concern to men over 55, the experts advise all men over 40 to get tested annually. The free booklets cover the specifics of diagnosis, treatment and prognosis. The prognosis is excellent if the condition is caught early enough. Call 800-4-CANCER.

Essential Cancer Hotline

If you were diagnosed with an advanced cancer, imagine how great it would be to find out that there is a clinical trial program with new and promising treatments for the type of cancer you have? In fact, there is a toll-free number you can call for help. The National Cancer Institute's Information Service provides the latest information about cancer, including causes, referrals to low-cost clinics, medical consultation, referrals to patient support groups and publications.

The hotline can provide you with literature and answer questions on various types of cancer and standard treatment. Call 800-4-CANCER (or 800-422-6237). Also visit the Web site at www.nci.nih.gov. For information on clinical trials, click on the "Clinical Trial" option. You may also *write to:*

> **National Cancer Institute**
> Public Inquiries
> 31 Center Dr., MSC 2580, Bldg. 31
> Room 10A31
> Bethesda, MD 20892

For Allergy and Asthma Sufferers

If you have questions about allergies or asthma, here's a place to find some answers. The Asthma and Allergy Foundation will answer any questions you have regarding the symptoms of allergies to different substances and foods and how allergies might be related to asthma. Call 800-7-ASTHMA, or visit their Web site at www.aafa.org.

Parent Resource Guide

It is important for children to develop good eating habits when they are young so they will grow up to be healthier, more active adults. The American Academy of Pediatrics has some important nutrition information just for the asking. *Send a business-sized SASE to:*

> **Nutrition Brochures, Dept. C**
> **The American Academy of Pediatrics**
> 141 Northwest Point Blvd.
> Elk Grove Village, IL 60007
> 847-434-4000
> www.aap.org

Fiber Facts

Research shows that eating fresh fruits and vegetables puts more fiber in your diet and helps you stay healthy. Finding out more about the vitamins, minerals and fiber in fruits and vegetables is essential to good health. "A Healthier You" also includes healthy recipes. Go online at www.aicr.org, or *send an SASE to:*

> **American Institute for Cancer Research**
> 1759 R St. NW
> Washington, DC 20009
> 800-843-8114

ABCs of Eye Care

The Vision Council of America and the Better Vision Institute have some important information about your eyes and how to take the best care of them. Topics include everything from the proper selection of eyeglass frames, to eye care for children and adults, tips on correct lighting, choosing the correct type

Bladder Control for Women. Causes of control problems...effective treatments.

Source: National Kidney and Urologic Diseases Information Clearinghouse, Three Information Way, Bethesda, MD 20892-3580. 301-654-4415.

Intimacy and Depression. How to keep depression and antidepressants from disrupting your personal relations.

Source: American Association for Marriage and Family Therapy, 1133 15 St. NW, Ste. 300, Washington, DC 20005. 202-452-0109. www.aamft.org

of sunglasses and more. Call 877-642-3253, or go online at www.visionsite.org, or *send a business-sized SASE to:*

> **Vision Council of America**
> **Better Vision Institute**
> 1700 Diagonal Rd., Ste. 500
> Alexandria, VA 22314

Depression Alert

Today, even though most of us are very aware of everything around us, we sometimes repress or deny the signs of depression in ourselves or those around us. There is some very useful information on depression published by the National Institute of Mental Health (NIMH). Learn all the facts and become aware. Call 800-421-4211, or go online at www.nimh.nih.gov.

Send a business-sized SASE and request the "Depression Awareness" information package:

> **NIMH Public Inquiries**
> 6001 Executive Blvd., Room 8184
> MSC 9663
> Bethesda, MD 20892-9663

Tension and Depression Hotline

Chronic tension and depression are two emotionally debilitating illnesses that you can do something about. The National Mental Health Association has a great deal of information on how to handle the problems of both tension and depression. If you have any questions about these conditions or want information, call the National Mental Health Association toll-free at 800-969-6642, or go online at www.nmha.org,

key in "Resource Center" in the search box.

Helping Others Have Healthy Teeth

We only get one set of permanent adult teeth which makes it essential to learn how to keep them strong and cavity free. For some, dental care is also a very important career opportunity that also allows you to help others take care of their teeth. If you know someone who may be interested in finding out more about career options, tell that person about this Web site at www.adha.org, or s*end a business-sized SASE to:*

> **American Dental Hygienists'**
> **Association**
> 444 N. Michigan Ave., Ste. 3400
> Chicago, IL 60611

The Mind-Body Connection

When used properly, the mind is a powerful instrument that can be used to stay well. To learn just how powerful your mind can be in controlling your body and to learn how your mind can help you heal yourself, get the free Resource Directory from The Institute of Noetic Sciences. Call toll-free 800-383-1586, or go to the Web at www.noetic.org.

Do You Really Need a Hysterectomy?

The American College of Obstetricians and Gynecologists has published a free brochure,

"Understanding Hysterectomy." It outlines what constitutes a medically necessary hysterectomy and describes what the surgery involves. Before having this operation, request a free copy from ACOG by calling 202-863-2518. www.acog.com

Hiking Fact Sheets

Whether you are walking to lose weight, exploring a tourist attraction or hiking to enjoy scenic trails, there are a number of guidelines to follow. *Send an SASE and ask for "Hiking Fact Sheets" from:*

American Hiking Society
1422 Fenwick Ln.
Silver Spring, MD 20910
www.americanhiking.org
Or you can download the information.

More Brain Power

Have you wanted to improve your creativity, enhance mental functioning, induce deep relaxation and reduce stress. It might sound too good to be true, but Comptronic Devices says it can be done through the use of a product called the DAVID Light and Sound devices. There is even a special application to improve sports performance. To get free information on this amazing device, *write:*

Comptronic Devices Limited
9008 51 Ave.
Edmonton, Alberta, Canada T6E 5X4
800-661-MIND (6463)
www.comptronic.com

Relax with Massage Therapy

Stress got you down? Maybe you need a good massage. The Massage Therapy booklet outlines detailed information about different methods of massage and the benefits of each type. It will also answer questions about stress and why massage therapy works. *Write to:*

American Massage Therapy Association
820 Davis St., Ste. 100
Evanston, IL 60201
www.amtamassage.org
Or you can download the information.

Consult with a Dietician

Are you curious about how your diet might be affecting your health? Call the nutrition hotline of the American Institute for Cancer Research and ask a registered dietician your personal questions on diet, nutrition and cancer. When you call, leave your question with an operator and a dietician will call you back within 48 hours to answer your question. Call between 9 a.m. and 5 p.m. EST, Monday through Friday. Call 800-843-8114.

Keep Your Child Healthy

A multitude of easy-to-use, free brochures and pamphlets on becoming a parent are available from Met Life. "Becoming a Parent," "Eating Right," "Little Miracles: Your Baby's First Years"and more. Call 800-MET-LIFE and ask about the Life Advice Program on Parenting.

Choosing a Psychiatrist. How to select the best one for you...referral sources. *Source:* American Psychiatric Association, Division of Public Affairs, Dept. BL99, 1400 K St. NW, Washington, DC 20005 ...or on the Web at www. psych.org, or call 888-357-7924.

The Sun, UV and You: A Guide to the UV Index and Sun-Safe Behavior.
Ultraviolet A, B and C radiation…melanoma and precancerous actinic keratoses…cataracts… sun-protection strategies.
Source: Consumer Information Center, Dept. 542E, Pueblo, CO 81009.

Facts About Iron

To understand the effects that iron and iron deficiency have on a child's health development, get a free brochure from the makers of Good Start Infant Formula and Follow-Up Formula. Ask for the "Iron" brochure. You will also learn that although iron is essential for your baby, it is just as essential to a mature adult. Call 800-782-7776. *Or send a business-sized SASE to:*

Nestlé Infant Nutrition
Iron Brochure Offer
PO Box AW
Wilkes Barre, PA 18703
www.nestleusa.com

Family Health Record— A Must

Every member of the family should keep a written medical record. It will be useful to you in filling out insurance forms, as well as school and travel documents. It can also be vital in helping a physician diagnose a medical problem a family member might have. Handy health record books are available from the March of Dimes. If you would like, they will also send you information on prenatal and natal care, a guide to a healthy pregnancy and information on children's growth and development. Also available are other informative brochures for teens about drugs and sexually transmitted disease. Call 888-MODIMES (663-4637), or *write to:*

March of Dimes Birth Defects Foundation
1275 Mamaroneck Ave.
White Plains, NY 10605
www.modimes.org

Health at Home

Cayce Care Health Products are manufactured and distributed by Baar, the official supplier of Edgar Cayce products for health, beauty and wellness. The catalog is filled with dozens of products to help you feel and look your best. There is everything including juices, vitamins and minerals. *Write to:*

Baar Products, Inc.
PO Box 60
Downingtown, PA 19335
800-269-2502
www.edgarcayce.org

Help for the Visually Handicapped

A useful series of publications is free to those with impaired vision. Printed in very large type are instructions for knitting, crocheting and gardening. Children's books are also available. Guides for the partially sighted include a dial operator personal directory.

For a complete listing, write:
National Association for Visually Handicapped
22 W. 21 St.
New York, NY 10010
212-889-3141
For Western states:
3201 Balboa St.
San Francisco, CA 94121
415-221-3201
Or go to their Web site at www.navh.org.

Johnson & Johnson Hotline

Where can you turn for answers to your questions concerning hygiene, personal care and baby care? To help you with answers to these questions, Johnson & Johnson has set up a toll-free consumer information hotline. Call with your questions Monday through Friday, between 8 a.m. and 6 p.m. EST. The toll-free hotline is 800-526-3967. www.jnj.com

Help for Deaf Children

Every year more than 200,000 children are born deaf or suffer hearing loss in the first years of life. The "Speech and Hearing Checklist" tells parents how to detect possible deafness in their children. Another useful booklet, "So Your Child Has a Hearing Loss: Next Step for Parents" is for parents of children who may be deaf or hard of hearing. *Both are free from:*

> **Alexander Graham Bell Association for the Deaf**
> 3417 Volta Pl. NW
> Washington, DC 20007
> www.agbell.org

Medical Supply Source

If you have a disability or illness that requires you to use medical equipment or supplies, you can order your medical supplies from home and save up to 40%–60%. Ask for a free catalog from America's leading mail-order medical supply catalog, Bruce Medical Supply. Call 800-225-8446. www.brucemedical.com

Questions About Medicare?

If you have questions or problems regarding Medicare, there is a toll-free number to call for help. You can get additional information regarding a Medicare claim, as well as general information about Medicare and its services. They can also help you with information on insurance supplements to Medicare, mammograms and lots more. Call 800-MEDICARE. www.medicare.gov

Physical Fitness for  Seniors

It is always a great idea to get in shape and stay in shape. Remember, if you take better care of your body, it will take better care of you. The President's Council on Physical Fitness and Sports has useful information that can add years to your life. The information includes an introduction to exercise, weight control, physical fitness, sports, running and lots more. Here are a few titles to consider:

• "Pep Up Your Life: A Fitness Book for Mid-Life and Older Persons"

• "Surgeon General's Report Fact Sheet—Older Adults"

• "Exercise and Weight Control"

• "Fitness Fundamentals: Guidelines for Personal Exercise Programs"

Call 202-690-9000, or *write to:*

> **The President's Council on Physical Fitness and Sports (PCPFS)**
> Department W
> 200 Independence Ave. SW, Room 738-H
> Washington, DC 20201-0004
> www.fitness.gov

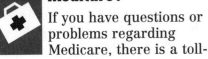

Grandparents' Guide for Family Nurturing And Safety. Safety checklist for caring for children from birth to age five.
Source: Consumer Information Center, Dept. 606E, Pueblo, CO 81009.

Now You Have a Diagnosis: What's Next? Help with making the best treatment decisions.

Source: Agency for Healthcare Research and Quality, 2101 E. Jefferson St., Ste. 501, Rockville, MD 20852. Or online at www.ahrq.gov.

What to Ask Your Doctor Before Surgery

If you are considering having any type of non-emergency surgery, be sure to get a free copy of "Questions to Ask Your Doctor Before You Have Surgery." It will help you be informed about the options and risks involved. Call the U.S. Public Health Service toll-free at 800-358-9295. Or visit the Web site at www.ahrq.gov.

Sexually Transmitted Diseases Hotline

If you suspect that you have contracted a sexually transmitted disease (STD), there is a toll-free hotline sponsored by the Centers for Disease Control to call for help and information. The specialists there will answer your questions concerning STDs, describe the symptoms that are the warning signs of disease and tell you how to get help. You will be referred to free or low-cost public health clinics or doctors in your area. They will also send you free brochures concerning STDs. Call Monday through Friday, between 8 a.m. and 8 p.m., 800-227-8922. www.cdc.gov

Eat Your Way to a Healthy Heart

Would like a copy of the American Heart Association's recommendations for a healthy heart, which include lists of good and bad foods, plus practical suggestions for cutting out the bad stuff? Ask for "Exercise Your Heart: A Guide to Physical Activity," "An Eating Plan for Healthy Americans,"

"Understanding and Controlling Your Cholesterol" and "Recipes for Low-Fat, Low-Cholesterol Meals." *Just send an SASE to:*

American Heart Association
National Center
7272 Greenville Ave.
Dallas, TX 75231
800-242-8721
www.americanheart.org

Avoiding Skin Cancer

Prevention is always far better than a cure. And one of the most preventable diseases is skin cancer. To find out what you can do to prevent this disease, get a copy of the free booklet "How to Spot Skin Cancer: If You Can Spot It, You Can Stop It." *Send a business-sized SASE to:*

The Skin Cancer Foundation
245 Fifth Ave., Suite 1403
New York, NY 10016
800-SKIN-490
www.skincancer.org

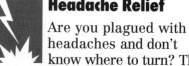

Headache Relief

Are you plagued with headaches and don't know where to turn? The American Council for Headache Education may be able to offer you a solution on how to lessen your pain and discomfort. Call them toll-free at 800-255-ACHE. www.achenet.org

Free Contact Lenses

If you wear contact lenses or are thinking of getting them, Johnson & Johnson would like you to try their Acuvue contacts. They have made arrangements with local optometrists throughout the country to supply you with your first pair. All you have to do is ask an optometrist in your area who carries Acuvue contacts for a free pair or visit www.acuvue.com.

Save 50% on Contact Lenses

To save up to 50% on contact lenses, consider buying them by mail order from a company called 1-800-CONTACTS, Inc. They carry a full line of first-rate contact lenses in all prescriptions from all manufacturers. The toll-free order line is easy to remember since it's the same as the company name: 800-CON-TACTS (or 800-266-8228). Or go to www.contacts.com.

Important Health Hotlines

To help answer various health questions here are some important toll-free hotlines:

Calcium Information Center
800-321-2681

Food Allergy Network
800-929-4040

Milk Consumer Hotline
800-WHY-MILK

American Dietetic Association
800-366-1655

National Osteoporosis Foundation
800-223-9994

Cancer Hotline

If you have been diagnosed with any type of cancer, call the toll-free Cancer Hotline. They will put you in touch with someone who has had the same type of cancer and will help you deal with the initial fear. Speaking with another person who has had to deal with the same disease that you have can be highly informative and enormously comforting. Call 800-433-0464.

Help Your Doctor Help You

Next time you are suffering from pain and discomfort and are unable to easily pinpoint exactly what hurts, follow this checklist. It will not only help you identify the problem but also could help the doctor diagnose the ailment.

• When did the pain or symptoms start?
• Did it follow an accident?
• Does it happen before meals or after meals?
• Did symptoms develop gradually or suddenly?
• Are the symptoms intermittent or constant?
• Are symptoms worse in certain positions, such as sitting or lying down, or at certain times, such as morning or evening, or during certain activities?
• How have the symptoms affected your normal activities?
• Make a list of prescription and nonprescription drugs you are taking.
• Describe your pain. Words like cramping, sharp, throbbing and aching, all give different information to your doctor.

The best way to assist your doctor is to provide accurate information about your medical concerns.

Don't Let Diabetes Get a Foothold on Your Life. Warning signs...dos and don'ts ...how your feet are affected by diabetes. *Source:* American Podiatric Medical Association, 9312 Old Georgetown Rd., Bethesda, MD 20814. Include a business-sized SASE. 800-FOOT-CARE, www.apma.org.

Warts. Conventional and alternative treatments for plantar, flat, genital and other warts. *Source:* American Academy of Dermatology, 930 N. Meacham Rd., PO Box 4014, Schaumburg, IL 60168-4014. 888-462-DERM. Available online at www.aad.org, then go to "Patient Education."

Apples, Yes—Cancer, No

A Finnish study of 10,000 adults who ate three apples a week appears to show a 58% reduction in risk of lung cancer. Apples are high in quercetin, an antioxidant that appears to be protective against lung cancer.

Everyday Exercise

Are you looking for a great exercise routine? No need to look any further. Here are a few tips to get you going:

• Do some spring cleaning around the house and scrub the floor a little harder.
• Do gardening and yard work.
• Clean out the attic and the garage.
• Walk, don't drive.
• Look for a fun aerobic workout or dance class. Try learning one of those new funky dance steps.

The Value of Vitamin E

In a recent survey of medical doctors asking which vitamins they took on a regular basis, it was found that 40% of the doctors took vitamin E. A study of men aged 50 to 69 found that those who took 50 mg of vitamin E daily for five to eight years lowered their risk of prostate cancer by 32%. Even among those who did get cancer, vitamin E reduced their chances of dying from it by 41%.

No one is quite certain just how vitamin E protects us against this cancer, but the vitamin's antioxidant powers are purported to prevent cell damage, which sets the stage for cancer. Other studies suggest that vitamin E may reduce the risk of heart attacks, too. If taking a supplement, consider taking 400 IUs of vitamin E for maximum protection. Be sure to buy natural vitamin E, which is absorbed by your system better than the synthetic form.

Chew Away Heartburn

If you are prone to getting heartburn after eating a hearty meal, try chewing gum for one-half hour after meals. Chewing gum boosts saliva production, which neutralizes stomach acid and washes it away from the esophagus where it can irritate tender tissues.

Another Reason to Stop Smoking

Along with all of the serious health risks that have been linked to smoking, there is now a new risk. A study shows that smokers are twice as likely to suffer age-related hearing loss as nonsmokers. Researchers speculate that smoking reduces blood flow to the ear.

Women—Cut Your Risk of Heart Attack

In a recent study of 80,000 women, Harvard researchers found that there was a greater risk of having a heart attack among women who eat lots of partially hydrogenated vegetable oils, also known as trans fats (found in margarine and many other processed foods), than among women who eat more saturated fats (found in butter, steak and other animal foods). Check food packages and cut back on those that list hydrogenated vegetable oils as an ingredient. If you use margarine, remember that the harder the spread, the more trans fats it contains. If you must, use soft or liquid margarine instead.

Sprains & Strains: What They Are, What to Do About Them

Now you can find out about the common sprains and strains in this free brochure. Write to the American College of Sports Medicine at PO Box 14401, Indianapolis 46202. Include a self-addressed, stamped, business-sized envelope.

Child Health Care

Send for a list of immunization schedules...tests...nutrition...more. Write to the Agency for Healthcare Research and Quality, PO Box 8547, Silver Spring, MD 20907.

Congestive Heart Failure: What You Should Know. Seven common causes...shortness of breath, fluid buildup and other signs of heart failure... dietary changes, medications, surgery and other treatments.

Source: American Heart Association, 7272 Greenville Ave., Dallas, TX 75231. 800-242-8721. www.american heart.org

Health
Web Sites

Health Web Sites

There is so much material on the World Wide Web that people new to the Internet often find searching for information a bit overwhelming at first. To help make your search simple and successful, there are a number of useful search resources you can use to locate a wide range of information.

For example, if you would like to explore the area of health, two of the best search engines to use are Lycos and Yahoo. Just by typing in their Web address and following the directions below, you will instantly be able to find the latest health-related news, information and answers to many of your health-related questions.

Lycos
www.lycos.com

Click on the "Health" button and you will be connected to Lycos Health with WebMD, a comprehensive source for health news.

Yahoo
www.yahoo.com

This may be your best bet. Yahoo Health offers a breakdown of about 50 categories, ranging from alternative medicine to hospitals to public health & safety.

...For America Online (AOL) Subscribers

AOL Time Warner has a Health channel with WebMD (keyword: "Health"). There you will find a health library, Diseases and Conditions with Mayo Clinic, and health resources, support groups and the very useful Drug database.

...Here Are Specific Health Sites to Visit on the World Wide Web

Health A to Z
www.healthatoz.com

This is designed to be a health navigational tool. Health A to Z is useful both for medical professionals and consumers. To locate information, you can either enter your own search words or click on one of about 30 categories for a listing of related sites.

Healthfinder
www.healthfinder.gov

This is a consumer health and human services information Web site produced by the US government. It leads you to online publications, clearinghouses, databases, related Web sites, support groups and government agencies that deal with health issues.

Medsite
www.medsite.com

Enter a medical or health keyword, click on the "Search" button and you will be on your way.

National Institutes of Health Information
www.nih.gov

This includes MEDLINE plus, patient information and journals. It is very well organized.

Mayoclinic.com
www.mayoclinic.com

Here you will find news and information on most medical conditions and guidelines, all from the world-renowned Mayo Clinic.

Ask Dr. Weil
www.drweil.com

Dr. Andrew Weil's site is for those who are interested in finding alternatives to traditional medicine.

Better Health. Prescription-drug database covers benefits of more than 4,500 medications...dosages... interactions. On the Web at www.rxlist.com

Health News You Can Use: Approved drugs, surgical techniques, etc.

Source: www.pslgroup.com.

Family Caregiver Alliance
www.caregiver.org

This site combines a clearing-house for publications, newsletters, diagnoses and research with a resource center for care services, public policy and links.

Arthritis Foundation
www.arthritis.org

For comprehensive information on arthritis, call the Arthritis Foundation toll-free at 800-283-7800. For a brochure on rheumatoid arthritis, call toll-free 877-467-3472, or visit the Web site.

...More Arthritis Information

For more information on the latest research on arthritis, you will also want to visit the following Web sites:

www.rheumatology.org
www.niams.nih.gov

Volunteer
Just for
The Health of It

Volunteer Just for the Health of It

We all know that it is better to give than to receive, but did you know that studies have shown that people who volunteer actually live longer, happier, healthier lives? Volunteering has been shown to reduce anxiety, plus it provides people with a renewed sense of purpose and a feeling of fulfillment.

Besides, seniors (folks 50+ years young) have a lot to give. They have a wealth of knowledge, talent and experience (not to mention a wealth of wisdom), to share with others. Remember, giving your time to help someone else helps you as well. Plus, one day you may be on the receiving end of such aid. If you have a little time and would like to make a difference in your life and in the life of someone else or if you currently need help, here are a few places to start.

The National Senior Service Corps for National Service

This is a network of more than one-half million seniors who are making a difference through the following programs:

Foster Grandparents

In this program seniors are caring for kids. They help children who have been abused or neglected. Also, they mentor troubled teenagers and young mothers and care for premature infants or children with physical disabilities.

Senior Companion Program (SCP)

Isn't it wonderful to help a friend in need? With this program there is help for seniors who have difficulty with day-to-day tasks or who have lost family and friends and need help getting things done. Senior Companions not only provide assistance and friendship but also help with such chores as paying bills, grocery shopping, providing a ride to medical appointments and more. Senior Companions receive training in Alzheimer's, stroke, diabetes and mental health, so they are able to alert doctors and family members to potential problems.

Retired Senior Volunteer Program (RSVP)

This program has helped people 55 and older put their skills and life experience to work for others. As an RSVP volunteer, you might teach English to immigrants, organize a neighborhood watch or help people recover from natural disasters. The number of hours you serve is flexible. You will receive appropriate on-the-job training from the agency or organization where you are placed.

For all of the above, call the National Senior Service Corps at 800-424-8867. Or contact them at www.seniorcorps.org.

Service Corps of Retired Executives (SCORE)

This program, sponsored by the US Small Business Administration, matches volunteers with

Steps to Enhancing Communication: Interacting with Persons with Alzheimer's Disease. How to better understand Alzheimer's disease…advice for improving communications…large-print format.
Source: Alzheimer's Association, 919 N. Michigan Ave., Ste. 1100, Chicago, IL 60611. 800-272-3900, or www.alz.org.

Being an Organ Donor. What organs can be donated...who can be a donor and how to become one.
Source: MetLife Consumer Education Center, 800-638-5433. Item #309. www.metlife.org

small businesses in need of advice. If you are thinking of joining the ranks of entrepreneurs, this is the place to get free advice from a seasoned pro. On the other hand, if you are a retired executive and would like to help other budding businesspeople get started on the right foot, call for information on how you can be of service. The toll-free number is 800-634-0245, or on the Web at www.score.org.

Global Volunteers Make a World of Difference

If you have always thought about joining the Peace Corps but hesitated because you were unable to make the required two-year commitment, Global Volunteers may be for you. For more than 14 years, Global Volunteers has sent people to 18 countries around the world for stays of two or three weeks. You will be a part of a team of 10 to 20 volunteers, plus host-country participants, and will work on projects that might include teaching English, improving health care, working on forest trails and teaching business practices.

Since Global Volunteers is a private nonprofit organization, participants pay their own transportation as well as a land package and administration fee that averages $2,000. But this entire outlay is tax-deductible, including the cost of transportation to and from the country.

What a great way to see the world and to help others at the same time. For more information about Global Volunteers, call 800-487-1074, or go online at www.globalvolunteers.org.

American Association of Retired Persons (AARP)

AARP provides a variety of volunteer programs, services and activities that help older Americans. One example is the Widowed Persons Service (for widows and widowers). With this program, a widowed person can meet with another widowed volunteer in his or her area for mutual friendship and support. Another service offered is a program that will refer you to organizations in your area either to volunteer your services or to be helped by a volunteer. For a full information package on all of the services offered, call AARP at 800-424-3410, or visit their Web site at www.aarp.org.

Peace Corps

The Peace Corps can give you a chance to immerse yourself in a totally different culture while helping to make an important difference in other people's lives. If you like helping people and want to get involved, get the Peace Corps information package. Call toll-free 800-424-8580, or go to www.peacecorps.gov.

Local Volunteering Is Fun, Too

Consider volunteer opportunities in your town and check the phone book for the local chapter of the following organizations to see which volunteer programs are active:

- American Cancer Society
- Chamber of Commerce
- Forest and Wildlife Service
- Forest Service Volunteers
- Hospice
- Lions Club
- National Parks Service
- Red Cross
- Respite
- Rotary Club
- United Way
- Vista

Volunteer Information On the Web

Check out these Web sites that specialize in information about volunteer opportunities:

SERVEnet
www.servenet.org

Action Without Borders
www.idealist.org

Habitat for Humanity
www.habitat.org

Americares
www.americares.org

Green Volunteers
www.greenvol.com

Volunteer Today
www.volunteertoday.com

When a Friend Has a Chronic Illness. What to say—and not to say. Also, how to help.

Source: Rest Ministries, PO Box 502928, San Diego, CA 92150. Include a business-sized SASE. Or call toll-free at 888-751-REST (7378). On the Web at www.restministries.org.

47

Free Health
And
Beauty Aids

Free Health and Beauty Aids

For many large companies the best way to promote their products is directly to the consumer. And what better way of doing it than by giving you a free sample? If you are satisfied with it, then most likely you will pass it on to your friends and family and ultimately the company will have more loyal customers. Everyone comes out ahead.

Some of the free samples listed below may have limited availability, so call soon.

10 Steps to Healthy White Teeth

The makers of Rembrandt toothpaste want you to be aware of how you can keep your teeth healthy and white. To show you how to do that they want you to visit "The Dentist Is In" on their Web site. You will be sent valuable information on aging teeth. And, along with a free coupon when you buy a tube of Rembrandt Low Abrasion Whitening Toothpaste or Dazzling White Bleaching System, you can receive a free 3oz tube of Rembrandt whitening toothpaste, they will send coupons worth a total of $7.00 off your next purchases of Rembrandt Oral Care Products. To get free samples and the coupons, call toll-free 800-548-3663. (Request option 2.) www.rembrandt.com

Canker Sore Aid

If you have canker sores in your mouth, call this toll-free hotline for information on a toothpaste specifically designed to relieve your problem. Call 800-548-3663. Request option 1.

Take Care of Your Skin

Alpha Hydrox will be happy to send you information about all of their skin products and how they can work for you. The company also has a consumer hotline updated monthly which describes their products and where they are available. If you are interested in finding out about facial, body care and foot care products, call 800-55-ALPHA. www.touchofscent.com/neoteric-cosmetics/index.html

Migraine Pain Management

For anyone who suffers from the excruciating pain of a migraine headache, "Chart Your Route to Relief" is a personal migraine management program which actually helps you find relief. It includes a comprehensive chart that will help you and your doctor pinpoint the cause. To get a free chart and a headache diary, simply request it when you *write to:*

Chart Your Route to Relief
PO Box 800
Wendell, NC 27591
800-377-0302
www.myparentime.com/articles/articles5134.shtml
Glaxo Wellcome, Inc.

Vascular Birthmarks. Causes of, and treatments for, the most troublesome—port-wine stains...macular stains ...hemangiomas.
Source: American Academy of Dermatology, Birthmarks, 930 N. Meacham Rd., PO Box 4014, Schaumburg, IL 60168-4014. Include a business-sized SASE. 847-330-0230
www.aad.org

Hand Eczema. Causes, treatments, how to protect your hands.
Source: American Academy of Dermatology, 888-462-3376. www.aad.org

Migraine Relief

If you suffer from migraine headaches, you will want to get the "Excedrin Migraine Tablets and Relief Guide." When you request it, you will also receive helpful information on dealing with migraine headaches. *Note:* You must be 18 or older to receive this offer.

Call them toll-free at 800-580-4455. Or visit their Web site at www.excedrin.com.

Free Earrings

Do your ears sting, turn black or become agonizingly painful when you put on your favorite gold earrings? Here is the answer to those sensitive ear woes. Once more you will be able to wear those fashionable earrings you always dreaded to put on because of the allergic reaction they caused. Simply Whispers will send you a catalog of their exclusive earrings made of top-quality surgical steel with the look of silver and 24-karat electroplated earrings for gold lovers. You will be sent a coupon valid for a free pair of earrings with your first order. Best of all, the earrings are guaranteed for life. You have a choice of pierced or clip-on styles. Call them toll-free at 800-451-5700. *Or write to:*
Simply Whispers
430 Court St.
Plymouth, MA 02360
www.simplywhispers.com

Pantyhose Problems?

The Hosiery Association (THA) would like to help you overcome the fear of stocking runs, snags and droops. The association will provide you with valuable information and helpful tips on how to determine your correct size, how to care for your stockings and how to make your hosiery last. When you call, you can also ask any specific questions you may have about stockings. Call 704-365-0913. Or go to www.nahm.com.

Leg Talk

Has this ever happened to you? You are down to your last pair of stockings and late for an important meeting when, for no apparent reason, the stockings run? Would you like to find out why this happens and what you can do about it? Send for a free copy of "Sheer Facts About Hosiery." *Send an SASE to:*
The Hosiery Association
3623 Latrobe Dr., Ste. 130
Charlotte, NC 28211
www.nahm.com

Ask the Hair-Color Experts

Are you thinking of changing your hair color? Having trouble finding the right shade? Can't cover that problem gray? The experts at Clairol have a toll-free hotline to call for answers to all of your hair-coloring questions. Their color consultants will also provide you with helpful tips to help you look your very best. They are available Monday through Friday, from 8:30 a.m. to 8:30 p.m., and Saturday from 9 a.m to 6 p.m., EST. Call them toll-free at 800-223-5800.

You can also visit the Clairol Women's Link Web site at www.clairol.com.

Hair Care Guidance and More

If you would like advice on how to manage your hair, how to color it or just how to keep it looking good, L'Oreal has the answers for you. Next time you are unable to decide which shampoo or conditioner is best for your hair type, call the toll-free L'Oreal Consumer Guideline, Monday through Friday, 10 a.m. to 7 p.m. EST, at 800-631-7358. *Or you can write to:*

L'Oreal Consumer Affairs
PO Box 98
Westfield, NJ 07091
Online at www.lorealusa.com

Healthy Diet, Healthy Looks

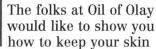 We have all heard the expression, "You are what you eat." Well, it appears to be true that the basics of looking good and feeling good start with healthy eating habits. The American Dietetic Association is making a concerted effort to get us back on a healthy eating track.

They have a toll-free line you can call weekdays for more information on healthy eating and for a referral to a local dietician. Call the Nutrition Information Line at 800-366-1655.

Keep It Clean

The folks at Oil of Olay would like to show you how to keep your skin clean and beautiful. When you click onto their Web site you will find a wealth of information, including makeup and cosmetic tips, plus hints on face and body care. You can even fill out a questionnaire online that will bring you free product samples. Check this out at www.oilofolay.com.

DOVESPA.com

When you visit the Dove Web site, you will be invited to join "My Dove." This club will give you access to join give access to: "Katie", your virtual skincare assistant, who will help you keep up with the latest in skincare and beauty information. You'll also get e-mail notification of exclusive offer and Dove promotions, an expanded gallery of e-cards and total access to past issues of *DoveDimensions Online*. 1-800-598-5005

Considering Cosmetic Surgery? Checklist to evaluate your doctor and his/her surgical facility. Free subscription to *About Face* on E.Zine®. *Source:* Robert Kotler, MD, FACS, 436 N. Bedford Dr., Ste. 201, Beverly Hills, CA 90210. Include a business-sized SASE. Or call 310-278-8721, Monday through Friday, 9 a.m. to 5 p.m. Also on the Web at www.bh4faces.com.

Cooking Up A Storm

Cooking Up a Storm

If you love to try new things, you are going to love the recipe collections in this section. The companies giving away these free cookbooks and recipe collections do so at great expense as their way of saying "thank you" to their loyal customers and also as a way of attracting new customers. They want to inspire you to even greater use of their products by showing you new and innovative ways of using them to create meals you and your family will enjoy.

Wonderful Cajun-Style Cooking

Get a free copy of Chef Paul Prudhomme's Magic Spice book and learn some of his cooking secrets. Imagine using the very same spices in your kitchen that he uses at his famous K-Paul's Louisiana Kitchen in New Orleans. Call toll-free 800-457-2857.

If you send either $1 or a business-sized SASE with 3 first-class stamps, he will send his most recent catalog, along with a sample of his Magic Seasoning Blends. *Send to:*

Magic Seasoning Blends
PO Box 23342
New Orleans, LA 70183-0342
www.chefpaul.com

If you sign up for Chef Paul's Fan Club, he will periodically send free recipes, tips, coupons, special holiday offers and more.

Delicious M&M Desserts

Everyone knows just how great M&Ms are all by themselves. But did you know they also make a great ingredient in desserts? The M&M recipe booklet tells you how to make delightful and fun desserts using M&Ms (unless of course you eat them all first). For a free copy call them toll-free at 800-627-7852. For a fun Web site with recipes, games, and more, go to www.m-ms.com.

Yummy Cranberries

Ocean Spray would like to show you some of the great things you can do with cranberries. The company will send you four different tasty recipe collections. Just ask for the "Lighten Your Style" brochure. Call toll-free at 800-662-3263, or go online at www.oceanspray.com.

Hints for a Healthier Diet

Today everyone is focusing on maintaining a healthy diet. Saco Foods will send you their excellent, "Hints for a Healthier Diet," which discusses oils, fats, fiber, snacks, meats and dairy products, fish and even the best canned foods. You will also receive free recipes for sinfully delicious cookies made with Saco delicious chocolate chunks. Call the "Bake Your Best" SACO foods consumer hotline toll-free at 800-373-SACO (or 800-373-7226), or visit the Web site at www.sacofoods.com. *Or write to:*

Saco Foods, Inc.
PO Box 620707
Middleton, WI 53562-0707

Soyfoods Guide. Where to find soy-containing foods in your supermarket...mail-order sources...nutritional content of soyfoods...more than 50 soy recipes. Free 24-page Soyfoods Guide 2001. *Source:* United Soybean Board, 800-989-USBI (8721). www.soybean.org

Pesticides and Food.
How to wash, peel and trim foods effectively ...special risks for children...resources for more information.
Source: Environmental Protection Agency, 800-490-9198. www.epa.gov

Fiesta Time

If you enjoy salsa and like to cook up those spicy Southwestern dishes, you will love this catalog of salsas and seasonings. You will surely enjoy the unique taste and the fun of trying some new ideas. To get a free catalog, call toll-free 800-43-SALSA (or 800-437-2572). *Or contact:*

Salsa Express
100 N. Tower Rd.
Alamo, TX 78516
www.salsaexpress.com

Wonderful Low-Fat Meals

If you would like to improve your diet with more low-fat meals, get "Simple Steps to Eating Smart" from Campbell's low-fat collection. In it is a wide variety of healthy, low-fat meals that are quick and easy to make. To get your collection, call toll-free at 800-257-8443, or go online at www.campbellsoup.com.

Low-Salt Recipes

If you would like to cut down on your salt intake without cutting down on taste, here is your chance. Try some of the tasty recipes using Nu-Salt, the salt substitute from the makers of Sweet 'N Low. In "Cooking with Nu-Salt" you will find a wide variety of sodium-reduced recipes—everything from light and healthy Spinach & Pasta Soup to Trout Almondine and Coq au Vin. For a copy, call the company toll-free at 800-206-9454. For more information, see their Web site at www.nusalt. com.

Eat More Grain

Near East Foods, the makers of great tasty rice, wheat and other grain products, would like to send you a free recipe booklet with interesting and delicious new ways to use healthy grains in your next meal. Call them toll-free at 800-399-4488. Also online at www.neareast.com.

Vegetarian Delight

Have you been thinking of becoming a vegetarian? Well, now is your chance. It's easy to stay on a vegetarian diet while you are home, but when you go on vacation, will you have to bring your own food? The Vegetarian Resource Group has a list of places throughout the US and Canada where you can enjoy vegetarian dining in addition to regular menus. To get a copy, *send a business-sized SASE to:*

The Vegetarian Resource Group
PO Box 1463
Baltimore, MD 21203
410-366-8343
Also available online at:
www.vrg.org/recipes/

200 Treats Under 200 Calories

Imagine trying some delicious low-calorie treats under 200 calories. Roman Meal has a terrific guide to low-calorie eating. It includes some great tips on calorie counting as well as tasty daily menus. They will even give you a diet nutrition plan to follow and some tasty recipe collections, including some baking ideas. *Write to:*

Roman Meal Co.
PO Box 11126
Tacoma, WA 98411
When you visit their Web site, there is a "family fun" section that includes projects, games and jokes.
www.romanmeal.com

Clam Lover's Special

Gorton's Seafood is delighted to send you their special recipe collection, "The Fisherman's Cookbook." You will be amazed at the myriad ways you can use Gorton's chopped or minced clams. You will learn new ways to make tasty appetizers as well as stuffed seafood and delicious pasta recipes. Call them toll-free at 800-222-6846, or go to www.gortons.com.

Mission Cafe Planner

Mission Foods has a wonderful recipe collection using a variety of tortilla products. You can start with the delicious strawberry breakfast crepes or try meatless tortilla lasagna. You will be delighted at all the tasty dishes you can make, from appetizers to main meals. They will also send you some coupons to try their products free. Call toll-free 800-443-7994. *Or write to:*

Mission Foodservice
PO Box 2008
Oldsmarr, FL 34677-7008
www.missionfoods.com

A-1 Steak Sauce and More

We all know that A-1 Steak Sauce makes a terrific addition to meat once it's on the plate, but did you know that it also make a great seasoning for all kinds of foods while they are being cooked? Learn about all of the great-tasting meals you can make by using A-1 Steak Sauce in new and innovative ways. Ask for the "A-1 Steak Sauce Recipe Book." Call 800-NABISCO. Or get featured recipes of all kinds on the company's Web site at www.nabisco.com.

Meat and Poultry Hotline

The US Department of Agriculture has a meat and poultry hotline to help you with questions dealing with food safety. There is a full series of recorded answers to the most commonly asked questions. And if you have specific questions, you can speak with a food safety expert. To speak with a specialist, call weekdays from 10 a.m. to 4 p.m., EST. For recorded messages, call 24 hours a day at 800-535-4555.
www.usda.gov

Creative Ways to Use Broth

The folks at College Inn Broth have a great recipe book to show you how to enhance all your dishes by using their chicken, beef and vegetable broths in new ways. To get a free copy, call them toll-free at 800-55-BROTH. Or go to their Web site at www.collegeinn.com.

Learn additional recipe ideas, serving tips, quick substitutions and more by subscribing to their free e-mail newsletter, *The Inn*.

The Guide to Gourmet Coffee. Flavors...roasts...types of pots and the right grind for them...recipes.
Source: Coffee Information Bureau, 800-299-2739. www.eightoclock.com, then click on "coffee shop"

Healthy Eating Away from Home. How to make healthy choices of all kinds in restaurants.
Source: American Institute for Cancer Research, 1759 R St. NW, Washington, DC 20009. Include a business-sized SASE. Online at www.aicr.org.

Flavorful Ways to Cut Back on Fat

Today we know just how important it is to cut back on our consumption of fat. But how do you do that without cutting back on flavor? For starters, try some great recipes using reduced-fat sour cream. Just ask for the "Changing Courses Recipe Collection." Call 800-782-9602 or visit www.landolakes.com

For Great Meals in Half the Time

Are you always in such a hurry that you never have the time to prepare a new nutritious main dish? Then now is the time to call the Rice-A-Roni/Noodle-Roni Main Dish Helpline. You will receive a recipe booklet full of rice and pasta recipes that are quick to prepare. Call them toll-free at 800-421-2444. *Or write to:*
> **The Golden Grain Co.**
> PO Box 049003
> Chicago, IL 60604-9003
> www.ricearoni.com

Free e-recipes and e-newsletter.

Prize-Winning Beef Recipes

If you would like to sample some of the best beef recipes in the nation, get a copy of the "National Beef Cook-off Prize-winning Recipes." You will find a host of delicious, easy-to-prepare meals, ranging from Chile Pizza to Grecian Skillet Ribeyes. Call toll-free 800-848-9088. *Or send an SASE to:*
> **National Beef Cook-off®**
> **Prize-winning Recipes**
> PO Box 3881
> Englewood, CO 80155

Also all recipes available online at: www.beefcookoff.org, then click on "Winning Recipes."

Sizzlin' Hot Stuff

Red Devil Hot Sauce is a zesty hot sauce that has a multitude of uses, in soups, stews, sandwiches and just about anywhere you want to add a lively taste to your food. For a compact collection of dozens of recipes, *send a postcard asking for "Wright with Liquid Smoke" and "Regina Cooking Wine".*
> **B&G Foods**
> PO Box K
> Roseland, NJ 07068
> 973-401-6500
> *Or go to:*
> www.bgfoods.com,
> and click on "Red Devil."

Fish Really Is Good for You

Research has shown that eating fish really is good for you. According to a study by the National Fisheries Institute, the average person eats a total of about 15 pounds of fish a year, or four ounces per week. Among the top 10 choices are salmon and catfish. The Catfish Institute has recipe brochures waiting for you. In them you will find a variety of ideas besides traditional high-fat frying. The brochures can be ordered free by sending an e-mail to The Catfish Institute. Go to www.catfishinstitute.com, then click on "Get free catfish stuff."
> **The Catfish Institute**
> PO Box 247
> 1118 Hayden St.
> Belzoni, MS 39038
> 662-247-4913

Cooking Light

We all know that what we eat affects our health. But exactly what foods are the best for our health? How do you prepare foods that are good for you? Now there is a toll-free number to call for answers to these and other questions you may have. This hotline, sponsored by *Healthy Cooking* magazine, will put you in touch with registered dietitians who will answer your questions about cooking light. Call between 8 a.m. and 4 p.m, CT weekdays. Call 800-231-3438.

Help for Bread Bakers

The Fleishmann's Yeast Bakers Help Line specializes in answering all of your questions about yeast and bread baking, including advice on using bread machines. Call this computerized hotline any time. Call 800-777-4959.

Tasty Sweet Nectar

Many people say that Golden Blossom Honey is the tastiest honey there is. To show you how to use their sweet and healthy nectar in new ways, you can access a multitude of recipes at http://209.67.56.157/home.htm. *Or write to:*

John Paton, Inc.
73 E. State St.
Doylestown, PA 18901

The Perfect Grill-Out

If you love to barbecue, you will adore the free booklet you can get simply by calling the Weber Grill Line at 800-GRILL-OUT. This toll-free phone number is in operation from April 1 to Labor Day each year, and each summer at new recipe booklet is available. You can also call the same hotline number to get answers to all of your barbecue questions, including cooking methods, fat-trimming tips, proper methods of clean-up and lots more. Or go to www.weber.com.

Fascinating Food Facts

The Department of Agriculture has a large package of fascinating and educational materials, including a handy food-pyramid guide waiting for you. Learn exactly what the USDA does in the areas of consumer services, food safety, nutrition and lots more. The pyramid guide is an excellent teaching and learning tool. *Write to:*

US Department of Agriculture
Publications Division
Washington, DC 20250
Or go to their Web site at:
www.usda.gov.

Fine Cheese Recipes

Six cheese recipes on file cards are available free from Marin French Cheese Company. Also included will be a mail-order price list for their fine line of cheeses. *Free from:*

Marin French Cheese Co.
7500 Red Hill Rd.
Petaluma, CA 94952
800-292-6001
www.marinfrenchcheese.com

Old-Fashioned Cookbook. Recipes for Scripture cake...bread and butter pickles... Civil War cornbread... scrapple...shepherd's pie...29 pages.
Source: West Virginia Department of Agriculture, 1900 Kanawha Blvd. E., Charleston, WV 25305.

What to Spread on Bread Instead.
Recipes for healthy and delicious spreads to make with olive oil.
Source: International Olive Oil Council, 800-232-6548.
www.internationaloliveoil.org

Poppin' Fresh Dough

The Pillsbury Doughboy brings you prize-winning recipes for cookies and pies. Make your next dessert a sweet and tasty delight. Call 877-975-BAKE to get recipes over the phone. *Or write:*
The Pillsbury Company
2866 Pillsbury Center
Minneapolis, MN 55402
Or go to their Web site at:
www.pillsbury.com

Just for Popcorn Lovers

If popcorn is one of your favorites, then the "Favorite Popcorn Recipes" collection is a must-have for you. It features mouth-watering popcorn balls, zesty treats and sweet and munchy snacks. *Send a postcard to:*
American Pop Corn Co.
PO Box 178
Sioux City, IA 51102
Or go to:
www.jollytime.com

Do You Have a Sweet Tooth?

Looking for new dessert ideas your whole family will enjoy? You will find lots of yummy dessert recipes and also learn how to cut the fat from sweets with "Prune the Fat" reduced-fat recipes. For a free copy and a discount coupon, *write to:*
Sokol & Co.
5315 Dansher Rd.
Countryside, IL 60525
800-328-7656
www.solofoods.com

Pasta—A Food for All Times

Here are three excellent booklets for the health conscious. There are terrific recipes plus lots of things you can add to pasta to come up with a new meal. There are even suggestions for quick microwave dishes. *Ask for "New World Pasta Recipes" from:*
New World Pasta
Consumer Relations
PO Box 126457
Harrisburg, PA 17112-6457
Or go to their Web site at:
www.nwpasta.com
Or call toll-free:
800-730-5957

Apple Sauce Deluxe

This great cookbook has some of the most delightful recipes using Lucky Leaf Apple Sauce. You will find recipes for everything from entrees to desserts to give your family new taste treats. It is yours *free from:*
Knouse Foods
800 Peach Glen Rd.
Peach Glen, PA 17375
717-677-8181
Or online at:
www.knouse.com

Do You Love Sausage?

Discover a host of tasty new ways to enjoy sausage with the Hillshire Farm Sausage recipe collection. For a free copy, call toll-free 800-328-2426. *Or send a postcard to:*
Hillshire Farms
PO Box 25111
Cincinnatti, OH 45225
Or online at:
www.hillshirefarm.com

Not for Dieters

Here is a scrumptious collection of "Hershey's Favorite Recipes," with such selections as Chocolate & Peanut Butter Praline Pie. It makes your mouth water just thinking about it. Call toll-free 800-468-1714. *Or send a card to:*

The Hershey's Kitchen
C/o Consumer Relations
100 Crystal A Dr.
PO Box 815
Hershey, PA 17033
www.hersheys.com

Potatoes—A Heart's Good Friend

It has been known for many years that potatoes are one of the healthiest foods you can eat. Now with the Heart Healthy recipe collection you will learn how to enjoy this nutritious vegetable in new ways. In addition to tasty recipes, you will discover some handy tips on buying and storing Idaho potatoes. There is also a free microwave cookbook available. Go to www.idahopotato.com on the Web. *Or Send a postcard to:*

Idaho Potato Commission
PO Box 1068
Boise, ID 83701
208-334-2350

Enjoy a Georgia Peach

Do you like peaches? Then you will love Georgia Peach Cobbler, peach salsa and other low-fat recipes using peaches. Send a business-sized SASE and ask for "Georgia Classic and Timeless Peaches." *Write to:*

Georgia Dept. of Agriculture
Commodities Promotion
19 Martin Luther King, Jr. Dr. SW
Atlanta, GA 30334
404-656-3685
www.agr.state.ga.us

Spice Up Your Life

Grey Poupon Dijon Mustard has a Web site that features more than 115 different ways to spice up a menu with Grey Poupon Dijon Mustard. There are tasty recipe ideas for red meat, chicken, pasta, fish and more. Go to the site at www.nabiscorecipes.com. Then click on "Easy Recipe Search", then Grey Poupon Dijon Mustard. Voilà—the 115 recipes will appear.
800-NABNET

Sweet as an...Onion?

An onion is probably the last thing that comes to mind when you think of sweet foods. But the Vidalia onion fans would like to change your mind. These special onions are mild and tasty. They are grown only in a small section of Georgia, where weather and soil conditions blend to make the "World's Sweetest Onion." Send today for the Vidalia onion recipe collection, which will also explain how to freeze and store these unique onions. *Send an SASE to:*

Vidalia Sweet Onions
PO Box 1810
Vidalia, GA 30474
800-892-3412
Or go to:
www.sweetvidalias.com

From Market to Mealtime: What You Should Know About Meat, Poultry and Seafood. How to buy...prepare...safe handling.
Source: National Consumers League, 1701 K St. NW, Ste. 1200, Washington, DC 20006. Send $1 for postage and handling, and include a business-sized SASE. Or go to www.nclnet.org.

If You Eat Raw Oysters, You Need To Know... Health considerations to keep in mind—and avoid potentially fatal illness.
Source: Food and Drug Administration, 5600 Fishers Ln., Rockville, MD 20857, 0001 or www.fda.gov.

Basket of Fresh Ideas

Just about everyone loves fresh strawberries. This collection of unique strawberry recipes will show you how to use this tasty fruit to make mouth-watering desserts and drinks. *Send a postcard to:*

California Strawberry Commission
PO Box 269
Watsonville, CA 95077

Or go to:
www.calstrawberry.com,
then click on "Strawberry Recipes."
e-mail address: info@calstrawberry.com

Sugarless Sweet Recipes

Equal Company has a nice package of easy-to-prepare recipes. Among other helpful items, you will receive some simple tips for making food-label information easy to understand. You will also be sent discount coupons. To get a free kit, call the toll-free number 800-323-5316 and ask for free recipes.

www.equal.com

Tortilla Chips Hits

This new recipe collection, "Fun Foods from Frito-Lay," will provide you with a host of innovative new ways to enjoy Tostitos Tortilla Chips. Enjoy Tex-Mex Turkey Bake or Salsa and Shells Supper Salad. You will also learn "The Story of Frito-Lay." *Free from:*

Frito-Lay
PO Box 660634
Dallas, TX 75266-0634
800-352-4471
www.fritolay.com

Eat a Yam for Dessert

How would you like to enjoy an Upside Down Pear Yam Cake or Grated Sweet Potato Pudding? These are just two of the tasty treats featured in the Sweet Potato recipe collection, with dozens of prize-winning yam recipes. *Free from:*

Louisiana Sweet Potato Commission
PO Box 2550
Baton Rouge, LA 70821-2550

Or go to:
www.sweetpotato.org

Spice It Up

Add a little zest to your next meal with recipes that call for Tabasco sauce. Send a card asking for a variety of recipes. There are dozens of tangy and tasty meal ideas and recipes for everything from Hot Crab Dip to Cajun Chicken Burgers. Put a little spice in your life and your meals. *Write to:*

McIlhenny Co.
Avery Island, LA 70513

Or go to the PepperFest at:
www.tabasco.com

New Adventures in Good Eating

Are you looking for new meal ideas your whole family will enjoy? Meals such as Pork and Pasta Dijon and Zesty Honey Chicken are among those found in the "Heinz Recipe Collection." *Free from:*

H. J. Heinz
PO Box 57
Pittsburgh, PA 15230

Or go online at:
www.heinz.com

Fabulous Figs

The fig has been with us ever since Adam and Eve decided that fig leaves made nifty apparel. Now the "Buyers' Guide to Dietary Fiber," along with "Fabulous Figs—The Fitness Fruit" and "This Fig Can Teach You a Lot About Nutrition" will give you delicious new ways to use this delightful and nutritious fruit. *Free from:*

> **Fig Advisory Board**
> 3425 N. First St., Ste. 109
> Fresno, CA 93726
> 800-588-2344
> www.californiafigs.com

Olive Oil Creations

When dinner is over you may receive a standing ovation from your family for the meal you just made with the help of this recipe collection. "How to Change Your Oil & Recipes" offers several dozen creative meal ideas using olive oil. You will also receive a store discount coupon. *Send a postcard to:*

> **Pompeian, Inc.**
> Dept. WS
> PO Box 8863
> Baltimore, MD 21224
> 800-POMPEIAN
> www.pompeian.com

Millionaire's Manhattans and More

The makers of the original cream sherry, Harvey's Bristol Cream, have a great recipe collection just for the asking. You will find Peachy Cranberry Sauce for pork, Millionaire's Manhattan, plus lots more. Ask for HBC's recipes. *Send a business-sized SASE to:*

> **HBC Recipe Collection**
> PO Box 767
> Holmdel, NJ 07733

Or go to:
www.harveysbc.com, and click on the "L" ice cube for Harvey's recipes.

Cookouts Are Fun

How would you like a grill chef's hat or a new set of barbecue tools? Be sure to get a free copy of the Grill Lovers Catalog. In it you'll find something every barbecue chef will enjoy having. *It's free from:*

> **Bradley Grill Lovers Catalog**
> Box 1300
> Columbus, GA 31902-1300
> 800-241-7548

Wonderful Almonds

For a change of pace, try using almonds to flavor your next meal. "All in Good Taste" is a recipe collection that will describe how to use almonds in everything from chocolate-almond apricot bread to turkey tetrazzini almondine and almond-blueberry fruit cake. Free at the Web site of the Almond Board of California. Go to www.almondsarein.com.

Saucy Recipes

This cookbook includes recipes of all kinds, using everything from soups to nuts. All these exciting meals feature Lea & Perrins Sauce. There's even a handy index to help you easily find the recipe

Pouch Potatoes!
Recipes for main dish, side dish, easy meals and more.
Source: National Potato Promotion Board, 755 E. Hampden Ave., #412, Denver, CO 80231. Include a business-sized SASE. www.potatohelp.com.

Catalog of Self-Heating Meals. Ideal for emergency preparedness and outdoor needs. Heat in minutes. Free catalog. *Source:* 21st Century Food Storage, 888-578-0200... or at www.storablefoods.com.

you want. Call 800-987-4674. Or go to www.lea-perrins.com, and click on "Recipes." You can download the full recipe booklet which contains many more recipes than what is on the Web site.

Butter Recipe of the Month

One call to the Best of Butter Hotline will reveal a world of ideas, recipes and tips on how to use Keller's Hotel Bar Butter in delightful new ways. To find out more about Keller's new recipes, cooking tips and product information, call 800-582-4382.
www.butter1.com

Sweet Potatoes and More

"Cooking with Sweet Potatoes" offers 28 tasty meals using sweet potatoes. You will enjoy the main dishes and colorful casseroles featuring sweet potatoes in combination with other vegetables and meats. For your copy, *write to:*

Sweet Potato Council
PO Box 14
1475 Marsh Hill Rd.
McHenry, MD 21541

Sweet Samples

For an envelope full of Sweet 'N Low samples, plus a handy carry case, just send an SASE and request "Sweet 'N Low Samples." *Send to:*

Sweet 'N Low
Cumberland Packing Corp.
Two Cumberland St.
Brooklyn, NY 11205
718-858-4200
www.sweetnlow.com

Florida Fresh

This wonderful package includes an outstanding collection of recipes and information on seafood and aquaculture. Discover how to make an Oven-Fried Hybrid Striped Bass and lots more. *Send a business-sized SASE to:*

Commissioner of Agriculture & Consumer Services
Bureau of Seafood & Aquaculture Marketing
2051 East Dirac Dr.
Tallahassee, FL 32310
850-488-0163
Or go to
www.fl-seafood.com

Muffin Mania

If you like Thomas' English Muffins plain, then you will also love them fancy. To get Thomas' English Muffin recipes, plus a discount coupon, call 800-356-3314, press 1.

Sweet Citrus Delights

This collection of mouth-watering citrus recipes comes to you from TexaSweet. Their Ruby Red grapefruit has a sweet, juicy flavor. The recipes cover breakfast, dinner, dessert and drinks, using this delectable citrus fruit. *Send a postcard to:*

TexaSweet Citrus Marketing, Inc.
900 Business Park Dr., #100
Mission, TX 78572-6007
956-580-8004
www.texasweet.com

A Sweet Way to Cheat

If you love sweets (and who doesn't?), but must watch your

weight, then "26 Ways to Get Back to Nature" is for you. For a free copy of the booklet plus four others, including "Cakes for All Occasions," *send a postcard to:*

Sugar Foods Corp.
9500 El Dorado Ave.
Sun Valley, CA 91353
818-768-7900
www.sugarfoods.com

Spread the Nutrition

Oscar Mayer sandwich spreads are easy and versatile to use. Try the spreads on crackers, breads and in other recipes. For a nice collection of recipe ideas, called "Nutrition Facts," *send a postcard to:*

Oscar Mayer
PO Box 7188, Dept. ST
Madison, WI 53707
Or get a new recipe each day at:
www.oscarmayer.com

Nuts About Nuts

If you're crazy about nuts, then the Mauna Loa catalog is the catalog for you. You can order anything from Macadamia nuts to Kona coffee. For a free copy, call 800-832-9993. *Or send a postcard to:*

Mauna Loa Gift Center
One Macadamia Rd.
H.C.01, Box 3
Hilo, HI 96720
www.maunaloa.com

Staying Young at Heart

Are you one of the 60 million Americans with high blood pressure? If so, you should learn how to eat

right. Send for the free booklet, "So You Have High Blood Cholesterol" *from:*

Information Center
National Heart, Lung & Blood Institute
PO Box 30105
Bethesda, MD 20824-0105
301-496-4236
www.nhlbi.nih.gov

Sizzling Lamb Recipes

The American Lamb Council has several recipe collections that will show you exciting ways to make your dinners more delightful. The collection includes "Make It Simple, Make It Sizzle" and "Festive Lamb Recipes," plus others. You will find wine-basted, marinated, grilled, roasted and broiled recipes using fresh American lamb. *Write to:*

American Lamb Council
6911 S. Yosemite St., Ste. 200
Englewood, CO 80112-1414
303-771-3500
www.lambchef.com

Bringing Home the Bacon

If you like bacon, be sure to get a copy of "Savor the Flavor, Round the Clock with Oscar Mayer Bacon." In it you will discover tasty recipes and cooking ideas featuring bacon. They will also include party and cookout recipes using Oscar Mayer's Little Wieners & Little Smokies plus "Nutrition Facts." *Send a postcard to:*

Bacon Booklets
Oscar Mayer Consumer Center
PO Box 7188
Madison, WI 53707
www.oscarmayer.com

Oyster Recipes.
Stew…salad…char-broiled…panned. Free.
Source: Louisiana Seafood Promotion and Marketing Board, 1600 Canal St., Ste. 210, New Orleans, LA 70112. Include a business-sized SASE. Or call 800-222-4017.

Baking with Wheat Substitutes. Free.

Source: Savory Palate, Inc., 8174 S. Holly, #404, Centennial, CO 80122-4004. Include a business-sized SASE. Or call 800-741-5418 for cookbooks for people with food allergies. Or go to www.savorypalate.com.

Delicious Beef

Are you looking for something easy but delicious for your family's meals? How about meals that are perfect for anyone watching his or her weight? Try something different...such as beef, pasta and artichoke toss or quick steak and vegetable soup. The Web site of the National Cattlemen's Beef Association is chock full of cut charts, cooking lessons, beef and veal basics, and a scrumptious recipe collection. Go to www.beef.org, then click on "Kitchen."

Secrets of Cooking with White Wine

Wine lovers delight in trying new wines and new ways to enjoy familiar wines. With this compact collection of recipes called, "White Wine Recipes," you will create tasty new meals using the fine wines of Widmer. *Free from:*

Widmer's Wine Cellars
Attn: Consumer Relations
116 Buffalo St.
Canandaigua, NY 14424
800-836-5253
www.widmerwine.com

Virgin Island Rum

Cruzan Rum is an exceptionally clean-tasting rum that works well with mixers or on its own. For 22 exotic drink recipes—Voodoo Juice, Patio Punch, Mama Wana, Sunsplash and more—plus great rum cake recipes, go to the Cruzan Web site at www.cruzan rums.com. You'll have a great time!

The Finest Cordial Recipes

Kahlua has put together a selection of more than 30 famous food and drink recipes from around the world. All of these recipes feature fine cordials. Just ask for "Kahlua Recipes." It's free. *Write to:*

Allied Domecq
Kahlua Brand Manager
355 Riverside Ave.
Westport, CT 06880
203-221-5400
www.allieddomecqplc.com

The Marvelous Liqueur

Chambord is a liqueur made with small black raspberries plus other fruits & herbs combined with honey. For new ways to enjoy this magnificent liqueur, send for the free "Chambord Recipe Book" *from:*

Chambord Recipes
La Maison Delan Et Cie.
2633 Trenton Ave.
Philadelphia, PA 19125
800-523-3811

For Home
And Garden

Get Rid of Germs

The makers of Bounty paper towels want to send you a handy booklet, "Trash Household Germs." The information in it will help reduce the spread of household germs. Most of us are not aware of how we can prevent the spread of germs before they cause serious problems. For example, using a paper towel to dry your hands after handling meat or poultry products and then discarding it reduces the risk of leaving bacteria to linger and multiply on a cloth dish towel. Learn how to have good home hygiene. Ask for "Trash Household Germs" when you call Bounty's toll-free number, 888-554-3767. On the Web at www.bountyfamily.com.

Secrets About Dirt

Get "The Wisk Garment Care Guide," a free brochure with tips on how to handle all those dirty laundry problems. To get a copy, call Wisk toll-free at 800-ASK-WISK (275-9475).

The Smart Mom

The people at iVillage provide an excellent site for women to get information about home decorating, beauty and skin care, parenting, food and much more. This site is perfect for the stay-at-home mom. www.ivillage.com.

Put Solar Energy to Work

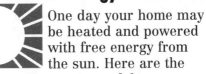

One day your home may be heated and powered with free energy from the sun. Here are the answers to many of the most frequently asked questions about putting solar and other kinds of renewable energy to work for you, from the Energy Efficiency and Renewable Energy Clearinghouse. *Write to:*

> **EREC**
> EE90
> 1000 Independence Ave. SW
> Washington, DC 20585-0121

There are also a large number of free booklets dealing with every aspect of energy efficiency and renewable energy. The booklets are available by calling 800-363-3732.

You can also access the Energy Efficiency and Renewable Energy Network of the Department of Energy on the World Wide Web. They even have free software to download. The Web site is located at www.eren.doe.gov.

Energy-Saving Tips

Saving energy not only makes America less energy dependent on other nations, but also it will save you a tidy sum of money. The Department of Energy has put together a package full of useful energy-saving information. Ask for the "Energy Saver" booklets. *They are free from:*

> **DOE Office of Science and Technology Information and Resources**
> PO Box 62
> Oak Ridge, TN 37831
> 865-576-8401
> 865-576-5728
> reports@adonis.osti.gov
> www.osti.gov

Biological Pollutants in Your Home. Where pollutants—animal dander, bugs, molds, bacteria and pollen—may be found... correcting water damage...inspecting a new home...prevention.
Source: American Lung Association, 1740 Broadway, New York, NY 10019 800-586-4872, or www.lungusa.org.

Carbon Monoxide Risks at Home. How to protect yourself... effects of exposure... safety checklist.

Source: National Fire Protection Association, Public Affairs, c/o Safety in the Home, One Batterymarch Park, Box 9101, Quincy, MA 02269-9101. Or go to www.nfpa.org on the Web.

Fiberglass Facts

"Home Energy-Saving Kit" is among the useful guides found in this information series. You will find out how fiberglass is made and how it is used for insulation, dust-stops and air filters. *Free from:*

Owens Corning
One Owens Corning Pkwy.
Toledo, OH 43659
800-438-7465
www.owenscorning.com

Let the Sun Shine In

If you are planning on building or remodeling a house, have you thought about which new windows and doors are right for you? "Windowscaping" displays and describes all of the various types of windows and doors available to help you decide for yourself. *The booklet is free from:*

Pella Co.
102 Main St.
Pella, IA 50219
888-84-PELLA
www.pella.com

Home Remodeling Ideas

Are you getting ready to build or remodel a home? If so, two booklets—the "Insider's Look at Building Your Home" and the "Insider's Look at Remodeling Your Home"—are essential items. Your creative juices will begin to flow as you thumb through these beautifully illustrated idea books. The answer books will provide help in solving your remodeling problems, whether you are adding a room or simply changing a win-

dow. Call 800-426-4261, ext. 2837. Or visit the Web site at www.andersenwindows.com.

Just How Secure Are Your Schools and Your Home?

The FBI would like every family to feel more secure. Learn how to better protect your family and your children. "A Parent's Guide to Internet Safety" and "The School Shooter: A Threat Assessment Perspective" are just two of the useful booklets available to help you keep your family safe. Available online at www.fbi.gov/publications.htm.

For these and other useful booklets, you may also write:

FBI Public Affairs Department
J. Edgar Hoover Building
935 Pennsylvania Ave. NW
Washington, DC 20535-0001
202-324-3000

Air Duct Cleaning

This helpful "Air Duct Cleaning Guide" will help you understand the importance of cleaning your air ducts. The quality of the air we breathe indoors has become an important environmental concern. You can schedule an air duct cleaning by going online to www.coit.com or call 800-FOR-COIT (367-2648) for a free brochure.

Coit Drapery & Carpet Cleaners
897 Hinkley Rd., Dept. ABJ
Burlingame, CA 94010

Residential Appliances

Answers to general questions about residential vacuums and appliances made by Míele. Míele produces state-of-the-art vacuums, dish-washers, steam ovens, laundry and cooking products. *For free brochures on all products call 800-843-7231.*

Miele Products
Nine Independence Way
Princeton, NJ 08540
fax: 609-419-4298
www.miele.com

Save Water, Save Money

Wasting water even from a slow leak over time can cost you quite a bit. To help you prevent this, here is a fully illustrated guide on how to pinpoint water waste in your toilet and what to do about it. You will also receive a free packet of dye to use to detect leaks. *Call or write:*

Fluidmaster
30800 Rancho Viejo Rd.
San Juan Capistrano, CA 92675
800-631-2011
fax: 949-728-2485
www.fluidmaster.com

Septic System Brochure

This brochure is listed on a Florida Department of Health Web site. It contains a great deal of practical information regarding the septic tank. After reading the brochure you will have a better understanding of the inner workings of your septic system. *Send a business-sized SASE to:*

Florida Dept. of Health
4025 Esplanade Way
Tallahassee, FL 32399
850-245-4443
www.state.fl.us.environment/osts/
brochure/index.html

Beautiful Historic Wallpapers

This catalog offers an excellent selection of high-quality wall cov-

ering products. These exclusively historic wallpapers are hand-print-ed in English tradition and are a perfect match for Victorian or historical homes. *Free catalog. Swatches: $1.00 per sample.*

J.R. Burrows & Company
PO Box 522
Rockland, MA 02370
800-347-1795
fax: 781-982-1636
merchant@burrows.com
www.burrows.com

Everything for Your Garden

You will find everything that you are looking for at Gardener's Supply Company. Seed-starting supplies and garden furniture, flower supports and greenhouses. *For a free catalog call or write:*

Gardener's Supply Company
128 Intervale Rd.
Burlington, VT 05401
888-833-1412
fax: 800-551-6712
info@gardeners.com
www.gardeners.com

 ## Brighten Your Home

In this handy "Guide to Paint and Varnish Removal" you will learn some clever ways to improve the appearance of your house. There are quick and easy methods for removing both mildew stains and paint or varnish from all interior and exterior surfaces. These helpful hints are a must for any tough cleaning or renovating job. Send for a free guide. *Write to:*

Savogran Company
PO Box 130, 259 Lenox St.
Norwood, MA 02062
800-225-9872
fax: 781-762-1095
www.savogran.com

Buying a New Roof and Getting Your Money's Worth. Includes listing of contractors in your area. *Source:* National Roofing Contractors Association, 10255 W. Higgins Rd., Ste. 600, Rosemont, IL 60018...or on the Web at www.nrca.net.

Propane Safety. How to tell if there's a leak ...steps to take if you smell gas...inspecting appliances...more.
Source: National Propane Gas Association, 1600 Eisenhower Ln., Ste. 100, Lisle, IL 60532...or on the Web at www.npga.org. Or you can e-mail info@npga.org.

The Complete Workshop

The Garrett Wade Company has a good assortment of hand tools, power tools, finishing products, hardware, books and home and living products. *For a free catalog call or write:*

> **Garrett Wade**
> 161 Avenue of the Americas
> New York, NY 10013
> 800-221-2942
> mail@garrettwade.com
> www.garrettwade.com

Put Out Fires

Learn how to put out fires by making a "fire pale" with baking soda. This free brochure could save a life. *Just call or write and ask for the "fire pale booklet."*

> **Arm & Hammer**
> PO Box 1625
> Horsham, PA 19044
> 800-524-1328
> www.armhammer.com

Stain Removal Guide

Most stains can be removed if you know how. The Maytag Corporation has an excellent stain-removal guide which will be sent to you just for the asking. Remember, once you master the steps, it's easy to remove just about any stain by referring to this handy guide. You will also receive "Low-Down on Laundry." *Just call or write:*

> **Maytag Corporation**
> Customer Service
> 240 Edwards St.
> Cleveland, TN 37311
> 800-688-9900

You can also download these guides at www.maytag.com.

Carpet Care

If you are thinking of adding or changing the carpets in your home but are confused by the many choices you have to make, call The Carpet and Rug Institute's information line for answers to your questions. Call 800-882-8846. Or on the Web at www.carpet-rug.com.

Stay Warm This Winter

Stay warm this winter with insulated clothing, outdoor equipment and toasty down comforters that you make yourself with the help of a Frostline kit. *For a free catalog, call or write:*

> **Frostline Kits**
> PO Box 3419
> Grand Junction, CO 81502
> 800-548-7872
> fax: 970-242-0286

Keep Your Silver Glistening

If you would like to keep your silverware shining like new, try storing it in Hagerty's Tarnish Intercept Bags. Once the silverware is placed inside the bag and the zipper is closed, tarnish is locked out. The inside of the bag will blacken when it has absorbed all of the corrosion-causing gases. Then the silver is removed and placed in a new bag. For information on this line of precious-metal care products, call 800-348-5162, ext. 103. You can also visit the Web site at www.hagerty-polish.com.
Or write to:

> **W. J. Hagerty & Sons, Ltd.**
> PO Box 1496
> South Bend, IN 46624

Shingle and Shake

Lots of remodeling ideas are contained in this terrific "Red Shingle & Shake" package. It shows how to use shingles and shakes both outside and inside your house. These guides also explain how to do it yourself and save money. *E-mail or write to:*

Cedar Shake & Shingle Bureau
PO Box 1178
Sumas, WA 98295-1178
info@cedarbureau.com
www.cedarbureau.org

Stain Out Hotline

Do you have questions about problem stains on your favorite garments? What do you do with an unknown mystery stain and you don't know where to begin? The Dow Stain experts, the makers of Spray 'N Wash, have some answers for you. Give them a call at their toll-free hotline, 800-260-1066. Or online at www.reckitt.com.

Free Spot Removal Guide

Here are lots of helpful tips on keeping your clothes clean, bright and stain free from the clean clothes professionals at Clorox. Ask for the "Stain Removal Guide." *Call or write:*

The Clorox Co.
1221 Broadway
Oakland, CA 94612
800-292-2200
www.clorox.com

Cleaning Your Carpet

If you need help dealing with a stained or spotted carpet, there is a 24-hour toll-free hotline to help you. Call 800-4 DUPONT (438-7668) for spot cleaning instructions and other carpet care techniques. Have paper and pencil ready for your step-by-step instructions. Or you can log onto www.dupont.com and use DuPont's search engine to find scores of useful household information.

Brighten Up Your Garden

Would you like to add a colorful look to your garden next spring? Consider planting Holland or domestic tulip bulbs. *For a full-color catalog, write to:*

Van Bourgondien & Sons, Inc.
Attn: Dutch Bulbs
PO Box 1000
Babylon, NY 11702
800-622-9997
blooms@dutchbulbs.com
www.dutchbulbs.com

Window Herb Garden And More

This catalog is packed with everything you can imagine to start a vegetable, flower or fruit garden. There are seed-starter kits and plants, garden helpers, bird houses and fun seed kits for kids. Free. Call 800-888-1447. *Or write to:*

Burpee Co.
300 Park Ave.
Warminster, PA 18974

Or sign up for a free e-mail newsletter for timely tips and gardening secrets at www.burpee.com.

Start a Community Garden

In the past few years backyard community gardens have been popping up all over the nation.

For the Birds. Learn how to attract different species of birds and build or buy suitable homes for them. Ask for brochure #357JJ. There is a 50¢ charge.
Source: Consumer Information Center, 888-878-3256. Or on the Web at www.pueblo.gsa.gov.

High Country Gardens. Catalog of mail-order plants that thrive in the Western US.

Source: High Country Gardens, 2902 Rufina St., Santa Fe, NM 87507-2929. 800-925-9387 or fax: 800-925-0097.

www.highcountrygardens.com

Community gardens bring people together and add beauty, too. It's also a good way to save money. In addition to other information, you will also receive teaching tools to help young minds grow. Ask for "Growing Ideas." *It's free from:*

National Gardening Association
100 Dorset St.
South Burlington, VT 05403
802-863-5251
fax: 802-864-6889
www.nationalgardening.com

Why Plants Fail

Why some plants fail to grow even when they are carefully tended to has always been somewhat of a mystery. Now Gurney Seed and Nursery would like to throw some light on the subject so you can have a more beautiful garden. The new Gurney catalog features more than 4,000 items, many shown in full color. You will discover how-to-grow-it tips, plus planting charts, moisture guides and countless special offers. *Write or call:*

Gurney Seed & Nursery Co.
110 Capital St.
Yankton, SD 57079
812-539-2499
www.gurneys.com

Oodles of Exotic, Imported Plants

Do you enjoy unusual and out-of-the ordinary plants? If so, this offer is for you. The new Stokes seed catalog features 1,300 plant varieties, including many imported from England, other parts of Europe and Canada.

Get a free catalog from:
Stokes Seeds, Inc.
PO Box 548
Buffalo, NY 14240
800-396-9238
www.stokeseeds.com

A Very Special Nursery Guide

From this nursery catalog and planting guide, you can order the seeds for a new seedless grape and virus-free berries. It includes several pages of tested recipes and a whole lot more. Miller Nurseries has put together a broad selection of their most popular nursery items. Ask for the new "Catalog & Planting Guide" from:

J. E. Miller Nurseries
5060 West Lake Rd.
Canandaigua, NY 14424
800-836-9630
www.millernurseries.com

Grow a Perfect Lawn

Here is a super five-star special for anyone with a lawn or garden. To help improve lawn, flowers, vegetable garden, trees and shrubs, call the experts at Scott Lawn Products on their toll-free line. They have the answers to any and all questions about lawn growing, diseases, fertilizing, problem areas and more. They will also give you a free subscription to *Lawn Care,* loaded with useful information and money-saving coupons. They will be happy to send you any of the dozens of booklets, magazines and brochures which can help you grow the perfect lawn or garden. This is an excellent resource. Call toll-free 800-543-TURF (8873). *Or write to:*

Scott Lawn Products
14111 Scotts Lawn Rd.
Maryville, OH 43041
www.scottscompany.com

Organic Gardening Catalog

Organic gardening is quite different from regular gardening. To learn about organic gardening and to shop for retail supplies, call or write Harmony Farm Supply. They sell tools, heirloom seeds, organic fertilizers, organic pest control and more. They even offer an organic farming consultation service.

Harmony Farm Supply
3244 Gravenstein Hwy. N.
Sebastopol, CA 95472
707-823-9125
info@harmonyfarm.com
www.harmonyfarm.com

Full-Sized Fruit from Dwarf-Sized Trees

If your yard is too small to hold as many fruit trees as you would like, take a look at this free catalog. These dwarf trees grow only 8 to 10 feet tall, yet still produce full-sized apples, peaches, pears, cherries or nectarines. The catalog features almost 400 varieties of fruit, shade and nut trees, plus shrubs, vines, ornamentals and award-winning roses. *Send a postcard for the catalog and special offers to:*

Stark Brother Nurseries
PO Box 1800, Highway 54 W
Louisiana, MO 63353
800-775-6415
www.starkbros.com

Free Fertilizer

Free manure is available to gardeners through Extension Services located throughout the country. To find the one nearest you that provides this service, call the local US Department of Agriculture Extension Service. The phone number can be found in the blue pages of your local phone book.

Great Gardens for You

Burrell Seed Growers has a nice seed catalog every home gardener will want to have. It features all kinds of wonderful ideas on creating a beautiful garden. Before you get ready to plant your next garden, be sure to get a copy of this catalog. *Call or write:*

D.V. Burrell Seed Growers Co.
PO Box 150
Rocky Ford, CO 81067
719-254-3318
fax: 719-254-3319
burrellseeds@rmi.net

Gardener's Handbook

If you want to learn how to have a beautiful, fruitful garden, get a free copy of "The Park Gardener's Handbook." In it you will find all kinds of useful information that will help you have more productive results from your gardening efforts. You can also choose from more than 3,000 new and rare varieties of flowers and vegetables, as well as the more familiar types. All are available in the full-color Park catalog. *Call or write:*

Park Seed Company
One Parkton Ave.
Greenwood, SC 29649
800-213-0076
www.parkseed.com

Healthy Lawn, Healthy Environment. How to take care of your lawn.
Source: US Environmental Protection Agency, 800-490-9198.

Martha's Got It

The Martha Stewart catalog has products for the home and includes cooking, gardening, crafts, holidays, weddings, babies and kids, books and so much more. She also has a Web site that contains a wealth of free information on home and garden improvement. Order your free Martha Stewart catalog by calling 800-950-7130 or log onto her Web site at www.marthastewart.com and you'll get many new and interesting ideas to help improve your quality of living.

Wild Bird Lover's Dream

The Audubon Workshop provides supplies, equipment and information for the wild bird enthusiast. If you love watching birds in your yard or elsewhere, then this is company for you. The Audubon Workshop also has a Web site chock full of resources and information on just about anything dealing with wild birds.

Audubon Workshop
5100 Schenley Pl.
Lawrenceburg, IN 47025
812-537-3583
fax: 812-537-5108
http://audubonworkshop.com

Making Country Life Easier

Country Home Products offers a wide variety of tools and products that make outdoor projects easier and more enjoyable. If you like working in the yard and would like to make it even more enjoyable, *call or write for a free catalog.*

Country Home Products
Meigs Rd.
PO Box 25
Vergennes, VT 05491
800-687-6575
fax: 802-877-1213
specialmkts@countryhomeproducts.com
www.countryhomeproducts.com

For
Pet
Lovers

Be Kind to Animals

If you care deeply for animals, the American Society for the Prevention of Cruelty to Animals (ASPCA) has an information packet, including booklets about caring for or traveling with your pets. To get a full list of the ASPCA's helpful information, visit the Web site at www.aspca.org.
Or write to:
American Society for the Prevention of Cruelty to Animals
Public Information Dept.
424 E. 92 St.
New York, NY 10128
212-876-7700

Looking for a Free Pet?

If you have ever stopped by a pet shop in the mall to play with the delightful puppy sitting in the window, you probably learned that taking that puppy home could be costly. But there is no reason to spend hundreds of dollars when local newspaper and supermarket bulletin boards may have ads giving away free kittens and pups. Also, animal shelters have delightful pets waiting for a good home. Typically at the shelters you will be asked to pay only for the animal's shots. Call your local animal shelter for more information.

Free Animal Calendar and Datebook

For pet lovers everywhere, the Animal Protection Institute has handy and informative fact sheets, on everything from animal testing to caring for exotic pets. If you love animals, this organization is definitely for you.

Call toll-free 800-348-PETS (7387). Visit the Web site at www.api4animals.org.
Or write to:
Animal Protection Institute
1122 S St.
Sacramento, CA 95814

Dogs Get Arthritis, Too

Does your dog have difficulty getting up after a nap or a hard time climbing stairs? When that happens to pets, most people just assume that it's old age and that nothing can be done about it. The problem may very well be osteoarthritis, which afflicts one dog in five. Pfizer Dog Care has a toll-free number you can call for information on what you can do if your dog suffers from this problem. Call 800-720-DOGS (3647). Online at www.rydimal.com.

Special Cat Care

Cat Chow Special Care is a cat food that helps maintain the health of a cat's urinary tract. It is made with real chicken for a great taste. For information call 800-7-PURINA (778-7462). Or go on the Web at www.purina.com.

Allergic to Pets?

If you would love to have a pet but are allergic to animal hair and dander, there may be a new way to help eliminate those allergies around the house with a new vacuum by Nilfisk, Inc. of America. Call 800-241-9420, ext. 2; or fax: 610-647-6427;or e-mail: questions@nilfisk-advance.com. Or on the Web at www.nilfiskamerica.com.

Animal Health Studies.
Free research information.
Source: Morris Animal Foundation, 800-243-2345.
www.morrisanimalfoundation.org

Canine Travel Tips.
Safety tips…cars, trains, buses, planes, boats…lodging… international.

Source: American Kennel Club, Customer Service, 5580 Centerview Dr., Ste. 200, Raleigh, NC 27606.
919-233-9767
fax: 919-816-3627
info@akc.org
www.akc.org.

Free Veterinary Care

If you live near a university that has a veterinary school, you may be able to get free care for your pet, especially if you are a senior citizen. Call and ask what services are offered.

Take Care of Your Pet

Are you sure that your pet's nutritional needs are being met? Do you have things in your home that may be hazardous to your pet? The Center for Veterinary Medicine will send you free brochures that will answer many of your health-care concerns and questions about your pet. *Call 301-827-3800 or contact:*

Center for Veterinary Medicine
US Food and Drug Administration
7500 Standish Pl.
Rockville, MD 20855
www.fda.gov/cvm

Loads of Dog Info

If you have a dog or are planning to get one, make sure you write for free pet information from the folks at Ralston Purina dog food products. They have an excellent freebie that will not only give you a brief history of dogs, but also provide you with tips on feeding, grooming, obedience training, keeping your dog healthy and traveling with your dog. They may also include discount coupons and a Purina dog food guide to balancing nutrients to meet your dog's needs. Also ask for the "Guide to Caring for Your Dog" and "Help…My Pet Refuses to Eat." These items are

a must if you have or are thinking about getting a pet dog. *Write to:*

Ralston Purina
Dog Food Division
Checkerboard Square
St. Louis, MO 63164
800-778-7462
www.purina.com

Potty Training Your New Puppy

If you've got a new puppy you want to be sure to train it properly so that it is properly trained to go outside to "potty." Petalia has a Web site that gives you complete instructions on how to train your dog. They also will give free health-care advice for your small pet. Get free information on cats, birds, fish and other small pets. *Visit www.petalia.com.*

Fish Are Fun

Fish are educational and can be enjoyed by the whole family. Now you can learn step-by-step how to set up a year-round backyard pond and stock it with hardy fish. Send for "Fish Are Fun" and "Guide to Creating the Perfect Pond." They're free. *Call or write:*

Tetra Second Nature
3001 Commerce St.
Blacksburg, VA 24060-6671
800-526-0650
consumer@tetra-fish.com
www.tetra-fish.com

What Are Quarter Horses?

 Whether you are presently an owner of horses or perhaps thinking of buying one, check out American Quarter Horses, the world's most popular breed of horse. For a fascinating booklet (and a colorful bumper sticker, too), *call or write:*

American Quarter Horse Association
PO Box 200
Amarillo, TX 79168
806-376-4811
www.aqha.com

Tennessee Walking Horse

Every equestrian will want to have this. Send a postcard and ask for the booklet, *Tennessee Walking Horse.* You will also receive a colorful postcard showing the three horses chosen by the breeder's association as the world's greatest pleasure and show horses.
Call or write:

Tennessee Walking Horse
PO Box 286
Lewisburg, TN 37091-0286
800-359-1574
twhbea@twhbea.com
www.twhbea.com

A Hot Spot for the Birds

 Learn how to care for your pet bird, about common bird diseases, and much more. An avian mall and reference center, "Hot Spot for Birds" is on the Internet and offers a free e-newsletter.

Hot Spot for Birds
27 Essex Dr.
Northridge, CA 91324
888-246-8776
fax: 781-459-7891
www.multiscope.com/hotspot/index.htm

More Than a Friend

For millions of people their pets are real members of their families. And love of animals has inspired many to follow a career path to becoming a veterinarian. The American Veterinary Association has an interesting booklet called "Today's Veterinarian" about the opportunities available today in this interesting field. For a free copy, *send a business-sized SASE to:*

American Veterinary Medical Association
1931 North Meecham Rd., Ste. 100
Schaumburg, IL 60173
847-925-8070
fax: 847-925-1329
www.avma.org

Take Good Care of Your Pets

 The American Humane Association has a whole series of informative booklets available for pet owners. The booklets explain how to care for dogs, cats, horses, birds and fish. For a complete listing, *write for the free catalog of publications from:*

American Humane Association
63 Inverness Dr. East
Englewood, CO 80112
800-227-4645
fax: 303-792-5333
www.americanhumane.org

Feral Cats

Feral cats can be a real problem, but they can also become pets. There is a wealth of information on the internet about taking care of feral cats. Learn how to deal with feral cats around your home by logging onto: amby.com/cat_site/feral.html or by calling the Feral Cat Coalition at 619-514-1222.

Dog and Cat Books. Many titles on such topics as health, food, training and behavior.
Source: Direct Book Service, Dept. ABL, PO Box 2778, Wenatchee, WA 98807-2778. Call 800-776-2665; fax: 509-662-7233; e-mail: mail@dogwise.com; or on the Web at www.dogwise.com.

Show Bunnies

If you have been thinking about getting a pet rabbit, then this is the place for you. The show bunny Web site will answer many questions about rabbit health care, hygiene, diet and other common problems that may arise during rabbit ownership. You will also learn of the many types of rabbits that are available to you. Log on to www.showbunny.com/home-sites/njwrc

Hard to Find Pet Books

If you have an unusual pet like an iguana, a chameleon, a box turtle or a python, then you might have difficulty finding information on your pet. Barron's provides books on many unusual pets. Go to www.barronseduc.com/pets-exotics.html or call them for a free listing of their books at 800-645-3476.

Barron's Educational Series
250 Wireless Blvd.
Hauppauge, NY 11788
info@barronseduc.com

The Cat Enthusiast

If you are one of many cat lovers, then *Cat Fancy* is the magazine for you. With its beautiful photographs, information and product listings, *Cat Fancy* is a fun and informative magazine. You can also find *Cat Fancy* online.

Cat Fancy Magazine
Three Burroughs
Irvine, CA 92618
949-855-8822
fax: 949-855-3045
www.animalnetwork.com/cats/default.asp

Freebies for Pet Owners on the Web

Visit PetRescue.com and you will find out about all of the wonderful things that people do in the name of pets. You will find things like free screen savers, posters, pet weight management kit, pet safety kit and much more. You can even send a free greeting card to those you love. *You can also write them at:*

PetRescue.com
PO Box 531057
Debary, FL 32753-1057
Info@petrescue.com
www.petrescue.com/free.htm

Crafts And Hobbies

Free Bead Supply Catalog

Are you looking for an interesting and challeng–ing hobby? The Frantz Bead Company has put together an informative supply catalog to help teach you the art of bead making. You will receive a free catalog with a full assortment of a wide range of bead supplies. Call 800-839-6712. *Or simply send a postcard to:*

> **Frantz Art Glass & Supply**
> 1222 E. Sunset Hill Rd.
> Shelton, WA 98584
> www.frantzartglass.com

Beautiful Christmas Ornament

If you love to collect truly unique Christmas ornaments, you will definitely want to get this one. It is a beautiful hand-made angel that will quickly become the cen-terpiece of your holiday decora-tions. Simply send $5 plus shipping and handling and *request the Buy 5 Small Angels and get 1 Free Christmas Angel from:*

> **Angelic Creations**
> PO Box 52
> Colfax, WA 99111
> http://users.colfax.com/dandtdra/

Fun with Ribbons

Learn to create colorful and fun projects with ribbons. You will be amazed at what you can cre-ate using ribbons of all sizes, col-ors and textures. This is a great rainy day project and you can even use the finished projects to raise money for a special cause. *Send an SASE to:*

Offray
857 Willow Cir.
Hagerstown, MD 21740
www.offray.com

Duplicate Bridge Anyone?

Do you enjoy playing duplicate bridge? If so, you will want this catalog and product source guide which cover just about anything you might want or need for this game. Call 800-2674-USA. *Or write to:*

> **American Contract Bridge League**
> Sales Department
> 2990 Airways Blvd.
> Memphis, TN 38116
> www.acbl.org

The Secret to Playing Better Chess

Learn the official rules of the challenging game of chess and also receive another publication to join the US Chess Federation. Chess helps you develop your ability to think analytically. Ask for "Ten Tips to Winning Chess." Call 800-388-KING, *or send a busi-ness-sized SASE to:*

> **US Chess Federation**
> 3054 NYS Route 9W
> New Windsor, NY 12553
> www.shopuschess.org

Crochet the Best Dolls

If you love to crochet, you will want this free pattern for a pair of Raggedy Ann and Andy dolls. Crocheting these dolls is just half the fun. Giving them as gifts and seeing the joy they bring is the

Robot Catalog.
Collection of miniature robot kits, books and parts.
Source: Mondo-tronics Inc., 4286 Redwood Hwy. PMB-N, San Rafael, CA 94903.
800-374-5764
www.robotstore.com

Catalog of Trademark Collectibles. Campbell's Kid figurine with mini-tractor...Cracker Jack Tins (set of 3)...Betty Boop Heart Lamp... Wizard of Oz figurines, etc.

Source: The Trademark Collection, 8806 Consolidated Dr., Soddy Daisy, TN 37379. www.tmcollection.com.

rest. *Send a business-sized SASE and $1 postage and handling to:*
NP Patterns
341 4th Terrace
Egg Harbor City, NJ 08215
asp.myfree.com/displayoffers/offers.asp?offercat=35

Add to Your Mechanical Toy Collection

If you are a collector of fine mechanical toys, this beautifully illustrated catalog is for you. In this catalog you will find a unique collection of toys and collectibles. Get your Lilliput catalog today. Call 800-TIN-TOYS (846-8697). *Or write to:*
Lilliput
PO Box 447
Yerington, NV 89447
www.lilliputmotorcompany.com

Protect Your Spirit

There's a Native American legend that says that by wearing a "spirit shield" you can protect yourself from evil spirits. Tandy Leather will send you instructions so you can make your own spirit shield. Call their toll-free number: 888-890-1611, or go on the Web to www.tandyleather.com.

Great Photos from Now On

This extensive packet of material in full color explains how to take the best snapshots under any circumstances. It is easy to understand and deals with topics such as lighting, flash photography, action and more. Start taking better pictures now. Call 800-242-2424, ext. 10. www.kodak.com

Home Sewing Basics

If you are thinking of decorating anything from a single room to an entire house, be sure to get "Sewing—It's Sew Soothing." Discover how much fun it is to make your own curtains, slip covers and pillow shams. To get a copy, *send a business-sized SASE to:*
Home Sewing Association
1350 Broadway, Ste. 1601
New York, NY 10018
www.sewing.org

Solve Your Polaroid Problems

Have your Polaroid photos been coming out the way you'd like? If not, there is a toll-free hotline to call where an expert will answer your questions. Call toll-free from 8 a.m. to 8 p.m. Monday through Saturday at 800-343-5000.

Polaroid has a wonderful policy of complete customer satisfaction. Your problem may lie with defective film which the company will replace at no charge. *Send defective film or photos to:*
Polaroid Customer Care Service
201 Burlington Rd.
Bedford, MA 01730
www.polaroid.com

Just for Knife Collectors

This catalog is packed with offers of hundreds of knives, swords, specialty and novelty knives, sharpening systems, accessories and more. Now you can find that special carving knife for meat, cheese or fruitcake. If you are a collector of swords and sheaths, there are several to choose from. *Write to:*
Smoky Mountain Knife Works
2320 Winfield Dunn Pkwy.
Sevierville, TN 37876
865-453-5871
www.ohwy.com/tn/s/smmtknwk.htm

A Photographer's Dream Site

Kodak has a great Web site that will help you take better photos. You will find top-10 techniques for good photos, remedies for problem pictures, picture-taking tips for special situations and subjects, plus a host of other topics. There are also chat rooms relating to digital, general and professional photography. Visit the Web site at www.kodak.com.

Enjoy Play Clay

Did you know that you can create your own unique gifts, decorations and jewelry with play clay? You can learn how to make play clay from Arm & Hammer Baking Soda. To get the "Amazing World of Play Clay," *call:*

Arm & Hammer
Play Clay Brochures
PO Box 1625
Horsham, PA 19044-6625
800-524-1328
www.armhammer.com

Create Beautiful Letters

 If you are interested in learning how to create handcrafted lettering, this is for you. With the "Lettering Charts" you will receive a super collection of Roman Gothic, Old English and Manuscript lettering charts plus helpful hints. *Call 704-838-1475 or download from their Web site.*

Speedball Art Products
PO Box 5157
2226 Speedball Rd.
Statesville, NC 28687
www.speedballart.com

The Art of Ventriloquism

Do you remember Howdy Doody, and Edgar and Jerry Mahoney? Now you can learn all the same techniques they used. Here is your chance to discover what a ventriloquist is and how to become one. You will also learn how to build a puppet, how to put together a show, what direction to go in and how to market a show. To receive the 32-page booklet, "Ventriloquism Revealed," *call 800-250-5125, or write to:*

North American Association of Ventriloquists
PO Box 420
Littleton, CO 80160
www.maherstudios.com/naav.htm

Not So Fast with That Old Zippo

 Somewhere in your attic or basement you may stumble across an old Zippo lighter. They were known for their reliability and quality for more than 50 years. Instead of throwing it out as junk, find out whether that old Zippo has any real value. Send for the "Collector's Guide to Zippo Lighters." *Write to:*

Zippo Manufacturing Co.
33 Barbour St.
Bradford, PA 16701
www.zippo.com

Stamp Collection

 There is a collection of 50 fantastic worldwide stamps waiting for you. Each stamp is 50 to 100 years old. The stamps are worth $2 at catalog prices, but can be yours for only $1. You will also

Catalog of Bow Ties.
More than 100 ties in various colors, patterns and fabrics.
Source: Beau Ties Ltd.,
800-488-8437
www.beautiesltd.com

Custom Flags & Banners Catalog. Design the size and shape to display your logo...trademark... organization emblem.
Source: National Flag & Display Co., Inc., 1080 Springfield Rd. N., Union, NJ 07083. 800-782-1510.

receive other stamps on approval, and there is no obligation to buy anything. Call 716-488-0763. *Or write to:*

Falcon Stamp Co.
341 E. 3rd St.
Jamestown, NY 14701
www.jamestownstamp.com

Start a Stamp Club

If you are interested in collecting stamps, you will probably enjoy the hobby more in the company of other stamp collectors. If this sounds like something you might be interested in, ask for a free copy of "You Can Start a Stamp Club." *Write to:*

American Philatelic Society
100 Oakwood Ave.
PO Box 8000
State College, PA 16803
814-237-3803
www.stamps.org

Free Numismatic News

Here is a newspaper every coin collector will want to have. Simply write and request a free sample copy of *Numismatic News Weekly.* You will enjoy its many interesting articles on all aspects of this fascinating hobby. *Send a card to:*

Numismatic News Weekly
Krause Publications
700 E. State St.
Iola, WI 54990
800-258-0929
Or go on the Web to:
www.krause.com

Crafts on the Web

The Internet is a wonderful source of information for the craft-minded. Get information on supplies, associations, crafts shows and more.

www.craftsfaironline.com
This site lists links to other craft-oriented pages—newsgroups, shows, etc.

www.craftweb.com
An online community that creates the opportunity for professional craftspeople, craft organizations and people interested in crafts to meet, share information and promote fine crafts worldwide.

www.craftassoc.com
Discover how to turn your art or craft into cash.

www.i-craft.com
Craft ideas for kids and seniors and a craft library.

www.makestuff.com
Do-it-yourself how-tos, tips, tricks and ideas.

www.artandcraftshows.net
Searchable database of craft shows in North America.

www.crochet.com
Learn how to crochet whether you are a right hander or a left hander. You can also order different patterns and subscribe to their bi-monthly print newsletter and their e-mail newsletter.

www.berroco.com

Stanley Berroco is one of the largest importers and wholesalers of handknitting yarns, patterns and supplies in the U.S. Visit their Web site for free patterns, viewing the *Update* newsletter, as well as locating a yarn shop near you.

www.elann.com

There are beautiful free patterns available on this Web site as well as a section to order needles and hooks.

Backyard Bird-Watching Year-Round

With the right equipment and feed, you can attract a beautiful and interesting variety of birds to your backyard...

Hummingbirds

These tiny birds appear from April through October all over the country and in warm climates year-round. Hummingbirds require a special feeder to hold their nectar.* Hang the feeder near flowering plants in your yard.

To make hummingbird nectar: Boil four parts water to one part white table sugar. Do not add dye. After sugar dissolves, let it cool and put in the feeder.

Finches

There are about 15 varieties of this brightly colored bird. Use either a *tube feeder*, which has individual feeding ports...or a *hopper feeder*, which allows lots of birds to feed together. Place

Bird feeders can be bought at specialty bird stores or any store that sells bird feed. Favorite mail-order resources for feeders and feed: Duncraft Birdfeeders, 800-593-5656...www.duncraft.com.

the feeder near trees or shrubs, in an easy-to-see place.

Black sunflower seeds specifically for birds work best—buy in bulk to save money.

Woodpeckers

These birds love suet, a type of beef fat. You can buy commercial suet mixes at stores that sell bird feed.

You'll need a suet feeder, which looks like a mesh cage. They are sold at pet-supply stores.

Hang the feeder in a tree or from a feeder pole near a wooded area.

Sparrows, Towhees, Doves and Quail

These birds prefer to feed on the ground—but in wet weather, birdseed can turn rancid.

Better: Use a platform feeder—a raised, horizontal piece of wood. You can make your own by affixing a piece of wood to a cinder block or a tree stump.

Provide *mixed seed*, which can be bought from a bird-supply store. Spread it on the platform.

Orioles and Tanagers

Use a fruit feeder—sold at bird stores—to lure these singing birds.

To make one: Put a nail in a fence post or deck railing. Cut an orange, grapefruit or apple in half, and impale it on the nail or on the feeder. Make sure the edible part of the fruit is showing.

Handyman Help

Visit www.naturalhandyman.com for home repair information. You can subscribe to their free *Home Repair Newsletter* and try a free issue of *Woodworker's Journal*.

J. Peterman Discoveries. Wonderful, unusual, vintage-inspired clothing and unique gifts from around the world, available on the Web.

Source: The J. Peterman Company, 1001 Primrose Ct., Lexington, KY 40511. Toll-free 888-647-2555. On the Web at www.jpeterman. com.

Computers
And the
Best Internet
Sites

Computers and the Best Internet Sites

There will be a time in the not-too-distant future when having a computer will be as common as having a telephone—and just as essential. One of the main reasons for having a computer is to gain access to the Internet (sometimes called the World Wide Web or just the Web). By simply typing in the address of a Web site, your computer is instantly transported to a place that could very well be on the other side of the world... and all for the price of a local phone call.

If you don't have a computer yet, but would like to see just what the Internet is all about, here are a number of ways to get started.

First, virtually all libraries across the nation have computers with access to the Internet, which can be used free of charge. Most of these computers are easy to use, and a librarian will be happy to show you how to get started.

Next, if your budget will allow it, you might want to get your own computer with a modem, which is the mechanism that hooks your computer to the Internet via a telephone line. The most affordable way to get started is with a used computer, which you might be able to find for as little as $300 or $500. Some stores sell only used computers, and you can also look in the classified ad section of your local paper. To have access to the Internet, it is not necessary to have the newest or fastest computer. However, it is a good idea to get a fast modem, which will speed your access to the Internet. A 56K modem starts at $89.00.

Finally, and again if your budget will allow it, there are various computer brands selling for under $1,000 which are already set up with everything, including a built-in modem. Now you can be online in a matter of 10 minutes.

Online Startup Services

One of the big advantages of owning a computer is that it puts the world right at your fingertips. At the touch of a key, you have instant access to people and sources of information beyond your imagination. In an instant you can surf the Internet where you will find thousands of fascinating Web sites. To get started with free software, and in many cases with free online trials, call these toll-free numbers:

America Online: 800-827-6364

Compuserve: 800-848-8199

AT&T Worldnet: 800-967-5363

Microsoft Network: 800-386-5550

Earthlink: 800-890-6356

Prodigy: 888-776-3449

Free Computer Supplies

There is intense competition going on between several nationwide computer retailers. Just to get you into their store, each of them offers printers or digital cameras with

About Buying a Computer. How to decide on an operating system...laptop vs. desktop...costs... warranties. Free.
Source: MetLife Consumer Education Center, 800-638-5433. Item #407.

Computer Products Galore. Catalog of products for small and home-based businesses, including computer cleaning and maintenance...workstation accessories...ergonomic hand and wrist protection...secure spacesaver lockers...more.

Source: Acctechllc, PO Box 1693, Newburgh, NY 12551. 800-284-5577.

rebates. Check your local newspapers for ads and inserts for Office Depot, CompUSA, Circuit City and other chain stores.

Look for the Best Deals

If you are looking for the best deals around in computers, software or accessories, some of the lowest prices you will find are from mail-order companies. Even if you decide to buy from a local store, calling mail-order companies will allow you to comparison shop to get the lowest price. Each of the companies listed here has been in business for a number of years and has an excellent reputation for customer satisfaction. When you call, ask for the latest catalog which will be full of important information to help you make an intelligent buying decision. Most companies have a 24-hour customer-service line and your orders arrive promptly, often the very next day.

1. **DataCOM**
   800-328-2261

2. **Dell**
   800-545-3771

3. **Mac Connection/PC Connection**
   800-800-0002

4. **MacMall**
   800-222-2808

5. **MacZone**
   800-248-0800

6. **Microcenter Catalog**
   800-634-3478

7. **PC Zone**
   800-258-2088

8. **Tiger**
   800-888-4437

Free Apple Assistance

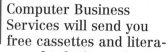

If you own a Macintosh or are thinking of buying one and have questions you need answered, there is a toll-free number you can call for help. It is the Apple Helpline at 800-SOS-APPL. Or visit the Web site at www.apple.com.

Get In on the Computer Business Boom

Computer Business Services will send you free cassettes and literature on one of today's quickest growing industries. We have seen the computer industry take off like a rocket, and now it's possible for you to be a part of it. To receive the cassettes and informational literature on various business opportunities, *write to:*

Computer Business Services
CBSI Playa, Ste. 1180
Sheridan, IN 46069

Supplies Galore

If you or your company owns a computer, you will want to get a copy of the Global Computer Supplies catalog. This full-color catalog lists thousands of computer-related products of all types. Call 800-8-GLOBAL (or 800-845-6225). *Or send a postcard to:*

Global Computer Supplies
11 Harbor Park Dr.
Port Washington, NY 11050

Lots for Free on the Internet

Thousands of types of software are available absolutely free on the Internet. If you have a computer and a modem, accessing the Internet is a simple and easy way to open up a whole new world. Among other things, you will find freeware, shareware and free software application upgrades waiting for you to download into your computer. You will also find the full text of hundreds of useful government booklets and reports on a host of fascinating subjects, all of which you can download free.

Web Sites Just for Seniors

Here are the Internet addresses of sites on the World Wide Web that are of special interest to mid-life and older Web users. When you type in the address, be sure to type it correctly. Even a small change, such as the addition or deletion of a space or period, will prevent you from accessing the site.

American Association of Retired Persons
www.aarp.org

AARP Guide to Internet Resources Related to Aging
www.aarp.org/cyber/guide1.htm

Achoo
www.achoo.com

Age of Reason
www.ageofreason.com

Andrus Foundation
www.andrus.org

Connections
homepage.mac.com/joyss/connec.html

Directory of Web Sites on Aging
www.aoa.dhhs.gov/aoa/webres/craig.htm

Elderhostel
www.elderhostel.org

ElderPage Information for Older Persons and Families
www.aoa.dhhs.gov/elderpage.html#wal

Family Caregiver Alliance
www.caregiver.org

Focus on the Internet
www.aarp.org/cyber

The Geezer Brigade
www.thegeezerbrigade.com

Generations United
www.gu.org

GriefNet
www.rivendell.org

Health A to Z
www.healthatoz.com

Life Expectancy Calculator
www.retireweb.com/death.html

MapQuest
www.mapquest.com

National Aging Information Center
www.aoa.dhhs.gov/naic

National Council on the Aging
www.ncoa.org

National Library of Medicine
www.nlm.nih.gov

New Lifestyles Online
www.newlifestyles.com

Older Jokes for Older Folks
seniors-site.com/funstuff/jokes97.html

Old-Time Radio Web Page
www.old-time.com

Online Resources for Financial and Retirement Planning
www.aoa.dhhs.gov/aoa/pages/finplan.html

Partnership for Solutions
www.chronicnet.org

Play Bridge Hand Generator
www.playbridge.com

Site-Seeing on the Internet. How to avoid fraud and deception while online.
Source: Federal Trade Commission, Consumer Response Center, CRC-240, Washington, DC 20580… or on the Web at www.ftc.gov.

Computer User's Guide to Better Vision. How to minimize or eliminate eye stress from your computer screen (visual display terminal).

Source: Communications Center, Dept. DP1, American Optometric Association, 243 N. Lindbergh Blvd., St. Louis, MO 63141. 888-396-3937. Include a business-sized SASE.

The Senior Center
www.senior-center.com

Senior Connection
www.senior.com

SeniorLaw Home Page
www.seniorlaw.com

SeniorNet
www.seniornet.org

Senior Staff Job Information Databank
www.srstaff.com

Silver Threads
www.winnipeg.freenet.mb.ca/sthreads

SPRY Foundation
www.spry.org

SSA Direct-Personal Earnings and Benefit Estimate Statement by Mail
www.ssa.gov/pebes

ThirdAge
www.thirdage.com

Time Zone Converter
www.timezoneconverter.com

Too Old for Computers?
www.seniorsincyberspace.org/old.htm

Weather Channel
www.weather.com

Welcome to Folks Online
www.folksonline.com

Writers' Consortium Seniors Site
www.seniors-site.com

Online Tips for Navigating The Web

Beginners Central
www.northernwebs.com/bc

The HelpWeb
www.imagescape.com/helpweb

Delphi Forums
www.delphi.com/navnet/faq

Internet Web Text Index
www.december.com/web/text

Big-Time Savings with Online Auctions

If you love shopping for bargains, you are in for the time of your life with these Internet auction sites. You can bid on everything from cameras to computers and golf clubs, any time day or night, 24 hours a day—all without ever leaving the comfort of your home. But remember, as with a traditional auction, you must be careful not to get caught in a bidding frenzy and bid too much just to get something you could have bought for less in a store.

Remember: Find out whether the item is new, used or refurbished.

Remember: New products should come with a manufacturer's warranty.

Remember: Always check the warranty and return policies.

When buying from someone online, be wary of sellers with E-mail accounts, which could be used to mask the seller's identity. Wherever possible, pay for your purchase with a credit card, which offers you the best protection in case there is a problem later. In some instances, you will be buying from a private individual, but in others (like at egghead.com), you buy directly from a large company, which adds an additional layer of protection.

Here are several of the most popular Internet auction sites:

www.ebay.com
This is the largest Internet auction site with everything imaginable, from antiques to Beanie Babies. To find the items

you are interested in, simply enter keywords. The site will do the work of finding a match for the item you are interested in.

www.ubid.com

At this auction site you will find not only computer products but all kinds of consumer electronics as well.

www2.warehouse.com

This site is operated by Micro/Mac/Data Comm Warehouse.

www.auctionx.com

A good site for computers and other technical equipment.

Free Internet Access

Did you know that you can not only use the Internet to search for free things and terrific bargains, you can actually get on the Internet itself for free? Instead of paying a monthly charge for access to the Internet, with the following companies you have no fees of any kind...ever! They make money by selling advertising which you will see while you are on their site. *For free Internet access check out the following:*

www.juno.com
www.netzero.net

Buying a Computer

Practical advice on how to buy a computer that fits your needs. Gives tips on protecting your computer and data, defines common computer terms and provides a helpful checklist to use when shopping for a computer. 10 pp. #618JJ. Free.

Dot Cons

While the Internet has made life easier, it has also opened a new frontier for con artists. Learn the top ten online scams, how you can protect yourself and tips for surfing the web without getting scammed. 3 pp. #312JJ. 50¢.

Internet Auctions: A Guide for Buyers and Sellers

Internet auctions offer a great way to buy or sell all kinds of products. Find out how auctions work, payment options and how to protect yourself. 18 pp. #359JJ. 50¢.

Internet Fraud: How to Avoid Internet Investment Scams

Before you invest in that "sure fire" online investment, use this guide to learn the warning signs of fraud, questions to ask about investment opportunities and what to do if you run into problems. 19 pp. #368JJ. 50¢.

Shop Safely Online

Is it really safe? Here are the facts about buying over the Internet and how to protect yourself. 2 pp. #361JJ. 50¢.

Online Brain Games: Crossword puzzles (including one from 1913—the world's first)...word searches...math games. On the Web at www.thinks.com.

Learning Something New

Learning Something New

One of life's true joys is exploring the world and discovering something we never knew before. We enter life with an enormous inborn curiosity about the world around us. Unfortunately, once we enter school for many of us learning becomes a chore, a job, something we are forced to do to get good grades or a good job. But once we reach a certain age and the pace of life becomes less frenetic, we can once again recapture that excitement of learning something new and feeling like a kid again.

Senior Summer School

That's right, summer school for seniors: two to 10 weeks of learning and fun, centered around eleven college campuses in the US and Canada. Here is your chance to meet new friends and see the world. And guess what? There are no marks, no grades and no mandatory attendance. The only requirement is a desire to learn something new. All of the programs offer social events, too. Call 800-847-2466, or visit their Web site at www.senior-summerschool.com. *Or you can write to:*

Senior Summer School
PO Box 4424
Deerfield Beach, FL 33442-4424

Back to School with Elderhostel

Elderhostel offers senior study programs around the world all year long. You will live in conference centers on college campuses and enjoy the cultural and recreational resources that are there. If you have an adventurous spirit and are looking to be challenged by new ideas and experiences, this is for you. You must be 55 years or older to be eligible. This is your chance to go back to college and experience dorm life as a more seasoned veteran.

For information, *get the free catalog of senior study programs from:*

Elderhostel
11 Avenue de Lafayette
Boston, MA 02111-1746
877-426-8056
www.elderhostel.org

Free College Extension Courses

If you have always wanted to return to college, there is no time like the present. First, check the section on "Colleges with Special Programs for Seniors" in the back of this book. They all offer free or low-cost tuition for seniors.

Also, check your local telephone directory for state and community college extension courses. These courses are not given for credit but are a lot of fun.

Next, contact local senior centers to see what they offer. Also, museums, nature centers, libraries and church groups offer courses and seminars that are educational and fun and in many

It's never too late to go back to school. Many universities offer older students classes at reduced tuition rates. *Example:* Pace Adult Resource Center at Pace University in New York allows anyone over age 50 to take regular accredited courses on a noncredit basis for one-third of the usual tuition (212-346-1288). Contact local universities about offerings in your area.

Source: Joan Rattner Heilman, author of Unbelievably *Good Deals and Great Adventures That You Absolutely Can't Get Unless You're Over 50.* McGraw-Hill.

Online auctions connect bidders with sellers directly. If you are the high bidder, you and the seller communicate by e-mail to arrange payment and delivery of the item. Always pay by credit card or COD if possible. Be sure to verify the seller's identity, and ask how you will get follow-up service if you need it. Find out about return policies. Important: Avoid impulse bids and purchases—you can overpay at an online auction, just as at other auctions. *Source:* Jodie Bernstein, director, Federal Trade Commission's Bureau of Consumer Protection, 614 H St. NW, Washington, DC 20001.

instances are free or almost free.

Finally, check your local newspaper for seminars and other educational activities in your area.

Are You a Sky Gazer?

If you enjoy studying the heavens, you will want to get a catalog of some of the finest astronomy books that will delight all star gazers. *Write to:*

Sky Publishing Corp.
49 Bay State Rd.
Cambridge, MA 02138
800-253-0245
www.skypub.com

A Share of America

"You and the Investment World" and "Topic Outline Brochure" are two fascinating guides that explain the history of the stock exchange, how the stock market works and the important role it plays in our nation's economy. The New York Stock Exchange also has an excellent series of educational aids, wall posters, ticker tape, teacher's guides and more. *Write to:*

NY Stock Exchange
Educational Services
20 Broad St., 3rd flr.
New York, NY 10005
www.nyse.com

Look to the Heavens

People have always been fascinated by the sky at night. With the recent discovery of new planets circling

around distant stars, one cannot help but wonder whether life exists elsewhere in the universe. To find out more about our distant neighbors, send for the "sky-watching series" of booklets dealing with our solar system and beyond. *Write to:*

Public Affairs Office
Harvard Smithsonian Center for Astrophysics
60 Garden St.
Cambridge, MA 02138
617-495-7450
//cfa-www.harvard.edu

The Facts About Oil

This nicely illustrated guide to petroleum tells all about the history of oil exploration and describes how the search for oil is conducted. Ask for the "energy information series" and you will receive a great package of excellent booklets dealing with many forms of energy including wind, nuclear, geothermal, coal, oil and more. Call 202-682-8000.

American Petroleum Institute
Publications Section
1220 "L" St. NW
Washington, DC 20005-4070
www.api-ec.api.org/intro/index_noflash.htm

Be a Smart Shopper

Everyone spends money, but not everyone knows how to do it right. Spending money wisely takes skill, time and experience. To help you learn how to be a smart shopper, the Federal Trade Commission and the National Association of Attorneys General have put together a fun activity booklet called "The Real Deal." *To get a copy, write to:*

Federal Trade Commission
600 Pennsylvania Ave. NW, Room 130
Washington, DC 20580
Or call toll-free 1-877-FTCHELP
www.ftc.gov

Would You Drive an Aluminum Car?

Today, through greater use of aluminum parts, our cars are getting far better mileage per gallon. This is just one of the many uses of aluminum. If you would like a better understanding of the history of aluminum, how it is made and how it is used, see "The Alcoa Story" at www.alcoa.com, then click on "History."

 ## Learn About Coal

If you are curious about coal and how it is found, extracted, transported and used, you can get informative booklets and a poster. All are available free from the American Coal Foundation. When you write, indicate exactly what your interests are so they can provide you with the appropriate materials.
A few of the items available include:
• *"Coal—Ancient Gift Serving Modern Man":* All about the history of coal
• *"Let's Learn About Coal":* Includes puzzles and word games explaining how coal is formed
• *"What Everyone Should Know About Coal":* Describes the different types of coal, how it is used and how it affects the environment
• *"Coal Science Fair Ideas":* Will help spark interest in coal, plus includes tips to help you get started with a learning project

• *Coal poster:* A large colorful poster with important coal information. Go to www.acf-coal.org to get online publications, activities and information.
Or write to:
American Coal Foundation
1130 17th St. NW, Ste. 220
Washington, DC 20036-4604
202-466-8630

A Pitch of a Sport

Did you know that many famous people used to pitch horseshoes? If you think you might find this sport interesting and would like to find out more about it, here is your opportunity. To discover more about this fun sport and to learn all the rules and tips for throwing the perfect horseshoe pitch, download the "Official Rules for Horseshoe Pitching" from the National Horseshoe Pitchers Association of America.

www.horseshoepitching.com

 ## Learn to Be More Romantic

Since the beginning of time, women have accused men of not being romantic enough. Finally there is help and it's called *RoMANtic Tip of the Week*. Each 1-page newsletter is filled with dozens of practical, creative and inspiring ideas and stories on dating, gift giving, anniversary celebrating and more. You can subscribe on the Web site at www.TheRomantic.com for the e-zines. 919-462-0900.

Join a free archaeological dig via the *Passport in Time* program. This program enables you to join activities such as archaeological excavation, site mapping, drafting, collecting oral histories, restoration and more. *Note:* You may have to pay your own food and lodging, depending upon the project.
Source: Passport in Time Clearinghouse, Box 31315, Tucson, AZ 85751. 800-281-9176, or www.passportintime.com.

Family connections.
No matter how far away family members may live, you can stay in close touch via the Internet. E-mail lets you send messages anywhere in the world, almost instantaneously. There's no postage, you don't have to wait weeks for letters to be exchanged and you can send far more than you could in an envelope.

Seniors Learn Something New

Visit www.seniornet.org/php/ and learn about computer technology and how to access the Internet to gather information on many different topics. When you join their free basic membership, you can be a part of over 600 discussions and chat rooms, as well as receive discounts on various products and a monthly electronic newsletter.

Free Courses and Seminars

Visit www.fathom.com and improve your skills in many different areas. There are free courses and seminars on a wide variety of subjects including "Early Contributions to Aviation," "George Washington and the Legacy of Character."

Money
For
College

Money for College

If you have children or grandchildren in college or about to go off to college, you know just how expensive it is. The good news is that there are all kinds of financial assistance programs available for virtually everyone. All that is necessary is to go through a series of steps in your search for the money you will need.

Listed here are several important and easy-to-use resources to help you effectively direct your search for college money. One of the most efficient ways of locating financial assistance that applies to you is to use the Internet. Naturally this means having access to a computer. If you do not yet own a computer, you can check with your local library or ask to use a friend's computer. Also most schools today have computers your child can use to help with this search.

Free College Aid

It is a little known fact, but there are literally billions of dollars in financial aid available to help students pay for their college education. The money is available from thousands of public and private sources. Much of it is available as outright grants that never have to be repaid. Still more money for college is available through low-cost loans and work-study programs.

The first place to check is with the financial aid office of the college of your choice. Counselors there will help you locate all the sources of money, including scholarships, grant-in-aid, work-study programs and low-interest, government-backed student loans. Next, you will definitely want to use the Internet as a resource in your search for financial assistance. Some of the most important Internet sources are described in the following articles.

Free Computer Search for Scholarships and Grants

Start your search with this Web site that was developed by the nation's financial aid administrators. At this site you will find a number of helpful scholarship search services that are entirely free. At many of the sites you will be asked to fill out a detailed questionnaire on the computer screen while you are online. The information about you and your background will be used to find appropriate sources of financial aid.

To begin your search go to the Web site, www.finaid.org.

Once you are at the finaid.org Web site, you will find several other sites (listed below) where again you will find the questionnaires that will begin your search. They will ask you to answer several pages of specific questions about your background and financial situation. Based on your answers to these questions, the site will set up a personalized profile that will match your specific skills, needs and interests. It will begin the search through its massive database for all of the money that is available for you. Once the search is completed, it will report to you exactly what assistance you qualify for and exactly how to get it.

Fulbright Scholar Program. Information for 2002–2003 grants for students.
Source: USIA Fulbright Student Program, 212-984-5400...or on the Web at www.iie.org.

Financial Aid: Student Guide.
Various loans and grants and how they work…phone numbers and Web sites.
Source: US Dept. of Education, Student Financial Assistance Programs, Washington, DC 20202. 877-4-EDPUBS

Despite the enormous value of this search and the fact that other organizations have charged up to $300 for similar services, there is no charge to you for these extensive searches! Here are some of the sites you will want to visit:

- **FastWEB:** www.fastweb.com
This is a database of more than 600,000 private-sector scholarships, grants, fellowships and loans. It is the Internet's largest free scholarship search site.

- **SRN Express:** www.srnexpress.com
This is a computerized version of the Scholarship Resource Network (SRN) database with information from several hundred thousand financial aid sources, with a special focus on scholarship information. They also have information on student-loan forgiveness programs for college graduates who need alternatives for loan repayment.

Low-cost Loans Pay for College

 Sallie Mae is the leading source of money for college loans. The folks there will be delighted to help you find the money you will need to pay for college.

One visit to the Sallie Mae Web site at www.salliemae.com is all you will need to see just how valuable it is. There you will be able to do a free online search for scholarship money available from more than 300,000 sources. Plus you can e-mail your financial aid questions and get quick advice from experts.

The College Answer Service is a toll-free hotline where you can speak to a financial aid expert who will answer your questions regarding paying for college, loans, aid packages, advice on financial aid applications, deadlines and lots more. You will also learn how to save hundreds of dollars with the lowest cost student loans available. Due to the low interest rates offered here, loans with Sallie Mae can cost a lot less to pay back. Call them Monday through Friday between 8 a.m. and 9 p.m. EST, at 800-239-4269.

Sallie Mae also has a number of helpful newsletters and fact-sheets including "Knowledge for College" and "Success by Sallie Mae: The Welcome Issue."

Student Loans and Grants

 If you are a college student or plan to be one and are short of money to continue your education, get a free copy of "Funding Your Education" and "The Student Guide." They are the most comprehensive resources of student financial aid from the US Department of Education. They cover major financial aid programs including Pell Grants, Stafford Loans and PLUS loans. Call the information hotline at 800-4-FED-AID.

For information on federal student aid backed by the US Government, you can visit the Department of Education's Web site at www.ed.gov.

How to Choose the Right College

Selecting the right college or university can be a challenging and time-consuming task but one that will bring immeasurable rewards for the rest of your life. To help you make the right choice, State Farm Insurance has a fantastic guide from *US News and World Report.* Nearly 300 pages long, this guide is filled with valuable information about tuition, room and board, financial aid, entrance requirements and lots more on more than 1,400 universities and colleges. To get a free copy of this important guide, *call State Farm toll-free at 888-733-8368.*

www.statefarm.com

College Planning

The "T. Rowe Price College Planning Guide" helps parents project what a college education may cost when the children are ready for higher education. It helps families plan ahead and start saving now. The guide is free. *Call 800-225-5132.*

Tax Credits Galore

Paying for college can be a huge burden, but now there is some relief—and hope. In fact, it's called the Hope Scholarship. It's even better than a scholarship because it's an income-tax credit beneficial to middle-income people. There are no applications to fill out. When you file your tax return, simply subtract the amount of the credit from the amount you owe. In effect, the government gives you up to $1,500 back per student. Here's how it works:

• The income tax credit can equal 100% of the first $1,000 paid in college tuition and fees, plus 50% of the next $1,000, for a total of $1,500.

• The credit is for you, your spouse or your dependent children in their first and second academic year so long as the students are enrolled at least half time in a two-year or four-year college or in a trade school.

• You can claim as many credits as you have qualified dependent students. For example, if you have two children in their first or second year of college, you will get a $3,000 credit on your income taxes for that year.

• To qualify for the full credit, your adjusted gross income (AGI) must be below $40,000 if you are single (between $40,000 and $50,000 you still qualify for a partial credit), or below $80,000 if you are married (between $80,000 and $100,000 you still qualify for a partial credit).

• Tuition must be paid in the same year as the credit is claimed. For example, you must have paid the tuition in 2001 to claim a credit on your 2001 tax return.

• In addition to the Hope Scholarship, there is also the Lifetime Learning Credit of $1,000 which can be taken for any student of any age, for any number of years, and even for a

Five Easy Ways Not To Get Admitted to a Competitive College. Pitfalls to avoid.

Source: Case Western Reserve University, Office of Undergraduate Admission, 10900 Euclid Ave., Cleveland, OH 44106-7055. Or call 216-368-4450.

Tax Benefits for Higher Education.
Learn how to claim a tax credit for part or all of tuition paid.
Source: IRS, Publication #970, 800-829-3676.

single adult education course. Currently this credit is worth up to $1,000 (20% of the first $5,000 paid in tuition and fees) and you can take just one credit per tax return no matter how many dependent students you may have in school. While you cannot take both credits at once for the same student, you can take the Hope credit for one and the Lifetime Learning Credit for another.

If you qualify, these tax credits can be an important source of additional money for college. For more detailed information, visit the IRS Web site at www.irs.gov/prod/tax_edu/teletax/tc605.html or your accountant.

Cars
And
Drivers

Tune-up in Time

Whether you have a new car or an older one, it is best to be prepared for any trouble you may encounter. Most of us are very trusting souls when it comes to our car repair needs. Usually we rely on the mechanic as the expert. When he tells us the car needs a tune-up or has any other problem, we have him check it out immediately. The Car Care Council wants us to be aware of tuning up our cars. They offer "Tune-up for Changing Seasons." This brochure is full of easy-to-understand advice on what to look for before it's too late. *To get a free copy, simply write to:*

The Car Care Council
Dept. T
42 Park Dr.
Port Clinton, OH 43452
www.carcarecouncil.org

Attention: Future issues of Car Care Corner will only be available via their web site.

Lemon Aid

If you are having problems with your car and can't seem to get satisfaction from the dealer or manufacturer, don't despair. Help is on the way. The Auto Safety Hotline is anxious to hear about your complaint so they can get to work on it. They have set up both a toll-free hotline and an Internet site for you to be able to report your problem. To make a report, call toll-free 800-424-9393. Or visit their Web site at www.nhtsa.dot.gov. *You can also write to:*

National Highway and Traffic Safety Administration
400 Seventh St. SW
Washington, DC 20590

NHTSA does not get involved in individual cases of complaints between the consumer and the dealer or manufacturer. If you have such a complaint, call the Federal Trade Commission for assistance at 877-382-4357. www.ftc.gov

Recall Resource Number

If you would just like to get information about recalls and auto defect reports, call the toll-free number operated by the Technical Information Services division of National Highway and Traffic Safety Administration (NHTSA). The number is 888-327-4236. Or try the Auto Safety Hotline at 800-424-9393.

Car Shopping on the Net

Are you thinking of buying a car? Interested in negotiating the best deal so you can save thousands of dollars? The Internet has scores of Web sites with automobile information. The most useful ones display invoice cost, road-test performance and rebates and incentives. *Try these:*

www.thecarconnection.com/
For up-to-date information, analyses and columns from auto industry experts at the Car Connection.

www.excite.com/autos
Use this Web site to go to the Auto Channel, which has links to every automaker's Web site for lease help, chat rooms and more.

www.edmunds.com
Edmund's Vehicle Price Guide is on the Web at this site. You can find out how much the car dealer pays for the car you are

How to Find Your Way Under the Hood and Around the Car.
Source: Car Care Council, Dept. BLB-UH, 42 Park Dr., Port Clinton, OH 43452. Include a business-sized SASE. www.carcarecouncil.org

Seven Sensible Signals. Official auto hand and headlight signals for drivers to show apology…danger ahead…etc.

Source: National Motorists Association, 800-882-2785. www.nationalmotorists association.org

thinking of buying. You will also discover the amount of the holdback allowance. The holdback allowance is an additional profit that the manufacturer later gives back to the dealer after the car is sold. It's approximately 3% of the suggested retail price. The site also has information on rebates and incentive plans.

www.kbb.com

The Kelley Blue Book Web site can give you a good idea what your trade-in is worth, as well as the real value of a used car you want to buy.

Don't Forget *Consumer Reports*

If you would like to see how *Consumer Reports* rates the car you are thinking of buying, visit their Web site. You will find evaluations of more than 120 makes of new cars. Access to their site costs $3.95 a month, but you can visit their "Best of the Best" page for free. The site is located at www.consumerreports.org. You can also get one-time reports for $12 for the first report, and $10 for others.

Save Thousands on Your Next Car

One of the best ways to save a lot of money on the purchase or lease of a vehicle is to use online vehicle brokers. They have nationwide networks of thousands of dealers of every make of auto or truck.

www.nationwide-auto.com

Nationwide Auto Brokers will obtain the best deals possible for their customers. For $11.95, for

the first quote ($9.95 each additional quote), they will supply you with a quote of the exact vehicle you're looking for. This quote contains a list of all equipment available, the dealer cost and suggested retail price. The car can be purchased directly through them or through a dealership.

www.carscost.com

Cars@Cost offers many models of new cars at dealer invoice plus their fee. They will locate your car, negotiate the price and set up delivery for $399.00.

Dealer Referral Services

As a smart shopper it is essential to inform yourself fully before you go out to buy your next car. One of the best ways to gather the information you will need to make an intelligent choice and get the very lowest price is by visiting these Web sites where you will not only learn lots of valuable information about cars, but also get referrals to auto dealers in your local area.

www.autobytel.com

With several million customers, Autobytel is one of the largest and most useful Web sites. It has links to six car-pricing sites, more than 5,000 dealers in their referral network and a great reputation. You will find a lease-buy comparison calculator and even an online finance application.

www.autoweb.com

At this site you will find well-organized information that will help you buy a new car, buy or sell a used car, explore insurance rates on the car you are thinking of buying, look into financing and find a list of dealers in your area. 1-888-ELOAN22.

www.autobuyer.com

There is not too much detailed information at this site but it is a great place to visit to get a dealer quote on the car of your choice without the pressure of a car salesman in the showroom.

www.carsmart.com

CarSmart is great consumer buying guide with loads of very useful information on such topics as financing, the best time to buy a new car, air bags, anti-lock brakes and much more. You can even get insurance and financing quotes, links to dealer and manufacturer sites and vehicle pricing reports.

www.carpoint.msn.com

Microsoft CarPoint previews various car models and offers "test drives" of selected cars. You will find lots of reviews, photos and reports on safety, road tests and more. It also has very useful features such as side-by-side comparisons and even an affordability calculator. Check it out before you buy your next car.

For AAA Members

If you're a member of AAA, you should know that they offer an excellent tour service. Contact your local AAA office and tell them your start point and your destination. They will give you detailed road maps with your route highlighted in colored ink.

Many local offices also offer members a car-buying service which could save you thousands of dollars on your next auto purchase or lease. 888-859-5161. www.AAAmidatlantic.com

Importing a Car

Can you save money by buying a foreign car on your next trip abroad? What are the customs requirements? What should you know about emission standards on a car you import yourself? For answers, send a postcard asking for "Importing a Car" and also "US Customs in Brief." *It's yours free from:*

US Customs Service
1300 Pennsylvania Ave. NW, Room 6.3D
Washington, DC 20229
www.customs.ustreas.gov/

10 Ways to Slash Auto Insurance Costs

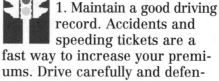

1. Maintain a good driving record. Accidents and speeding tickets are a fast way to increase your premiums. Drive carefully and defensively. Consider walking or taking other means of transportation or car pooling to reduce the risk of accidents.

2. Raise your deductibles. The deductible is the amount you must pay for any loss before your insurance kicks in. If your current deductible is $250 or less, raising it to $500 can save you 15% to 30%.

3. Protect against theft. Security devices, such as car alarms or having the car's serial number etched on the window, saves you 15% on your comprehensive auto insurance.

Underhood Tips to Help You Keep Your Cool. Car air-conditioning-system tips.
Source: US Environmental Protection Agency, EPA430F95092, National Service Center for Environmental Publications, Box 42419, Cincinnati, OH 45242. 800-490-9198.

Keys to Vehicle Leasing: A Consumer Guide. Leasing versus buying...sample form...rights and responsibilities.

Source: Federal Trade Commission, Consumer Response Center, CRC-240, Washington, DC 20580...or on the Web at www.ftc.gov. You may also call 877-FTC-HELP.

4. Ask about discounts. Insurance companies offer special deals and discounts if you are retired, belong to a business association, have been insured with the company for a certain number of years or have multiple policies with the same company, such as insuring both car and home with the same firm.

5. Take a driver improvement course. For example, AAA has a Driver Improvement Program for people 55 and older. Taking the course will lead to car insurance discounts.

6. Reduce your coverage or eliminate coverage no longer needed. For example, many new cars now come with towing or road service included. If that's the case, eliminate that particular coverage from your auto insurance.

7. Look for an insurer who gives discounts to drivers over 50 or cars with low annual mileage. Some insurers give students with good grades a 5% discount. If your child maintains a B average or better in school or has taken driver's education, you may be eligible for discounts. If your child is at a college more than 100 miles from home and the car stays home, depending on the insurance company, you may also be eligible for discounts. Rates are also much lower when a teenage driver is considered only an occasional driver of the parents' cars.

8. Check insurance rates before you buy a car. The cost of insuring a Porsche is much higher than the cost of insuring an inexpensive family car or a domestic car.

9. Shop around. Talk to friends and neighbors about their insurance coverage and rates. Get quotes from several companies. Compare rates and coverage.

10. Get a car with anti-lock brakes and air bags and save an additional 5%.

Guide to Leasing

If you can't decide whether to buy or lease a vehicle, you need to have this guide: "A Consumer Guide to Vehicle Leasing." It is free from the Federal Reserve Board. 202-452-3244 or 3245. www.federalreserve.gov

What to Do if You Have a Car Accident

• Write down names and addresses of all persons involved and all witnesses.

• Notify the police immediately.

• Get medical attention if needed.

• Contact your insurance agent and do not admit liability or discuss your accident with anyone except your insurance representative or the police.

Free Designated Driver Kit

State Farm wants to help give you, your college, civic group or professional organization free designated driver presentation items. They are a colorful way to remind friends and associates of the importance of safe driving. State Farm will send your group a free designated driver kit. It has a presentation guide, video and sample speeches. To get one, contact a State Farm agent or regional office near you. www.statefarm.com

Keep Your Tires Safe

Did you know that when you keep your tires properly inflated, the air provides a cushion of protection when you hit a pothole? If the tire is under-inflated, you could damage the wheel. If it is over-inflated, the tire will be damaged. For the best information about the care and protection of tires, send for a free copy of "The Motorist Tire Care and Safety Guide." *Send a business-sized SASE to:*

> **RMA**
> PO Box 3147
> Medina, OH 44258
> 800-325-5095, ext. 242
> www.rma.org

Shopping for a Safe Car

Before you go shopping for your next car, be sure to get a copy of "Injury, Collision & Theft Losses" and "Shopping for a Safer Car." These informative booklets will help you make an intelligent choice about which is the safest vehicle for you. They include excellent safety and loss comparisons of hundreds of passenger cars, vans, pickups and utility vehicles. *Write to:*

> **Insurance Institute for Highway Safety**
> **Highway Loss Data Institute**
> Communications Department
> 1005 N. Glebe Rd., Ste. 800
> Arlington, VA 22201
> 703-247-1500
> *Or go to the Web at:*
> www.hwysafety.org/pubs.htm

Automobile Hotline Numbers

If you are thinking of buying or leasing a car in the near future, be sure you get all the information you need to make an intelligent decision before you go to a dealer showroom. The first step is to call the toll-free hotline phone number for the make of car you are interested in. The manufacturers will send you illustrated product information booklets and even videotapes featuring their cars.

Acura	800-TO-ACURA
BMW	800-334-4BMW
Buick	800-4-RIVIERA
Cadillac	800-333-4CAD
Chevrolet	800-950-2438
Chrysler	800-4-A-CHRYSLER
Dodge	800-4-A-DODGE
Ford	800-392-3673
GMC	800-GMC-TRUCK
Honda	800-33-HONDA
Hyundai	800-826-CARS
Infiniti	800-826-6500
Isuzu	800-726-2700
Jaguar	800-4-JAGUAR
Jeep	800-925-JEEP
Land Rover	800-FINE-4WD
Lexus	800-USA-LEXUS
Lincoln	800-392-3673
Mercedes	800-FOR-MERCEDES
Mercury	800-241-8450
Mitsubishi	800-55-MITSU
Nissan	800-NISSAN-3
Pontiac	800-2-PONTIAC
Porsche	800-PORSCHE
Saab	800-582-SAAB
Subaru	800-WANT-AWD
Suzuki	877-697-8985
Toyota	800-GO-TOYOTA
Volkswagen	800-DRIVE-VW
Volvo	800-550-5658

Alone Behind the Wheel. What to do to ensure safety when driving by yourself.
Source: Shell Oil Co., 800-376-0200.

Free
For
Sports Fans

Senior Sports

Healthy eating and exercise are the keys to keeping fit, feeling great and living longer. Keeping physically active also keeps us alert mentally. Whatever your favorite sport, go out and do it. If you are unable to participate in a fitness program, then walking is just fine.

Did you know that there is a Senior Softball World Championship and a Senior Softball World Series each year?

Believe it or not, Senior Softball was started in 1930 by a hotel owner in Florida who was looking for something for her elderly guests to do. She organized the Three-Quarter Century Club. Members had to be at least 75 years old. Think about that the next time you think you are too tired and feel you can't exercise.

For more information on Senior Athletic Competition like Senior Softball, *write to:*

> **National Senior Games Association**
> 3032 Old Forge Dr.
> Baton Rouge, LA 70808
> 225-925-5678
> www.nsga.com

Also contact your local senior center, city recreation department, library or YMCA to see what senior sports they are sponsoring.

Women's Sports Foundation

This is an organization that encourages women to get involved in sports. They offer any group or school free films of women in sports to help encourage other women to be active and stay active. They also publish a guide listing scholarships to American colleges and universities for women who are into sports. It's a myth that only men get sports scholarships to college. Call them toll-free at 800-227-3988. Or visit their Web site at www.womenssports foundation.org.

Outdoor Sports

L.L. Bean, the outdoor-sporting specialists for 67 years, would like to send you a copy of their catalog. It features fine-quality apparel and footwear for people who love the outdoors, as well as equipment for camping, fishing, hiking and canoeing. Call toll-free at 800-441-5713 or visit their Web site at www.llbean.com.

The Story of the Olympic Games

"The History of the Olympics" gives you the complete story of the Olympics, starting with the earliest recorded game in 776 B.C. It traces the game's history right up to the present. This, along with much more fascinating information, is available at www.olympic-usa.org.

Free Baseball Cards

Every baseball fan will want to send for this freebie. When you request it, you will receive 12 trading cards each featuring a different player and player stats. To get your cards, just *send a business-sized SASE and 50¢ to:*

> **DANORS, Dept. F**
> 5721 Funston St., Bay 14
> Hollywood, FL 33023
> www.expage.com/page/freestuffforkids

Women's Sailing School. Newsletter and brochure of courses and events...both domestic and international.
Source: Sea Sense, Inc., Box 1961, St. Petersburg, FL 33731. 800-332-1404. www.seasenseboating.com

How to Buy Exercise Equipment for the Home. Features to look for in a treadmill, rowing machine, elliptical trainer or heart-rate monitor.

Source: Sporting Goods Manufacturers Association, 200 Castlewood Dr., North Palm Beach, FL 33408-5696 561-842-4100 www.sportlink.com/fitness

Free from Your Favorite Team

Do you love sports? How would you like to receive photos of your favorite teams? Most sports clubs have all kinds of freebies for their loyal fans, which often include team photos, souvenir brochures, stickers, fan club information, playing schedules, catalogs and lots more. All you have to do is write to your favorite sports teams at the following addresses. Tell them you are a loyal fan and ask for a "fan package."

Even though it is not always necessary, it's a good idea to send along business-sized SASE so they can send your freebie in your own envelope or you can send your information via their Websites. Also, if you have a favorite player on the team, write his name on the envelope.

Sometimes it takes a while to get an answer since most teams are flooded with mail. Just be patient and you'll hear from them.

Hockey

National Hockey League
One International Blvd.
Rexdale, Ontario
Canada M9W 6H3
www.nhl.com

Eastern Conference

Atlanta Thrashers Hockey Club
Atlanta, GA 30348-5366
www.atlantathrashers.com

Boston Bruins
One FleetCenter, Ste. 250
Boston, MA 02114-1303
www.bostonbruins.com

Buffalo Sabres
Marine Midland Arena
One Seymore H. Knox III Plaza
Buffalo, NY 14203
www.sabres.com

Carolina Hurricanes Hockey Club
Entertainment & Sports Arena
1400 Edwards Mill Rd.
Raleigh, NC 27607
www.caneshockey.com

Florida Panthers Hockey Club
One Panthers Pkwy.
Sunrise, FL 33323
www.floridapanthers.com

Montreal Canadiens
Molson Centre
1280 de la Gauchetiere St. W
Montreal, Quebec
Canada H3B 5E8
www.canadiens.com

New Jersey Devils
Continental Airlines Arena
50 Route 120 North
E. Rutherford, NJ 07073
www.newjerseydevils.com

New York Islanders
Nassau Veterans Memorial Coliseum
1255 Hempstead Tnpk.
Uniondale, NY 11553
www.newyorkislanders.com

New York Rangers
Madison Square Garden
Two Penn Plaza, 14th flr.
New York, NY 10121
www.newyorkrangers.com

Ottawa Senators Hockey Club
Corel Centre
1000 Palladium Dr.
Kanata, Ontario
Canada K2V 1A5
www.ottawasenators.com

Philadelphia Flyers
First Union Center
3601 S. Broad St.
Philadelphia, PA 19148
www.philadelphiaflyers.com

Pittsburgh Penguins
Mellon Arena
66 Mario Lemieux Pl.
Pittsburgh, PA 15219
www.pittsburghpenguins.com

Tampa Bay Lightning
Ice Palace Arena
401 Channelside Dr.
Tampa, FL 33602
www.tampabaylightning.com

Toronto Maple Leafs
Air Canada Centre
40 Bay St.
Toronto, Ontario
Canada M5J 2X2
www.mapleleafs.com

Washington Capitals
Market Square North
401 Ninth St. NW, Suite 750
Washington, DC 20004
www.washingtoncaps.com

Western Conference

Anaheim Mighty Ducks
Arrowhead Pond of Anaheim
2695 Katella Ave.
Anaheim, CA 92806
www.mightyducks.com

Calgary Flames
Pengrowth Saddledome
PO Box 1540, Station M
Calgary, Alberta
Canada T2P 3B9
www.calgaryflames.com

Chicago Blackhawks
United Center
1901 W. Madison St.
Chicago, IL 60612
www.chicagoblackhawks.com

Colorado Avalanche
Pepsi Center
1000 Chopper Cir.
Denver, CO 80204
www.coloradoavalanche.com

Columbus Blue Jackets
Nationwide Arena
200 W. Nationwide Blvd.
Suite Level
Columbus, OH 43125
www.bluejackets.com

Dallas Stars
Dr. Pepper StarCenter-Valley Ranch
211 Cowboys Pkwy.
Irving, TX 75063
www.dallasstars.com

Detroit Red Wings
Joe Louis Arena
600 Civic Center Dr.
Detroit, MI 48226
www.detroitredwings.com

Edmonton Oilers
Skyreach Centre
11230 110 St.
Edmonton, Alberta
Canada T5G H7
www.edmontonoilers.com

Los Angeles Kings
Staples Center
1111 S. Figueroa St.
Los Angeles, CA 90015
www.lakings.com

Minnesota Wild
317 Washington St.
St. Paul, MN 55102
www.wild.com

Nashville Predators
501 Broadway
Nashville, TN 37203
www.nashvillepredators.com

Phoenix Coyotes
Alltel Ice Den
9375 E. Bell Rd.
Scottsdale, AZ 85260
www.phoenixcoyotes.com

St. Louis Blues
Savvis Center
1401 Clark Ave.
St. Louis, MO 03103-2709
www.stlouisblues.com

San Jose Sharks
San Jose Arena
525 W. Santa Clara St.
San Jose, CA 95113
www.sjsharks.com

Vancouver Canucks
General Motors Place
800 Griffiths Way
Vancouver, BC
Canada V6B 6G1
www.canucks.com

Basketball

Atlanta Hawks
One CNN Center
Ste. 405
Atlanta, GA 30303
www.nba.com/hawks

Boston Celtics
FleetCenter
151 Merrimac St., 5th flr.
Boston, MA 02114
www.nba.com/celtics

About Fitness and Exercise. Types of exercises and calories burned per hour... safety issues...preventing boredom.
Source: MetLife Consumer Education Center, 800-638-5433.

Little League. How to organize a Little League baseball or softball program. Free.
Source: Little League Baseball Inc., PO Box 3485, Williamsport, PA 17701.

Charlotte Hornets
100 Hive Dr.
Charlotte, NC 28217
www.nba.com/hornets

Chicago Bulls
United Center
1901 W. Madison St.
Chicago, IL 60612-2459
www.nba.com/bulls

Cleveland Cavaliers
One Center Court
Cleveland, OH 44115
www.nba.com/cavs

Dallas Mavericks
American Airlines Center
2500 Victory Ave.
Dallas, TX 75201
www.nba.com/mavericks

Denver Nuggets
PO Box 4568
1635 Clay St.
Denver, CO 80204
www.nba.com/nuggets

Detroit Pistons
Palace of Auburn Hills
Two Championship Dr.
Auburn Hills, MI 48326
www.nba.com/pistons

 Golden State Warriors
1011 Broadway, 20th flr.
Oakland, CA 94607
www.nba.com/warriors

Houston Rockets
Two Greenway Plaza, Ste. 400
Houston, TX 77046
www.nba.com/rockets

Indiana Pacers
125 S. Pennsylvania St.
Indianapolis, IN 46204
www.nba.com/pacers

Los Angeles Clippers
Staples Center
1111 S. Figueroa St., Ste. 3100
Los Angeles, CA 90015
www.nba.com/clippers

Los Angeles Lakers
Staples Center
555 N. Nash St.
El Segundo, CA 90245
www.nba.com/lakers

Miami Heat
American Airlines Arena
601 Biscayne Blvd.
Miami, FL 33132
www.nba.com/heat

Milwaukee Bucks
Bradley Center
1001 N. Fourth St.
Milwaukee, WI 53203
www.nba.com/bucks

 Minnesota Timberwolves
600 First Ave. N
Minneapolis, MN 55403
www.nba.com/timberwolves

New Jersey Nets
390 Murray Hill Pkwy.
E. Rutherford, NJ 07073
www.nba.com/nets

New York Knicks
Madison Square Garden
Two Pennsylvania Plaza
New York, NY 10121
www.nba.com/knicks

Orlando Magic
TD Waterhouse Centre
One Magic Pl.
600 West Ameila
Orlando, FL 32802
www.nba.com/magic

Philadelphia '76ers
First Union Center
3601 S. Broad St.
Philadelphia, PA 19148
www.nba.com/sixers

Phoenix Suns
America West Arena
201 E. Jefferson St.
Phoenix, AZ 85004
www.nba.com/suns

Portland Trail Blazers
One Center Court, Ste. 200
Portland, OR 97201
www.nba.com/blazers

Sacramento Kings
Arco Arena
One Sports Pkwy.
Sacramento, CA 95834
www.nba.com/kings

San Antonio Spurs
100 Montana
San Antonio, TX 78203
www.nba.com/spurs

Seattle Sonics & Storm
351 Elliott Ave. W., Ste. 500
Seattle, WA 98119
www.nba.com/sonics

Toronto Raptors
Air Canada Centre
40 Bay St.
Toronto, Ontario
Canada M5J 2X2
www.nba.com/raptors

Utah Jazz
Delta Center
301 W. South Temple
Salt Lake City, UT 84101
www.nba.com/jazz

Washington Wizards
MCI Center
601 F Street NW
Washington, DC 20004
www.nba.com/wizards

Football

National Football League
280 Park Ave.
New York, NY 10017
www.nfl.com

American Conference

Baltimore Ravens
11001 Owings Mills Blvd.
Owings Mills, MD 21117
www.ravenszone.net

Buffalo Bills
One Bills Dr.
Orchard Park, NY 14127
www.buffalobills.com

Cincinnati Bengals
One Paul Brown Stadium
Cincinnati, OH 45202
www.bengals.com

Cleveland Browns
80 First Ave.
Cleveland, OH 44146
www.clevelandbrowns.com

Denver Broncos
Mile High Stadium
1900 Eliot St.
Denver, CO 80204-1721
www.denverbroncos.com

Indianapolis Colts
7001 W. 56 St.
Indianapolis, IN 46254
www.colts.com

Jacksonville Jaguars
One ALLTEL Stadium Pl.
Jacksonville, FL 32202
www.jaguars.com

Kansas City Chiefs
One Arrowhead Dr.
Kansas City, MO 64129
www.kcchiefs.com

Miami Dolphins
Pro Player Stadium
2269 NW 199 St.
Miami, FL 33056
www.miamidolphins.com

New England Patriots
60 Washington St.
Foxboro, MA 02035
www.patriots.com

New York Jets
Giants Stadium
East Rutherford, NJ 07073
or
1000 Fulton Ave.
Hempstead, NY 11550
www.newyorkjets.com/index2new.php

Oakland Raiders
1220 Harbor Bay Pkwy.
Alameda, CA 94502
www.raiders.com

Vintage-style Football Jersey Catalog. Historic minor league and semi-pro T-shirts, caps and jerseys.
Source: Ebbets Field Flannels, 800-377-9777.
www.ebbets.com

Skiing: Links to Thousands of Sites on Ski Resorts... equipment...snow conditions. Covers snowboarding, too. On the Web at www.skicentral.com

Pittsburgh Steelers
PO Box 6763
Pittsburgh, PA 15212
www.steelers.com

San Diego Chargers
PO Box 609609
San Diego, CA 92160-9609
www.chargers.com

Seattle Seahawks
11220 N.E. 53 St.
Kirkland, WA 98033
www.seahawks.com

Tennessee Titans
Baptist Sports Park
460 Great Circle Rd.
Nashville, TN 37228
www.titans.com

National Conference

Arizona Cardinals
8701 S. Hardy Dr.
Phoenix, AZ 85284
www.cardinals.com

Atlanta Falcons
4400 Falcon Pkwy.
Flowery Branch, GA 30542
www.falcons.com

Carolina Panthers
Ericsson Stadium
800 S. Mint St.
Charlotte, NC 28202
www.panthers.com

Chicago Bears
Halas Hall
1000 Football Dr.
Lake Forest, IL 60045
www.chicagobears.com

Dallas Cowboys
Texas Stadium
2401 East Airport Freeway
Irving, TX 75063
www.dallascowboys.com

Detroit Lions
1200 Featherstone Rd.
Pontiac, MI 48342
www.detroitlions.com

Green Bay Packers
1265 Lombardi Ave.
Green Bay, WI 54304
www.packers.com

Minnesota Vikings
Winter Park Administrative Offices
9520 Viking Dr.
Eden Prairie, MN 55344
www.vikings.com

The New Orleans Saints
5800 Airline Dr.
Metairie, LA 70003
www.neworleanssaints.com

New York Football Giants
Giants Stadium
East Rutherford, NJ 07073
www.newyorkgiants.com

Philadelphia Eagles
Veterans Stadium
3501 S. Broad St.
Philadelphia, PA 19148-5201
www.eagles.com

San Francisco 49ers
4949 Centennial Blvd.
Santa Clara, CA 95054
www.sf49ers.com

St. Louis Rams
901 North Broadway
St. Louis, MO 63101
www.stlouisrams.com

Tampa Bay Buccaneers
One Buccaneer Pl.
Tampa, FL 33607
www.buccaneers.com

Washington Redskins
21300 Redskin Park Dr.
Ashburn, VA 20147
www.redskins.com

Baseball

Major League Baseball
350 Park Ave.
New York, NY 10022
www.majorleaguebaseball.com

American League

Anaheim Angels
angels.mlb.com
2000 Gene Autry Way
Anaheim, CA 92806
www.angelsbaseball.com

Baltimore Orioles
Oriole Park at Camden Yards
333 W. Camden St.
Baltimore, MD 21201
www.orioles.mlb.com

Boston Red Sox
Four Yawkey Way
Boston, MA 02215-3496
www.redsox.mlb.com

Chicago White Sox
333 W. 35 St.
Chicago, IL 60616
www.whitesox.mlb.com

Cleveland Indians
Jacobs Field
2401 Ontario St.
Cleveland, OH 44115-4003
www.indians.mlb.com

Detroit Tigers
Commerce Park
2100 Woodward Ave.
Detroit, MI 48201
www.tigers.mlb.com

Kansas City Royals
One Royal Way
Kansas City, MO 64129
www.royals.mlb.com

Minnesota Twins
Metrodome
34 Kirby Puckett Pl.
Minneapolis, MN 55415
www.twins.mlb.com

New York Yankees
Yankee Stadium
161st St. and River Ave.
Bronx, NY 10452
www.yankees.mlb.com

Oakland Athletics
7677 Oakport St., Ste. 200
Oakland, CA 94621
www.athletics.mlb.com

Seattle Mariners
SAFECO Field
1250 First Ave. S.
Seattle, WA 98134
www.mariners.mlb.com

Tampa Bay Devil Rays
Tropicana Field
One Tropicana Dr.
St. Petersburg, FL 33705
www.devilrays.mlb.com

Texas Rangers
1000 Ballpark Way, #400
Arlington, TX 76011
www.rangers.mlb.com

Toronto Blue Jays
One Blue Jays Way, Ste. 3200
SkyDome
Toronto, Ontario
Canada M5V 1J1
www.bluejays.mlb.com

National League

Arizona Diamondbacks
Bank One Ballpark
PO Box 2095
Phoenix, AZ 85001
www.diamondbacks.mlb.com

Atlanta Braves
PO Box 4064
Atlanta, GA 30302-4064
www.braves.mlb.com

Chicago Cubs
Wrigley Field
1060 W. Addison
Chicago, IL 60613
www.cubs.mlb.com

Cincinnati Reds
100 Cinergy Field
Cincinnati, OH 45202
www.reds.mlb.com

Athlete's Foot.
Prevention...most
effective treatment.
Source: American Academy of
Dermatology, 888-462-3376
(DERM). www.aad.org

Colorado Rockies
Coors Field
2001 Blake St.
Denver, CO 80205-2000
www.rockies.mlb.com

Florida Marlins
Pro Player Stadium
2267 Dan Marino Blvd.
Miami, FL 33028
www.marlins.mlb.com

Houston Astros
PO Box 288
Houston, TX 77001-0288
www.astros.mlb.com

Los Angeles Dodgers
Dodger Stadium
1000 Elysian Park Ave.
Los Angeles, CA 90012-1199
www.dodgers.mlb.com

Milwaukee Brewers
One Brewers Way
Milwaukee, WI 53214-3652
www.brewers.mlb.com

 Montreal Expos
PO Box 500
Station "M"
Montreal, Quebec
Canada HIV 3P2
www.expos.mlb.com

New York Mets
Shea Stadium
123-01 Roosevelt Ave.
Flushing, NY 11368-1699
www.mets.mlb.com

Philadelphia Phillies
Veterans Stadium
3501 S. Broad St.
Philadelphia, PA 19148
www.phillies.mlb.com

Pittsburgh Pirates
PNC Park at North Shore
115 Federal St.
Pittsburgh, PA 15212
www.pirates.mlb.com

 St. Louis Cardinals
250 Stadium Plaza
St. Louis, MO 63102
www.cardinals.mlb.com

San Diego Padres
PO Box 12200
San Diego, CA 92112-2000
www.padres.mlb.com

San Francisco Giants
Pacific Bell Park
24 Willie Mays Plaza
San Francisco, CA 94107
www.giants.mlb.com

Money Matters

How to Find a Good Financial Planner

Are you are always having difficulty making ends meet? Maybe you would like to have more money to enjoy your retirement. You might need the help of a financial planner. "When & How to Choose a Financial Planner" is a free booklet available from the National Endowment for Financial Education. The information in this booklet will help you choose a planner. The guide gives basic information on when to seek advice, as well as how to go about choosing a financial planner. *To get a free copy, send an SASE to:*

National Endowment for Financial Education
5299 DTC Blvd., Ste. 1300
Greenwood Village, CO 80111
303-741-6333
www.nefe.org

Find the Right Financial Adviser

Everybody with assets to protect, regardless of their age, should have a financial advisor. Remember, you worked hard for your money and now it's time to make your money work harder for you. Oppenheimer Funds has published a guide, "Finding a Financial Adviser" kit which will take you step-by-step through the process of selecting names, conducting interviews, making the final decision and maintaining a relationship that will be profitable. This is a must for anyone looking for help in making intelligent financial planning decisions. To order a free copy, call 888-470-0862. www.oppenheimerfunds.com

Making Educated Investments

American Century Investments is offering free investor education materials you might find useful. Here are some of the more popular ones:

• "IRA Choices and Challenges" is a 16-page booklet that compares the different types of IRAs.

• "Investing with a Purpose" is a 26-page booklet that explains the concepts of diversification and asset allocation. It offers four sample portfolios based on your stage in life, and includes a do-it-yourself investor profile questionnaire.

• "College Planner" is a slide-rule calculator for determining college costs.

• "Post-Retirement Calculator" is a slide-rule calculator for determining how long your savings will last, depending on how much you spend.

• "Fast TaxFacts" is a laminated card with tax rates and general information on IRA rules and IRA rollovers and much more.

For a free copy of any or all of these booklets or calculators, call American Century Investments toll-free at 800-345-2021. www.americancentury.com

10 Questions to Ask When Choosing a Financial Planner.
Source: Certified Financial Planner Board of Standards, 888-237-6275. www.cfp.board.org

Tax-Saving Investments

If would like to lower your income taxes, you might want to consider investments that are completely or partially free of federal, state or local income tax. Lebenthal, one of the nation's leading municipal bond dealers, has the "Bond Information Kit." It will explain the advantages of invest-

Small Businesses Targeted by Big Scams: Suggestions to protect yourself against phone service schemes …Internet fraud… loan sharks…more.

Source: Call For Action, Inc. 5272 River Rd., Ste. 300, Bethesda, MD 20816. Include a business-sized SASE. Or call 800-647-1756. 301-657-8260. www.callforaction.org

ing in tax-exempt bonds. For a free kit, call them toll-free at 800-425-6116. www.lebenthal.com

Franchise Savvy

Did you ever think of starting your own business, or perhaps buying one of the thousands of franchises that are available? Before you decide to make your mark as a franchise entrepreneur, you owe it to yourself to learn more about franchising. Here are two valuable sources to contact:

www.entremkt.com

The Franchise Update Directory is the most comprehensive database of franchise information on the World Wide Web. This site lists more than 2,500 franchises.

www.ftc.gov

The Federal Trade Commission has an excellent pamphlet, "A Consumer Guide to Buying a Franchise." You can read it on the FTC's Web site.

Free Help Starting a Business

Service Corps of Retired Executives (SCORE) can give you free advice on starting a small business. This is a group of working and retired executives and business owners who donate their time and expertise to provide individual, confidential business counseling and business workshops for aspiring entrepreneurs and small-business owners. To find the SCORE office nearest you, call them at 800-634-0245. www.score.org

Startup Money for You

For some seniors the definition of retiring is to stop doing their usual job and starting up something new. If you have always wanted to start a business, now's your chance. The US Small Business Administration (SBA) is a great resource. The SBA has a variety of programs, including a loan guarantee program you might want to use. There are offices throughout the US. To find out more, first call the SBA Answer Desk at 800-827-5722. Or visit the SBA Web site at www.sbaonline.sba.gov.

Best Mortgage Loans

Before shopping for a new mortgage, find out what rates are being charged in your area, and learn about mortgage trends and how to use repayment calculators. Often even a slightly lower interest rate can save you thousands of dollars over the repayment period of your loan. Once you have become an informed consumer, then you can shop intelligently for a mortgage loan either on the Internet or at a local financial institution.

Here are three online sites where you can find up-to-date rate information and lots more. They do not offer mortgages directly but will provide you with all kinds of highly useful information.

www.fanniemae.com/index.html

Fannie Mae has all kinds of mortgage and home refinancing information. The site also lists the co-ops, condos and houses owned by Fannie Mae because of foreclosures throughout the nation.

This is a great place to shop for a terrific buy on your next home.

www.interest.com/rates.html

On its Web site, the Mortgage Market Information Service employs an easy-to-use click-on map that will help you locate up-to-date information about mortgage rates and lenders in specific areas around the country.

www.monstermoving.com

With Monstermoving, you can learn about mortgages and shop for the best rates online. Visitors can access more than 1400 participating lenders covering more than 124 different loan programs for real-time, side-by-side comparisons of mortgage rates. Mortgage calculators help predict mortgage costs and determine qualifications for a specific loan.

Online Mortgage Savings

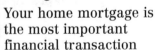

Your home mortgage is the most important financial transaction your family is likely to ever make. But if you have ever shopped for a mortgage you know how long, tedious and expensive the process can be. Now there may be a better way: online mortgages.

By filling out the application on your home computer and sending it electronically, this method offers you a combination of speed, convenience and cost savings. Financial experts agree that getting a mortgage online can save you money. In fact, sometimes the savings can total tens of thousands of dollars over the term of the mortgage! The reason is that the online mortgage companies, who deal with lenders throughout the country, are constantly searching for the very best rates to offer you. Also, online mortgage approval can sometimes take a matter of minutes instead of the weeks or even months that it can take the traditional way.

Plus, several of the online mortgage companies offer you a variety of additional services which include help in finding a home, tips on negotiating, help in inspecting the home you plan to buy and lots more. Here are three of the leading online mortgage companies you can contact directly through their Internet sites:

> **Quicken Loans:** www.quickenmortgage.com
> **E-Loan:** www.eloan.com
> **iOwn:** www.iown.com

Do You Have Unclaimed Money Waiting for You?

Did you know that there are actually more than $300 billion in unclaimed funds waiting for the rightful owners to come along? Often what happens is that people move and forget to notify everyone of their new address. Or someone may have a bank account from years ago which still has money in it that was never withdrawn. Also, there are three million stock-brokerage accounts with securities that belong to shareholders who are currently unaccounted for. If you think that there is even a remote possibility that you have funds or securities you have forgotten about, check at the following Web sites to see what you have and how you can claim your funds. It could be like winning the lottery!

At the first Web site, you can conduct a search for lost funds. The company is called "The

How to Buy a Home With a Low Down Payment. A consumer's guide to buying a home with as little as 5% down.
Source: Federal Consumer Information Center, Pueblo, CO 81009. Read online at www.pueblo.gsa.gov.

Saving and the American Family, a money-management guide for parents and children.
Source: Merrill Lynch, 800-637-7455.

[handwritten margin notes]
ALSO →
HomeBasics.com
RefundSweepers.com
SmartSource.Com

CapitaLink Group." Their Web address is www.ifast.com.

And, the 25 states with Web sites have a combined site where you can search by name for unclaimed property that is being held. Check out this Web site at www.unclaimed.org (National Association of Unclaimed Property Administration–NAUPA).

Download Coupon Savings

One of the traditional ways to save money is to clip coupons and use them when shopping. Unfortunately it can take a lot of time to scour the newspapers to find the right coupons. Now there is an easier way to get those same savings without the hassle: download them from the Internet.

One of the leading companies that can help you get online coupons is called CoolSavings. This electronic method of couponing has met with great success and this Web site has quickly become one of the most visited Internet sites. The way it works is that you go to the Web site and fill out a brief online questionnaire, select the coupons you want, download them into your computer and print them out. You'll find a vast array of companies at this site, including everything from local pizza delivery stores to national chains like J. C. Penney, Toys "R" Us and McDonald's. To check out the Web site, go to www.coolsavings.com.

Know Your IRAs

You probably know that Individual Retirement Accounts, commonly known as IRAs, exist to help you save tax-sheltered money for retirement. But do you know what the difference is between an IRA and a Roth IRA? To help taxpayers learn more about the different types of IRAs so you can determine which is right for you, the IRS has updated its "Publication 590" which focuses on these types of accounts. Call the IRS at 800-829-1040. Or visit their Web site at www.irs.gov.

Avoid Phone Scams

Unscrupulous individuals and companies have a phone scheme that preys on consumers and especially on seniors. Without your knowledge they "slam" or "cram" your phone.

Slamming means switching your phone service to their company without your permission. Cramming is the practice of charging you for services you never ordered.

Here are some suggestions from the National Fraud Information Center on how to avoid slamming and cramming, and what to do if you think you have been defrauded.

• Check every page of your phone bill as soon as you get it for unauthorized charges. If you find something that is unclear, call your local phone company.

• Read the fine print before filling out any contest form or coupon offer.

• Take care when calling 800 or 900 numbers.

• Be especially wary of following instructions that say, "Enter activation code numbers," or of answering yes to questions that may result in your authorizing unwanted telephone services.

Here's what to do once you feel you have been defrauded:

• Call the National Fraud Information Center at 800-876-7060. ww.fraud.org

• Send a letter describing what happened and enclose a copy of your bill to:

Federal Communications Commission
445 12th St. SW
Washington, DC 20554
(or call 888-225-5322)
www.fcc.gov

• File a complaint with your local attorney general and telephone regulators.

Retirement Planning Pays Off

Whether you are just starting to invest or already have a plan, Charles Schwab has a free booklet that will help you with important financial decisions. "Smart Answers for Today's Market" will help you plan for a more secure financial future. It describes Charles Schwab's investment strategy for volatile times. Ask for "Smart Answers for Today's Market" when you call 877-476-2370. www.schwab.com

Women and Money

The Moneyminded Web site is designed specifically for women. It addresses questions about saving, family goals and investing, mostly from a woman's perspective. On the site you will find featured entrepreneurs and financial risk-takers who offer terrific advice and important information for women and their money. The Web address is www.moneyminded.com/index.htm.

Best Online Broker

Gomez.com rates Charles Schwab as the #1 overall online broker. If you buy or sell securities on the Internet and would like to get important financial information about Schwab's brokerage services, visit their Web site at www.schwab.com.

Understanding Mutual Funds

"A Guide to Understanding Mutual Funds" is available free from the Investment Company Institute, the mutual fund industry's principal trade group. This guide describes the various types of funds and explains the risks involved. It also discusses how funds are structured and how to set up an investment plan. The booklet includes advice about important tax considerations and gives you a guide to finding and analyzing information on funds yourself. To get a free copy, call 202-326-5800. www.ici.org

Mutual Fund Report Card

Are you holding the right mutual funds? Charles Schwab has a series of report cards for various mutual funds that include the funds' ratings, performance and growth records. You can request up to three reports for any mutual fund even if it is not available through Schwab. There is no cost or obligation. Call Schwab toll-free

Look at 401(k) Plan Fees. Factors that impact fees...why cheaper is not necessarily better... Web sites...more.
Source: US Dept. of Labor, Pension and Welfare Benefits Administration, 800-998-7542. www.dol.gov/dol/pwba/

What to Do When You Receive a Large Cash Payout. How not to let your emotions rule…how to find professional advice and invest for the long term.
Source: Forum for Investor Advice, 301-656-7998.

at 877-476-2370. Or visit their Web site at www.schwab.com.

Mutual Fund Info

TD Waterhouse will send you the "Top Performing Mutual Funds Guide" and the "Mutual Funds Information and Comparison Guide." If you invest in mutual funds or are thinking of investing, these are two guides you will want to have. They are free when you call toll-free at 800-934-4448. Or visit the TD Waterhouse Web site at www.tdwaterhouse.com.

Get Your Budget in Shape

To help you keep your budget in shape, the Internet has a number of sites that can help you, like:

> www.healthy.net/library/articles/cash/
> assessment/assessment.htm

Are you an overspender? Are there things you can do to avoid the devastating effects of this habit? To discover your "Spending Personality," take a self-test online at Healthy Cash at the HealthWorld Online Web site.

Five Ways to Get Financially Fit

• Pay off your credit card debt in order to reduce interest expenses. Start with the credit cards that have the highest finance charge. If possible pay off your balance every month.

• Switch to credit cards that have no annual fees.

• Be a smart shopper and always shop around before you buy something, especially big-ticket items.

• If you find it necessary to carry balances on your credit card, be certain you are not using a card that charges a high percentage rate on unpaid balances. Remember, you can get the interest rate lowered on most credit cards just by asking for a lower rate. Tell the company you are thinking of dropping the card and using another one that charges a lower interest rate. You will be amazed at how often they will offer you a substantially lower rate rather than lose you as a customer.

• Join a credit union if you are eligible. Generally credit unions charge lower fees than banks, especially if you maintain only small balances in your checking and savings accounts.

Money Facts

The Federal Reserve Bank of Atlanta has a free fascinating booklet which describes how currency is designed, printed, circulated and eventually destroyed. There is even a section on how to redeem bills that might have been damaged in a fire or chewed up by the family dog. Ask for "Dollars and Cents: Fundamental Facts About U.S. Money." *Write to:*

Federal Reserve Bank of Atlanta
Publications Dept.
1000 Peachtree St. N.E.
Atlanta, GA 30309-4470
404-498-8020
www.frbatlanta.org

Your Mortgage Can Make All the Difference

"Choosing a Mortgage That's Right for You" is an easy-to-read guide that can help you. It walks you through the mortgage shopping process in three easy steps. Discover what size mortgage loan you can afford, how to choose the mortgage that's right for you and how to compare terms commonly used among lenders. The guide is free when you call 202-274-8000. *Or contact:*

> **Fannie Mae Foundation**
> Consumer Resource Center
> 4000 Wisconsin Ave. NW
> North Tower, Suite One
> Washington, DC 20016-2804
> www.fanniemaefoundation.org

Retirement Investing That Makes Sense

"How Do I Choose the IRA That's Right for Me?" is a free brochure that explains tax-sheltered retirement investing. It can help you get the most from your investments. It is published by the AARP Investment Program from Scudder Investments, a group of no-load mutual funds designed for AARP members, but open to investors of any age. (No-load means there is no sales commission.) For a free copy, call 800-322-2282.

Other free AARP publications include "Strategies for Managing Taxes in Retirement" and "Investing in Your 50s." These and other publications are also available to read online at www.aarp.scudder.com.

Find the Right Tax Professional

When tax time comes around it is always an excellent idea to have a tax professional help you. To assist you in the difficult process of choosing the right one, you might want to start by getting the names of professionals in your region and interviewing several of them. For the names of tax experts in your area, call the National Association of Enrolled Agents at 301-212-9608. www.naea.org

Before Going into Business

If you have ever thought of going into business and starting a new corporation, here is a booklet you will definitely want to get. "Starting Your Own Corporation" will answer many of your questions regarding setting up the right kind of corporation. For a free copy, call the Company Corporation at 800-542-2677. www.corporate.com

Personal Finance Helplines

If you are not sure where to turn for good advice regarding personal finances, here are several toll-free hotlines you can go to for help. They will either provide you with the information you need or tell you where you can get further assistance.

> **American Institute of Certified Public Accountants' Personal Financial Planning Division:** 888-777-7077
> **American Society of Financial Service Professionals:** 800-392-6900
> **The Financial Planning Association:** 800-282-7526
> **National Association of Personal Financial Advisers:** 800-366-2732

Bear Markets: A Historical Perspective on Market Downturns. What they are…how to prepare…survival strategies…hypothetical case studies. *Source:* The Vanguard Group, 800-523-7731.

Find Out How to Order T-bills under new US Treasury Department rules—making it easier for individual investors.
Source: Bureau of the Public Debt, 202-691-3550.
www.publicdebt.treas.gov

Is Your Stockbroker Right For You?

The best way to find a good stockbroker is to ask for referrals from friends, professional acquaintances or family. If you have any questions and would like to check on a particular broker's background, call the National Association of Securities Dealers at 800-289-9999. www.nasd.com

Know the Value of Your Bonds

Did you know that all Series E savings bonds issued since 1941 are still earning interest? If you own any bonds tucked away in a safety deposit box and would like to know exactly how much they are worth today, look for "Tables of Redemption Values for Savings Bonds" at the official Web site at www.savingsbonds.gov. *Or write to:*

Bureau of the Public Debt
Savings Bond Operations Office
Parkersburg, WV 26106-1328

Buying US Government Securities

Americans have been buying Series E savings bonds for many years. But few people know they can also buy Treasury bonds and bills which pay even higher interest. For more information on how you can get in on this no-risk, high-yield investment, visit www.publicdebt.treas.gov, or write for *Treasury Direct Investor kit from:*

TreasuryDirect
PO Box 9150
Minneapolis, MN 55480-9150
800-722-2678

Secret Service Financial Duties

Did you know that the Secret Service does more than protect the President? It was originally created to suppress counterfeiting, a job they still perform. To learn more about this duty of the Secret Service, you can read "Know Your Money" online at www.ustreas.gov/usss/ to learn how to detect a counterfeit bill. *Write to:*

US Secret Service
Procurement Division
950 H St. NW, Ste. 730
Washington, DC 20001
202-406-6940

Recover Lost Money

Did your dog chew up some money you left on the table? Did it get partially destroyed in a fire? Did you know that the US Department of Treasury can help get that money back for you? Send them a note with a plausible, detailed explanation. Once the claim is processed and verified, the actual payment is made by federal check. For more information, call 202-874-3019, *or write to:*

US Department of the Treasury
Bureau of Engraving and Printing
14th and C Streets, SW
Washington, DC 20228
www.moneyfactory.com

Mortgage Know-how

If you are looking for a new mortgage either to buy a house or refinance one you already own to take advantage of lower mortgage rates, it is important that you learn how to evaluate the type of mortgage that is best for you. As

a first step you might call First Financial Equity on their toll-free number for more information and for answers to your mortgage questions. Call 888-951-1010. www.ffec.com

Investment Savvy

Before you make any significant investment, learn what to look for to find the one that's best for you. Also discover how to evaluate your investment and determine how well it meets your objectives. Begin by visiting the Neuberger Berman Web site at www.nb.com. Call toll-free at 877-672-7329. *Or write to:*

Neuberger Berman
Private Asset Management
605 Third Ave., 36th flr.
New York, NY 10158-3698
www.nb.com

Savings Just Because You're Over 50

Now that an ever-growing part of the population is over 50 years old, there are lots of bargains and discounts available just for the asking. Remember, if you don't ask, you'll never know. In any store you shop in always check to see if there are certain days or times when seniors are offered discounts or specials. Many hotels offer discounts on their rooms as well as in their restaurants. You can also apply for a travel club card if you are a member of AARP, the American Association of Retired Persons. Their toll-free phone number is 800-424-3410.

Learn About Mutual Funds

If you would like to learn all about mutual funds and find out which are the best ones for you, check out the Strong Equity Performers from Dreyfus. Call them toll-free at 800-782-6620. Or visit a Dreyfus Financial Center via the Internet at www.dreyfus.com.

Utilities Fund

Basic utilities, such as water and electricity, are always in demand and telecommunications is growing in all countries. That is why the Franklin Utilities Fund might be a growth fund for you. They will manage a portfolio especially designed for you. If this sounds like something you would consider, call today for a free brochure and prospectus from 800-632-2301. *Or write to:*

Franklin Templeton Investments
PO Box 997152
Sacramento, CA 95899-7152
www.franklintempleton.com

Low-cost Life Insurance— Guaranteed

If you are looking for maximum life insurance coverage at the lowest cost, this information is for you. A company called Quotesmith actually guarantees that they will find the lowest term life rates in America or they will send you $500. That might be quite a claim, but one worth checking out.

When you request a quote, Quotesmith will scan over 300 insurance companies in their database and give you the lowest price quotes found by the search. There is no charge for this service. You can call them at 800-556-9393

What You Should Know About Your Pension Rights. Whether benefits are guaranteed...what happens in case of a corporate merger... your spouse's rights. *Source:* US Dept. of Labor, Pension and Welfare Benefits Administration Publications. 800-998-7542. www.dol.gov/dll/pwba.

or get instant quotes online: www.quotesmith.com.

Fund-raising Kit

If your school or organization needs money, this free fund-raising kit will teach you how. For example, it will give you some ideas on how your group can collect members' recipes and publish them into a great cookbook. *Write for a free kit:*

> **Fundcraft**
> Box 340
> Collierville, TN 38027
> www.fundcraft.com

Mutual Funds for Investors Over 50

If you have worked hard to save money for your retirement and to help it grow, you will want to make sure you do everything you can to preserve and protect that important investment. "Understanding Mutual Funds: A Guide for Investors Aged 50 and Over" defines the basics to help older individuals choose funds appropriate for their needs. It is yours free! Call 800-322-2282, *or contact:*

> **AARP Investment Program**
> 811 Main St.
> Kansas City, MO 64105-2005

Check out Money Market Funds

If you want higher interest than you will get in a bank but still want instant access to your money, be sure to check out money market funds. To find out more about these funds, *contact one or more of the larger funds and ask for a prospectus and information package:*

Dreyfus Service Corp.
200 Park Ave.
New York, NY 10166
800-645-6561
www.dreyfus.com

Fidelity Investments
Box 770001
Cincinnati, OH 45277-0011
800-544-3902
www.fidelity.com

American Express Financial Advisers
70100 AXP Financial Center
Minneapolis, MN 55474
800-AXP-FUND
finance.americanexpress.com/finance

Tax-Free Income Fund

If you are in a high tax bracket and would like to lower the tax bite, did you know you can start earning tax-free income with instant liquidity and no sales or redemption fee? For more information on tax-free investing, call T Rowe Price at 800-638-5660. www.troweprice.com

Let the IRS Help You for Free

Few people realize that the IRS is committed to giving taxpayers every legitimate deduction they are entitled to. The IRS has toll-free numbers throughout the country to call for assistance and/or forms. As a start, for answers to your income tax questions, call the IRS tax hotline toll-free at 800-829-1040.

The IRS also has a series of helpful publications such as "Federal Income Tax," available free of charge. Call the toll-free number for this publication or a list of the others available or visit www.irs.gov.

The IRS also has a toll-free number to assist deaf or hearing-impaired taxpayers who have access to TV-Phone/Teletype-writer equipment. That number is 800-829-4059.

"Congratulations! You've Just Won..."

Even though the world is full of people who would never think of doing anything dishonest, there are still plenty of people out there who would not give a second thought to conning you out of your life savings. One of the most common scams is calling elderly people with an exciting announcement such as, "Congratulations, Mr. Jones, your name has been selected as the winner of an exciting cruise. Isn't that great? All you need to do to claim your prize is to put up a good-faith deposit by sending us a check for $$$$$$."

If you receive such a call, hang up the phone immediately. One rule to always follow is: Never... EVER buy anything or pay money to claim your "free prize." No reputable company would ever ask you to send money to get a so-called free prize.

For more information on these and other scams and what you can do to keep from falling prey to one, get a free copy of "Telemarketing Travel Fraud." *It is free from:*

Public Reference
Federal Trade Commission
CRC-240
Washington, DC 20580
877-FTC-HELP (382-4357)
www.ftc.gov.

Be Your Own Broker

If you have a computer and would like to make your own investment decisions without the help of a stockbroker, this one may be for you.

For a listing of online brokers who allow you to trade for a small fraction of what it would cost you from a full-service broker, see the listings at the end of this section.

Six Ways to Protect Your Family with Estate Planning

1. **Create a will.** The will is an essential part of your estate plan. It should detail how and when to distribute your assets and who will manage your estate upon your death. If your children are minors, under age 18, you also should appoint legal guardians in case both you and your spouse die. In the event that you don't name a guardian, the court will select one for your children. In addition, if family members fight over custody, your estate pays the legal fees. Also, if you die without a will, the court chooses an executor to distribute your assets. In many cases, a court administrator is chosen who will get paid out of the funds from your estate. The court, regardless of your intentions, may divide your assets between your surviving spouse and children, even if your spouse needs the children's share to meet day-to-day expenses.

2. **Take advantage of tax exemptions.** With proper planning, you can structure your estate plan to take advantage of valuable tax

When Your Broker Calls, Take Notes! Fill-in-the-blank form that prompts you to ask (and record) why the investment broker thinks you should buy/sell... risks involved.
Source: Investors Take Note, North American Securities Administrators Association (NASAA), 10 G St. NE, Ste. 710, Washington, DC 20002. 202-737-0900 www.nasaa.org

Invest Wisely.
Selecting a broker...
making investment
decisions.
Source: US Securities and
Exchange Commission,
800-732-0330. Read this
publication online at
www.sec.gov.

exemptions. A new law allows an increasing amount of your estate to pass tax exempt to your heirs. In 2001, the first $675,000 of assets is exempt from federal estate and gift tax. This exemption jumps to $1 million in 2002, $1.5 million in 2004, $2 million in 2006, $3.5 million in 2009. At the same time the top estate tax rate gradually drops from 55% in 2001 to 45% in 2009. In 2010, the estate tax is completely repealed—but in 2011 the current rules come back into play. After that, a marital deduction allows the transfer of an unlimited amount of property tax-free to your spouse.

3. Use trusts to reduce your taxable estate. If you have more than the exemption amount, a By-Pass Trust allows you to pass more assets directly to your heirs. A typical Bypass Trust enables the surviving spouse to receive income from the trust. At his or her death, the principal would then pass to the heirs. Since the assets are in a trust, they are not included in the taxable estate of your spouse.

4. Consider gifting. If your assets far exceed any possible use you may have for them in your lifetime, you might consider giving portions of your assets to those you would want to have them. But watch for new gift tax rules.

5. Understand the value of your estate. Simply put, your estate includes everything you own. Most of us don't realize how quickly assets add up. Make a personal financial statement that totals up the value of your home, any other real estate, stocks, bonds and investment interests, even the value of your

life insurance policies, as well as any valuables you may own.

6. Speak to a professional. Recent tax laws are confusing and make planning extremely difficult. Before you decide on any estate plan, be sure to consult with an accountant or attorney who specializes in tax law.

Save Hundreds of Dollars on Every Stock Trade by Trading Online
16 Online Brokers Charging $20 Per Trade or Less

If you are an active trader or investor in stocks and make all of your own buying and selling decisions without the advice of a broker, you can save a lot of money on your trades by using an online broker.

Here are stock brokerage firms that charge $20 per transaction or less for online trades. Some, like Ameritrade and Datek, even charge less than $10 for trades that would cost several hundred dollars at a full-service firm. The services offered, speed of execution and investor financial requirements vary from one firm to the next. Most firms also let you trade using their toll-free phone number, but generally will charge somewhat more for such trades than the ones made online. To find out more, check out the Web sites listed here or call the brokerages' toll-free numbers.

Ameritrade
www.ameritrade.com   800-669-3900

Brown & Co.
www.brownco.com   800-965-1191

Buy and Hold Securities
www.buyandhold.com   800-646-8212

CSFB Direct
www.csfbdirect.com   800-825-5723

Datek Online
www.datek.com   877-328-3521

*Dreyfus Brokerage Services
www.edreyfus.com   800-421-8395

E*trade
www.etrade.com   800-786-2575

Fidelity Investments
www.fidelity.com   800-544-6666

*Freedom Investments
www.freedominvestments.com
    800-944-4033

Investex Securities Group
www.investexpress.com   800-392-7192

JB Oxford & Co.
www.jboxford.com   800-656-1776

Preferred Trade
www.preferredtrade.com   888-889-9178

Quick & Reilly
www.quick-reilly.com   800-368-0446

Scottrade, Inc.
www.scottrade.com   800-619-7283

Strong
www.estrong.com   800-342-8941

TD Waterhouse
www.tdwaterhouse.com   800-934-4448

Wallstreet Electronica
www.wallstreete.com   888-925-5783

Understanding Opportunities and Risks in Futures Trading. Trading strategies...how to participate...choosing a contract...buying and selling options. *Source:* National Futures Association, 800-621-3570.

* For the low commission price, trades must be done through the Internet.

Travel Free Or at Huge Savings

The Best Ways to Travel for Free

Most people don't know it, but there are many ways you can get free or almost free travel. Here are a few of the best.

If you have a unique skill or hobby, many cruise lines will give you a free trip in exchange for giving a lecture about your specialty on one of their cruises. Often cruises have a theme and your speciality might fit in with that theme. For example, if you are a fitness specialist, you could teach aerobics on board. Or perhaps you are an amateur magician or a financial advisor. The cruise line might give you a free trip just for spending an hour a day instructing others during the cruise. Check the travel section of your local newspaper or a toll-free directory for the phone numbers of the cruise lines. If you have a computer, you can also reach the cruise lines via the Internet. (Also see the Internet listings later in this chapter.)

There are some courier services that will ask you to carry a package for them. You get a discounted trip for carrying the parcel. Sometimes you can stay a few extra days so long as you can catch their plane on the return flight. For more information, contact the International Association of Air Travel Couriers at 352-475-1584 or see their Web site at www.courier.org.

A common practice of all airlines is to overbook their flights since they know from experience that a certain percentage of people do not show up and the airline wants to leave with a full plane. When too many passengers show up, the airlines will offer free tickets to anywhere they fly just for changing your flight. One great method of getting free airline tickets is as soon as you get to the airport for your next trip, volunteer to take the next flight out if they are overbooked in exchange for a free ticket on a future flight.

Frequent flyer programs are still a good deal and cost you nothing. Many credit card companies will give you frequent flyer miles just for using a particular card. Check with your charge card company. Also, make sure you are a member of the airline's frequent flyer club. Many airlines don't put a time restriction on using the miles.

Some families look for house sitters to take care of their place while they travel on business or vacation. In return for watching someone's home, you get a free place to live. If you like to travel, you can even trade apartments and homes with people in other parts of the country (or the world) through different real estate exchanges. Check the classified section of your local newspaper.

Adventure Tours for Seniors

Many seniors who are in fairly good physical condition want to go on trips that involve challenges and cultural learning experiences. These seniors are looking for new adventures and also want to learn about local culture and nature in such places as Africa and South Africa. Elder Treks specializes in senior adventure tours to 50 different

Travel Tips for Older Americans. Advice on health...insurance...safety...where to find additional information.
Source: Consumer Information Center, Dept. WWW, Pueblo, CO 81009. 888-878-3256 or www.pueblo.gsa.gov.

Defensive Flying.
Best ways to avoid delayed flights and missed connections… replace a lost ticket, etc.
Source: Aviation Consumer Protection Division (C-75), US Department of Transportation, 400 Seventh St. SW, Room 4107, Washington, DC 20590. 202-366-2220 or www.dot. gov/airconsumer/defensive. htm.

countries including Africa and South Africa. If you are looking for that adventurous tour, call Elder Treks at 800-741-7956. Or visit their Web site at www. eldertreks.com.

Golden Passport to Fun

Did you know that as a senior you can buy a lifetime entrance to national parks, monuments, historic sites, recreation areas and national refuges for a one-time fee of just $10? This also entitles you to a whopping 50% discount on fees for such activities as camping, swimming, parking, boat launching and cave tours. This comes to you via the Federal Golden Age Passport and it could be worth its weight in gold. And for the blind and disabled, there is the Federal Golden Access Passport which is completely free. To get your passport, call the National Park Service at 202-208-4747 or 202-619-7289.

What to Do When Your Flight Is Overbooked

Many flights get overbooked. That means that the airline has sold more tickets than there are seats on the plane. When a flight is overbooked, the airline must offer inducements to passengers to voluntarily take a later flight. The inducement generally will be a voucher for a free flight on their airline. If the flight is very overbooked, you might be able to get an even better deal, which might include vouchers for more than one flight, an upgrade to

first class on the next flight, an overnight hotel stay if there are no more flights until the next day and sometimes even cash. Here are 10 useful suggestions to take advantage of these situations:

1. Volunteer before airline representatives offer vouchers, if you think your flight may be oversold.

2. Make an informed decision. Ask how long it will be until the next flight leaves for your destination.

3. If there are no takers after a voucher is announced for a low amount and it's a popular flight, don't raise your hand right away. The voucher value will most likely increase.

4. Use the voucher as soon as possible. Most expire within a year and are not replaceable if lost or stolen.

5. Ask for a meal voucher as well.

6. When using a travel voucher, plan in advance. In some cases, limited seating may make it more difficult to redeem your free or discounted travel exactly when you want to.

7. If you have a travel agent, show him or her the front and back of your voucher to determine whether it qualifies for a particular flight.

8. Read the fine print. Some vouchers may not be used on certain days and holidays.

9. Many vouchers themselves are not transferable. But generally the recipient can get a ticket for someone else.

10. Be polite, but don't be afraid to ask for more. For example, in addition to a travel voucher, you might ask for an upgrade to first class on the next flight out.

Remember, the airline must get people off the overbooked flight and will offer whatever it takes.

Travel Bargains for Seniors

 One of the great benefits of becoming a senior is receiving discounts on just about everything from "senior day" at retail stores to movies, the theater, restaurants and, the best of all, travel. Next time you plan to venture out on a trip, be sure to ask about senior discounts.

There are a number of ways seniors can get discounted travel. For example, the airlines offer discount booklets you can purchase for substantial savings on your airfare.

Next, don't forget to become a member of the American Association of Retired Persons (AARP). You don't have to be retired but you or your spouse must be 50 years of age or older. For a membership fee of $10 per year (which includes your spouse), you will receive a magazine, *Modern Maturity*, regular updates and a membership card which is good for discounts on just about everything (hotels, insurance, drugs and more). Once you are a member, to get these discounts you simply show your membership card. To join, call the AARP member services toll-free number at 800-424-3410. Or visit the Web site at www.aarp.org.

Airline Discounts

Most of the airlines offer special programs for seniors. Before you make a plane reservation, check with the airline you are planning to travel on to be sure they offer at least a 10% discount for people 62 and older. Many airlines also have programs where you can purchase coupon booklets or passports that allow you to travel domestically and internationally at substantial discounts.

Continental Airlines has a Freedom Trip booklet and Freedom Flight Club program which allow you to enjoy discounted domestic and international travel. Call them at 800-441-1135. www.continental.com

Delta Airlines has a discount program for domestic and international travel for seniors 62 and older. Call 800-221-1212 for domestic travel and 800-241-4141 for international travel. www.delta.com

For information on American Airlines Senior Discount program, call American Airlines at 800-237-7981. www.aa.com

Lowest Airfares

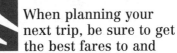 When planning your next trip, be sure to get the best fares to and from the cities you will be visiting. There are a number of companies that specialize in finding the lowest fares available. They check constantly with the various airlines and track their prices to ensure that when you contact them you will get the best fare. While fares change constantly, savings are available to and from many major cities both within the US and on international flights. To check these low-cost fares, call 888-777-

Smart Travelers Planning Kit. Includes information about advantages of packages and tours.

Source: United States Tour Operators Association, 275 Madison Ave., Ste. 2014, New York, NY 10016. 800-468-7862.

Fly Rights. A consumer guide to air travel covers delayed and canceled flights, overbooking and tips for filing complaints. *Source:* US Department of Transportation Aviation Consumer Protection Division. Read online: www.dot.gov/airconsumer

2222. Or visit the Web site at www.lowestfare.com.

Also check the following Web site where you can actually name your own price for hotels and airfare: www.priceline.com. Or call them at 800-PRICELINE.

Airline Coupons for Seniors

Senior citizens are eligible to purchase Senior Citizen Airline Coupons. Currently, with these coupons you can fly anywhere an airline flies domestically for no more than $298 round trip, and even less on some airlines. Airlines that go to the US Virgin Islands, Puerto Rico and the Bahamas, and several that fly to Canada, even include those destinations for the same low price.

Typically the coupons are sold in a book of four one-way flights. Each coupon is good for a one-way fare. While some airlines require a 14-day advance reservation, you can also use the coupons to fly standby. You don't have to travel round trip, which means there is no minimum stay. Senior Coupon travel also earns you frequent flyer miles.

Note: With most airlines a couple cannot share a coupon book. To use the coupons you must travel with a qualifying senior. America West and US Air both allow a senior to share a coupon book with a grandchild aged 2 to 11.

Also, don't forget to check with all the airlines for special seniors clubs and senior discounts. For example, American, Delta and United have senior clubs that offer zoned fares ranging from

$98 to $298, round trip, depending on the distance. In other words, you pay no more than the usual senior-coupon price for a long trip, and get an even better price on shorter trips. Those clubs also offer discounted international travel which is not available with the regular coupons.

Remember, as a senior you get at least a 10% discount, but check with the airline for an even bigger discount and the best travel deal.

50% Discount on Hotels

Do you want to save a lot of money the next time you book a hotel reservation in a large city? Try using a hotel broker. Like airline ticket consolidators, hotel brokers are outlets through which hotels rent some of their vacant rooms at low prices.

Hotel brokers are given blocks of discounted rooms in big city hotels. They in turn pass the bulk of the savings onto you. They concentrate mainly on big cities, such as Boston, Chicago, Los Angeles, New York, San Francisco, Washington and others. A few even handle larger cities overseas, such as London, Sydney, Paris and Hong Kong. Consolidators can cut your hotel costs by as much as 50%. These brokers are classified into two groups.

• Booking-Agent Brokers: Some brokers make a reservation for you at the discounted rate. Once you have a confirmed discounted reservation, you simply check in at the hotel as you ordinarily would and pay the discounted amount when you check out.

•Prepay Brokers: Other brokers are like tour operators. They sell hotel rooms at the same reduced rates as in package tours. Here you must prepay for your entire stay in order to get the best rate, and the broker sends you a voucher, which you use as proof of payment upon arriving at the hotel.

When comparing the two types of brokers, just keep in mind that with the first method, where you pay at the checkout, you don't have to worry if you are forced to cancel or reschedule your trip.

•Hotel Reservations Network (HRN) is the largest prepay-voucher broker. Their toll-free number is 800-964-6835. Or visit their Web site at www.hoteldiscount.com.

• Quikbook is the largest booking-agent broker. Call them toll-free at 800-789-9887. Or visit their Web site at www.quikbook.com.

• Express Reservations is another booking-agent broker. They specialize in hotel bookings only in New York, Chicago and Los Angeles. Call them toll-free at 800-407-3351. Or visit them at their Web site at www.express-res.com.

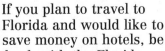 **Florida Hotel Savings**

If you plan to travel to Florida and would like to save money on hotels, be sure to check with the Florida Tourist Bureau, Inc. Despite the official sounding name, they are not a state agency but rather a private travel company that specializes in saving you up to 50%

on your hotel accommodations throughout Florida. They work on the prepaid voucher system, which means you book your room and pay in advance in exchange for a very substantial discount at the best hotels and motels. Call them toll-free at 321-868-0091. www.2000floridatravel.com

Half-Price Hotels

Many people have found that membership in a discount club is an excellent way to save money on travel. If you spend more than a few nights a year in hotels, the annual price of membership in a good hotel discount club can be a good investment.

Most clubs promise a 50% discount off rack rate, subject to availability and the occupancy level expected by the hotel. Here is one of the largest discount programs:

www.travelersadvantage.com: 800-835-8747

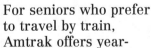 **Save with Amtrak**

For seniors who prefer to travel by train, Amtrak offers year-round discounts for anyone 62 and older. These discounts include 15% off regular fares, special one-way fares, Explore America Fares and special group fares. They also have beautiful brochures describing their fun vacation packages. Call Amtrak toll-free at 800-USA-RAIL (or 800-872-7245). Or visit the Web site at www.amtrak.com.

153

Jet Vacations

If you plan to travel to France and want to save money on everything— quality air travel, hotels, car rental, ski packages, sightseeing —call Jet Vacations. The company specializes in trips to Paris and to the Riviera. Plan your trip early and save. Call them toll-free and learn how you can enjoy France 3,435 different ways. Call 800-538-0999.

Travel Care

Are you planning a trip? Before you go you will want to get a copy of "Pack-It." This handy booklet is filled with how-to ideas on packing and caring for luggage. Call 800-262-8282 or *send a postcard to:*

Samsonite Consumer Relations
PO Box 90124
Allentown, PA 18109
www.samsonite.com

Chocolate Town, USA

If you are looking for a really fun time, why not try a special theme weekend at the fun Hershey Park in Hershey, Pennsylvania? For more detailed information, call 800-HERSHEY. www.hersheypa.com

TraveLodge Directory

You can have a free directory of the more than 500 TraveLodge motels and motor hotels. It lists location, room rates and a map for each TraveLodge. You will also find information on their new group rates, family plan and bargain break weekends. Call 800-578-7878. www.travelodge. com

Days Inn Directory

"Quality accommodations for the American traveler at economical rates" has been the motto of Days Inn since its founding in 1970. For a free directory of the over 1,800 inns with their rates, maps, toll-free numbers and more, call 800-325-2525. www.daysinn.com

Holiday Inn Directory

For a complete listing of all Holiday Inns both in the US and worldwide, request a free copy of their huge directory. In seconds you can locate any of the thousands of Holiday Inns with room rates, list of recreation activities, even a map for each hotel. Call toll-free at 800-HOLIDAY. www.sixcontinentshotels.com/holiday-inn

Enjoy a Club Med Vacation

Club Med's unique vacation resorts have delighted thousands of people tired of the same old thing. If you are interested in a fun vacation that really is something different, send for the free color travel booklet. To get a free booklet or for more information on their clubs, call 800-CLUB-MED (or 800-258-2633) or visit their Web site at www.clubmed.com.

Barefoot Adventure Cruise

Are you ready for something different? For a vacation unlike any you have ever been on, consider sailing a tall ship to a small island in the Caribbean. The full-color "Barefoot Adventure" will tell you all about Barefoot shipboard adventures aboard schooners that once belonged to Onassis, Vanderbilt and the Duke of Westminster. Call toll-free at 800-327-2600. www.windjammer.com

Safety Guide

Did you ever wonder if you should be concerned about your health and safety when you travel to foreign destinations? Travel Medicine has a free "Travel Safety Guide." It offers practical quick tips on insect protection, medical kits, mosquito nets, protective clothing, water filters and more. Before you venture out on your next travel excursion, be sure to send for this free guide. *Write to:*

Travel Medicine Inc.
369 Pleasant St.
Northampton, MA 01060
800-872-8633
www.travmed.com

Foreign Exchange Online

If you plan to travel abroad, did you know that you can now buy francs, pounds and yen over the Internet? This service can be useful for travelers who want to have small amounts of currency upon arrival in a foreign country. At their Web site, International Currency Express lists rates at which they sell foreign currency.

If you decide to buy, you can pay by check or credit card and receive currency in two to four days via express mail. You can call them toll-free at 888-278-6628. Or visit their Web site at www.foreignmoney.com.

Fight Jet Lag

Do you travel frequently and find that you suffer from jet lag? If so, this free wallet-sized card should help. It summarizes the amounts and types of food you should eat and tells you the best times to eat to reduce the effects of jet lag. Ask for "The Anti-Jet Lag Diet." To get a copy, call 630-252-5575 or *send a business-sized SASE to:*

Argonne National Laboratory
Jet Lag Diet
9700 S. Cass Ave.
Argonne, IL 60439
www.anl.com

Volunteer for a Free Vacation

Regardless of how young or old you are, one of the most fascinating ways to enjoy a wilderness experience in a national park is by being a volunteer. A variety of government agencies including the US Forest Service, the National Park Service, the US Army Corps of Engineers and various individual state park systems welcome volunteers to serve as campground hosts in exchange for a free stay. Every year hundreds of thousands of people who love the outdoors volunteer their services for anywhere from one day to a full year.

In addition to acting as hosts, volunteers also help as caretakers, researchers, ranger assis-

Magellan's Passport to Travel Photography. Techniques for photographing scenery, people, parades and festivals.

Source: World Headquarters Magellan's International, Magellan's Catalog, 110 W. Sola St., Santa Barbara, CA 93101. 800-962-4943 www.magellans.com

Catalog of Summer Adventures for Young Adults.
Information on hiking and biking tours in the Swiss Alps and the US.
Source: Overland, 413-458-9672. www.overland adventures.com

tants, trail repair crews, plumbers and carpenters. This reflects the growing interest in active vacations or educational travel. In exchange for their services, volunteers may receive free camping and other recreational privileges, which often include cabins, house trailers or bunkroom accommodations at no cost. While some volunteers are given an expense allowance, most should expect to pay for food and transportation costs.

If this sounds like a vacation you might enjoy, contact the park, forest, refuge, fish hatchery or other facility which you are interested in or *check with the following:*

National Park Service
Volunteers in Parks Coordinator
1849 C St. NW, Ste. 7312
Washington, DC 20240
202-208-4747

They are looking for 112,000 volunteers each year who are interested in a stay of from one to three months in one of the nation's over 320 participating parklands. Volunteers help with trail projects, species control and campground hosts. To get a brochure listing all of the parks in the US, along with an application, send a postcard to the address above.

US Forest Service
800-281-9176
Check the local information operator or the blue pages of the phone book for the number of the nearest US Forest Service office. In their Volunteers in the National Forests Program they have up to 100,000 volunteers every year to serve in one of the nation's 155 national forests or 22 national grasslands.

The US Forest Service also has a program called *Passport in Time*. This program welcomes families for one-day to one-week stays which focus on archaeological digs and historical restorations. Call the toll-free number listed above.

Bureau of Land Management
Environmental Education and
Volunteer Program
1849 C St. NW, Mail Stop 406 L Street
Washington, DC 20240
202-452-5078

Approximately 20,000 volunteers are needed each year for the National Volunteer Program sponsored by the Bureau of Land Management. Volunteers restore watersheds, build trails, staff visitor centers, patrol cultural sites, write brochures and conduct educational programs in federal lands, mostly in the West.

US Fish and Wildlife Service
Division of Refuges
National Volunteer Coordinator Office
4401 North Fairfax Dr., Room 670
Arlington, VA 22203
800-344-9453

This service oversees hundreds of wildlife refuges and fish hatcheries throughout the nation. Volunteers are needed to help with raising fish, banding birds, restoring fragile habitats and conducting tours of the habitats and fisheries. To get a visitors guide and map with all of the national wildlife refuges, call the toll-free number listed above.

US Army Corps of Engineers
800-865-8337
They manage 460 lakes throughout the country. Volunteers are needed to help with a variety of programs which include archaeological digs, pest control and campground hosts.

Alaska Division of Parks and Outdoor Recreation
Alaska State Parks Volunteer Coordinator
550 W. 7th Ave., Ste. 1380
Anchorage, AK 99501
907-269-8708
www.alaskastateparks.org

Alaska has one of the most extensive summer volunteer programs. Volunteers help out as archaeological assistants, backcountry ranger assistants, researchers and trail crew members. The service pays transportation expenses from Anchorage plus a small expense allowance for commitments of two weeks to three months.

To volunteer closer to home, try checking your local phone directory for your state's Department of Parks and Recreation and ask about their volunteer programs.

Healthy Travel to Foreign Lands

 If you are on medication and plan to travel abroad, be sure to consult the International Society of Travel Medicine Clinic Directory available free on the Web at www.istm.org. It lists over 500 medicine clinics in 44 countries (including the US). You will also find answers to many of your questions about the health risks in the countries you are visiting, which shots are needed, which medicines to pack and how to get medical assistance while you are in that country.

Before you travel, you may also want to check with the following organizations for updates on illnesses in the countries you will be visiting:

Pan American World Health Organization
202-974-3000
www.who.int

Centers for Disease Control and Prevention
800-311-3435
www.cdc.gov

International Association for Medical Assistance to Travellers
716-754-4883
www.iamet.org

Links travelers to doctors in 130 countries.

Internet Sites for Travelers

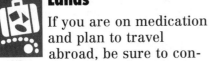 Surfing the World Wide Web is one of the easiest and most convenient ways to simplify your travel planning and to save money. If you are planning to travel and have access to the Web either at home, work or your public library, here are a number of sites you will want to visit.

www.travelocity.com

If you would like to quickly check for the lowest plane fares from any major city to any other major city in the US, check out this site. Updated on a daily basis, you will find a listing of the lowest air fares at that time. You will also find several other features of interest including:

• Hot Deals: For steals, deals and all-around great travel bargains worldwide.

• Flight Paging: Keeps you informed of changes to your flight's departure or arrival times and gate assignments, all sent to your alphanumeric pager.

• Fare Watcher e-mail: Sends low fare updates directly to your e-mail quickly and reliably.

Australia Vacation Planner. What to see and do...where to stay and dine...how to get around...in each of Australia's nine major regions.
Source: Australian Tourist Commission, 800-369-6863.

The Dude Rancher.
Directory of more than 100 ranches. Listed by state.
Source: The Dude Ranchers' Association, Box F-471, LaPorte, CO 80535. 970-223-8440 or www.duderanch.org.

• Shop Safe Guarantee: Protects every credit card transaction you make on Travelocity.

• Reviews: For independent, non-biased reviews of vacation choices.

• Weather Forecasts: Complete updated weather forecasts for cities around the world

Are you looking for the best fares to the world's big cities? While at Travelocity's Web site, if you enter codes for multiple cities, Travelocity will search for the lowest fare available at all metropolitan airports. Here are a few cities where this feature can be used:

New York City (NYC)
Washington, DC (WAS)
Chicago (CHI)
London (LON)
Paris (PAR)
Dallas (QDF)
Houston (QHO)

In addition, you may enjoy significant savings if you are willing to fly into nearby airports. For example, when traveling to Los Angeles (LAX), you may want to consider flying into either the Burbank (BUR), Orange County (SNA) or Ontario (ONT) airport.

Similarly, the cost of a trip to San Francisco (SFO) might be reduced by flying into San Jose (SJC) or Oakland (OAK), while travel to Miami (MIA) may be less expensive if you fly into Ft. Lauderdale (FL).

www.weather.com

What's the weather like in the city you are about to fly to? Are there any flight delays due to bad weather? For answers, go to this Web site, a service of the Weather Channel. Before your next trip, check to see what weather's in store for you.

www.frommers.com

Arthur Frommer's budget travel site has expert advice and travel discounts. You will find a daily newsletter, the hot spot of the month, and Arthur's tip of the day. The site also features destination information, bargain airfares, cruises, lodging and car rentals. You can book your travel reservations. Check the many vacation ideas, travel tips and photo contest.

www.trip.com, 800-874-7266

This site is designed to save money for travelers. You can book airline tickets, hotel rooms and car rentals at lower rates. To help you save money, this service will automatically search for flights from alternate airports and for connecting flights. You will also find Destination Guides with restaurants and hotel reviews, plus maps with point-to-point directions to and from anywhere in the US.

http://travel.yahoo.com

Yahoo! Travel is a comprehensive travel planning resource. You can make reservations and check flight times, create a dream map of where you want to go and how much you want to spend, and get daily coverage of travel-related deals and values. You'll also find message boards, chat and a daily poll.

www.expedia.com

This is Microsoft's travel Web site. While it is primarily geared toward leisure travelers, business travelers will find a number of useful features including city maps and restaurant listings. Another nice feature is expedia's low-fare tracker which will alert you to discount fares for cities selected by you.

www.webflyer.com

The ultimate site for the frequent flyer. You will find all kinds of special bonus mileage offers and exclusive discount fares available only online. Its best feature is the fact that it tracks all airline, hotel and car rental discounts by city and saves you time by listing them all at one site.

www.quikbook.com

Consumer Reports Travel Letter named this site one of the Web's best sites for hotel discounts. Here you will find out where you can get big hotel discounts of up to 60% in major cities like New York, Atlanta, Los Angeles and Boston, to name a few.

www.epicurious.com

This is the site of *Gourmet* magazine and Conde Nast.

http://travel.excite.com

http://travel.discovery.com

Cruise Line Web Sites

If you are thinking of taking a cruise but are not sure which cruise is right for you, before you book, check out the Web sites of the cruise lines you are considering. Here's a selection of some of their Web sites:

Carnival Cruise Lines
www.carnival.com

Celebrity Cruises
www.celebritycruises.com

Clipper Cruise Line
www.clippercruise.com

Cunard Lines
www.cunardline.com

The Delta Queen Steamboat Co.
www.deltaqueen.com

Holland America Line
www.hollandamerica.com

KD River Cruises of Europe
www.rivercruises.com

Norwegian Cruise Lines
www.ncl.com

Radisson Seven Seas Cruises
www.rssc.com

Regal Cruises
www.regalcruises.com

Royal Caribbean International
www.royalcaribbean.com

Silversea Cruises
www.asource.com/silversea

Windjammer Barefoot Cruises
www.windjammer.com

Windstar Cruises
www.windstarcruises.com

World Explorer Cruises
www.wecruise.com

Better Ways to Save Money On Plane Travel

Finding the lowest fare isn't always easy. Discount fares typically have restrictions that can be difficult and sometimes frustrating to interpret. If you are looking for the lowest fare, here are a few suggestions that will help.

1. Make your reservation early. Many discount fares require that you make a reservation 7, 14 or 21 days before your trip. The fare can be affected by the amount of lead time. The best international fares often require a reservation 30 days in advance. By making a reservation as soon as you know your travel dates, you increase your chances of finding a fare you can live with.

2. Flying on a weekday usually costs less. Flights on Tuesday,

Virtual Ship Tours. Read helpful Guides for First-Time Cruisers and enjoy panoramic 360-degree views of cabins, dining rooms, casinos, pool decks and more for ships of 20 major cruise lines online at www.travelco.com.
Source: Cruises Only, 800-777-0707.

159

Magellan's Passport to Compact Packing.
Source: World Headquarters Magellan's International, 800-962-4943.
www.magellans.com

Wednesday and Thursday usually have the lowest fares. Fares are sometimes (but not always) higher on Monday and Friday than on other weekdays. Saturday flights occasionally have discount fares, but as a rule it's more expensive to fly on a weekend than a weekday.

3. Stay over a Saturday night. Most low fares require that you stay over at least one Saturday night before your return flight. However, some fares may only require you to stay a minimum of three or four days.

4. One airline is better than two. It is almost always less expensive to use only one airline for the entire trip. In fact booking two airlines can, in some cases, cost hundreds of dollars more.

5. Try an earlier or later flight if you can't find the fare you want or, if possible, consider flying on another day. Airlines sell only a limited number of seats at the lowest fares. When those seats sell out, the price goes up. If you don't succeed with your first choice, try an earlier or later flight. To get the lowest round-trip fare, that fare must be available on both the departing and return flights. If the fare is sold out on either leg of the journey, the final price will be much higher.

Traveling the US

Planning ahead can make all the difference in the world between having great fun and having a run-of-the mill trip. Some of the very best sources of information you can use in your planning are the tourist offices in the various states you plan to visit. These offices are set up to provide maps, brochures and other information about their states' tourist attractions, climate, restaurants and hotels.

When you call a state's tourist office, tell them which areas of the state you plan to visit, what time of year, and also indicate any special sight-seeing interests. Often they can provide you with additional materials on the areas in which you are most interested.

The following is a list of state tourism offices, including toll-free numbers and Web sites.

ALABAMA
800-ALABAMA
www.touralabama.org

ALASKA
907-929-2200
www.travelalaska.com

ARIZONA
602-230-7733
www.arizonaguide.com
www.azot.com

ARKANSAS
800-NATURAL
www.arkansas.com

CALIFORNIA
800-GO-CALIF
www.gocalif.ca.gov

COLORADO
800-433-2656
www.colorado.com

CONNECTICUT
800-CT-BOUND
www.ctbound.org

DELAWARE
800-441-8846
www.delaware.gov

DISTRICT OF COLUMBIA
800-635-6338
www.washington.org

FLORIDA
888-735-2872
www.flausa.com

GEORGIA
800-VISIT-GA
www.gomm.com

HAWAII
800-464-2924
www.gohawaii.com

IDAHO
800-635-7820
www.visitid.org

ILLINOIS
800-2CONNECT
www.enjoyillinois.com

INDIANA
888-ENJOYIN
www.enjoyindiana.com

IOWA
888-472-6035
www.traveliowa.com

KANSAS
800-2-KANSAS
www.kansascommerce.com

KENTUCKY
800-225-TRIP
www.kentuckytourism.com

LOUISIANA
800-964-7321
www.louisianatravel.com

MAINE
888-624-6345
www.visitmaine.com

MARYLAND
800-MD-IS-FUN
www.mdisfun.org

MASSACHUSETTS
800-447-MASS
www.massvacation.com

MICHIGAN
800-5432-YES
www.michigan.org

MINNESOTA
800-657-3700
www.exploreminnesota.com

MISSISSIPPI
800-WARMEST
www.visitmississippi.org

MISSOURI
800-877-1234
www.missouritourism.org

MONTANA
800-VISIT-MT
www.visitmt.com

NEBRASKA
800-228-4307
www.visitnebraska.org

NEVADA
800-NEVADA-8
www.travelnevada.com

NEW HAMPSHIRE
800-FUN-IN-NH
www.visitnh.gov

NEW JERSEY
800-VISITNJ or 800-JERSEY-7
www.visitnj.org

NEW MEXICO
800-733-6396 or 800-545-2040
www.newmexico.org

NEW YORK
800-CALL-NYS
www.iloveny.state.ny.us

NORTH CAROLINA
800-VISIT-NC
www.visitnc.com

NORTH DAKOTA
800-HELLO-ND
www.ndtourism.com

OHIO
800-BUCKEYE
www.ohiotourism.com

OKLAHOMA
800-652-6552
www.travelok.com

OREGON
800-547-7842
www.traveloregon.com

PENNSYLVANIA
800-VISIT-PA
www.experiencepa.com

About Travel Safety.
Hotel, car and sightseeing safety...scams, thieves and pickpockets.
Source: MetLife Consumer Education Center, 800-638-5433.

161

Discover America Tourism Offices Vacation Guide.
Toll-free numbers.
Source: Travel Industry Association of America, 1100 New York Ave. NW, Ste. 450 Washington, DC 20005. Include a business-sized SASE. 202-408-8422
www.tia.org

RHODE ISLAND
800-556-2484
www.visitrhodeisland.com

SOUTH CAROLINA
800-872-3505
www.travelsc.com

SOUTH DAKOTA
800-SDAKOTA
www.travelsd.com

TENNESSEE
800-836-6200
www.state.tn.us/tourdev

TEXAS
800-8888-TEX or 800-452-9292
www.travelTex.com

UTAH
800-200-1160
www.utah.com

VERMONT
800-VERMONT
www.1-800-vermont.com

VIRGINIA
800-VISIT-VA
www.virginia.org

WASHINGTON
800-544-1800
www.experiencewashington.com

WASHINGTON, DC
See District of Columbia

WEST VIRGINIA
800-CALL-WVA
www.callwva.com

WISCONSIN
800-432-TRIP
www.travelwisconsin.com

WYOMING
800-225-5996
www.wyomingtourism.org

US TERRITORIES
American Samoa
684-633-1093
www.amsamoa.com

Guam
800-US-3-GUAM
www.visitguam.org

Puerto Rico
800-223-6530
www.prtourism.com

US VIRGIN ISLANDS
US Virgin Islands Tourism
1270 Ave. of the Americas, Ste. 2108
New York, NY 10020
800-372-8784
www.usvi.net

NATIONAL PARKS
Department of the Interior
National Park Service
Washington, DC 20240
202-208-4747

Enjoy the great outdoors. Get back to nature. Visit our beautiful national parks. There is a series of interesting guides to the seven most popular national parks. These guides are free for the asking. Send for any (or all) guides you'd like:

• Rocky Mountain National Park, Colorado
• Mt. McKinley National Park, Alaska
• Mesa Verde National Park, Colorado
• Hot Springs National Park, Arkansas
• Hawaii National Park, Hawaii
• Yellowstone National Park, Montana
• Carlsbad Caverns, New Mexico

You might also want the free map of the National Park System. Request by name the guides you would like. Write to the address above.

INTERNATIONAL VACATIONLAND— 1000 ISLANDS

The 1000 Islands region features the best of two countries: the US and Canada. Some of the many attractions include fishing, golf, tennis, biking, hiking, houseboat rentals, shopping and recreational sports in all seasons. Three tour packages are available for the asking:

1. 1000 Islands, 43373 Collins Landing, PO Box 400, Alexandria Bay, NY 13607. In Canada, write to 1000 Islands, PO Box 69, Lansdowne, Ontario, Canada KOE 1LO. 800-8-ISLAND

2. Kingston Bureau of Tourism, PO Box 486, 209 Ontario St., Kingston, Ontario, Canada K7L 2Zl. 888-855-4555 www.kingstoncanada.com

3. Rideau Lakes 1000 Islands, PO Box 125, Perth, Ontario, Canada K7H 3E3.

Visit www.1000islands.org for more information.

Travel Through Auction

Visit www.skyauction.com to find wonderful travel bargains with leading airlines, hotels, resort chains and cruise lines.

Cruises, Cruises, Cruises

Visit www.vacationstogo.com for savings of up to 75% on last-minute crises. For example, they will map out which cruises are recommended for families with kids. These particular cruises offer baby-sitting, teen center/disco, youth center or playroom and a youth staff.

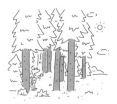

Shenandoah National Park Information Packet.
Source: Aramark Shenandoah National Park, Box 727, Luray, VA 22835. 800-778-2851 or www.visitshenandoah.com.

More Foreign Travel

More Foreign Travel

Before you travel abroad, be sure to contact the tourist office of the countries you plan to visit. They will be delighted to send you a beautiful package of travel brochures, places to visit and much more.

Antigua and Barbuda

Antigua and Barbuda Dept. of Tourism
610 Fifth Ave., Ste. 311
New York, NY 10020
888-268-4227
www.antigua-barbuda.org

Argentina

Argentina Embassy
1600 New Hampshire Ave.
Washington, DC 20009
202-238-6400
www.embajadqargentina-usa.org

Aruba

Aruba Tourism Authority
1000 Harbor Blvd.
Weehawken, NJ 07087
800-TO-ARUBA
www.aruba.com

Go sailing or scuba diving in the turquoise Caribbean, enjoy yourself at casinos, discos and lots more.

Austria

Austrian National Tourist Office
PO Box 1142
New York, NY 10108-1142
212-944-6880, fax: 212-730-4568
www.austria-tourism.at

Write for the Austrian information package and you will be sent a beautiful assortment of travel guides and student education opportunities.

Bahamas

Bahamas Tourist Office
800-422-4262
www.bahamas.com

Barbados

Barbados Tourism Authority
800 Second Ave.
New York, NY 10017
212-986-6516, 800-221-9831
www.barbados.org

Discover the many sides of Barbados that make it a luscious vacation spot. A nice visitor's package is yours for the asking.

Belize

Belize Tourism Board
New Central Bank Bldg., Level 2
Gabourel Lane
PO Box 325
Belize City
Belize
Central America
800-624-0686
www.travelbelize.org

Bermuda

Bermuda Dept. of Tourism
205 E. 42 St., 16th flr.
New York, NY 10017
800-237-6832 for brochures

Are you thinking of traveling to Bermuda? Don't go without this information package. It includes travel tips, a map, hotel rates and more.
800-223-6106 Dept. of Tourism
www.bermudatourism.org

Tips on Avoiding Baggage Problems: Packing...check-in... claims.
Source: US Department of Transportation, 202-366-2220. www.dot.gov/air consumer.

About...Travel Safety: Securing your home...choosing a hotel...car...sightseeing ...protecting against scams and pickpockets. *Source:* MetLife, Consumer Education Center. 800-638-5433. www.metlife.com

Brazil

Brazil Reservations
1050 Edison St., Ste. C
Santa Ynez, CA 93460
800-544-5503
www.brazilres.com

British Virgin Islands

British Virgin Islands Tourist Board
370 Lexington Ave., Ste. 1605
New York, NY 10017
212-696-0400
www.bviwelcome.com

Britain

British Tourist Authority
551 Fifth Ave.
New York, NY 10176
800-462-2748
www.travelbritain.org

There is always something new to discover in England, Wales, Scotland and Ireland. Send a card requesting the Britain information package and you'll receive a beautiful color magazine, photos, maps, tour suggestions and more.

Britain on Track

Europerail International Inc.
691 Richmond St.
London, Ontario, Canada N6A 5MI

Tour scenic Britain by rail. EuropeRail passes offer unlimited travel on most rail, bus and ferry routes. For rail passes, fares and maps, visit www.britainontrack. com. 888-667-9734.

Canada

Canadian Tourism Commission
235 Queen St., 8th flr. West
Ottawa, Ontario
Canada K1A OH6
www.canadatourism.com

A variety of guides will describe the many exciting tours of Canada. You will learn where to go, what to see, what clothes to bring and much more. There is more to do in "our neighbor to the north" than you had ever imagined.

Canada-Nova Scotia

Nova Scotia Information
2695 Dutch Village Rd., Ste. 501
Halifax, Nova Scotia
Canada B3L 4V2
800-341-6096
www.checkinnovascotia.com

"Nova Scotia Doer's and Dreamer's Travel Guide" is a beautiful book that tells all about things to see, history, legends, customs, crafts and more. Call or write to ask for yours.

Cancun and Cozumel

Caribbean Tourism Organization
80 Broad St., 32nd flr.
New York, NY 10004
212-635-9530
www.doitcaribbean.com

Caribbean Sun Fun

Caribbean Tourism Organization
80 Broad St., 32nd flr.
New York, NY 10004

Discover the fun and excitement each of the Caribbean islands has to offer. Ask for the free travel package.
212-635-9530
www.doitcaribbean.com

Cayman Islands

Cayman Islands Tourism
420 Lexington Ave., Ste. 2733
New York, NY 10170
212-682-5582
www.cayman.org/tourism

Curaçao

Curaçao Tourist Board
800-445-8266
800-328-7222
www.curacao-tourism.com

Egypt

Egyptian Tourist Authority
630 Fifth Ave., Ste. 1706
New York, NY 10111

Travel back in time to the cradle of civilization. Explore the pyramids and discover the old and new wonders of Egypt. Ask for the Egypt information and maps.

212-332-2570
www.egypttourism.org

France

French Government Tourist Office
444 Madison Ave., 16th flr.
New York, NY 10022
212-838-7800

The France information package is a mini-tour of France with a large full-color tour book, plus Paris on a budget, tips on tours of Paris, information on hotels and motels, off-season packages and more.

410-286-8310 for brochures
www.francetourism.com

Germany

German National Tourist Office
122 E. 42 St., 52nd flr.
New York, NY 10168-7200
212-661-7200
www.visits-to-germany.com

Germany by Train

DER Travel Services
9501 W. Devon Ave., Ste. 1E
Rosemont, IL 60018
888-337-7350
www.dertravel.com

If you are planning a trip to Germany, one of the best ways to tour the country is by train. With German Rail you will have unlimited travel plus discounts on many bus and boat routes. For free information, write to German Rail.

800-660-5300
www.eurorail.com/germrail.htm

Greece

Greek National Tourism Organization
645 Fifth Ave., 9th flr.
Olympic Tower
New York, NY 10022
212-421-5777
www.gnto.gr

To help you make your trip to Greece more enjoyable, here's a large packet of brochures, maps and booklets on the beautiful Greek Islands. Request the Greece tour package.

Grenada

Grenada Board of Tourism
800 Second Ave., Ste. 400K
New York, NY 10017
800-927-9554
www.grenada.org

Guyana

Guyana Tourism
c/o Caribbean Tourism Organization
80 Broad St., 32nd flr.
New York, NY 10004
212-635-9530
www.doitcaribbean.com

University Vacations catalog. Stay and learn at one of 13 famous universities— Harvard…Oxford… Trinity College, Dublin… University of Bologna …University of Paris, Sorbonne…etc.
Source: University Vacations, 800-792-0100. www.universityvacations.com

Free Things to Do and See in Tokyo and Kyoto. Free.

Source: Japan National Tourist Organization, One Rockefeller Plaza, Ste. 1250, New York, NY 10020. Include a business-sized SASE. 212-757-5640.

Hong Kong

Hong Kong Tourism Board
115 E. 54 St., 2nd flr.
New York, NY 10022
212-421-3382
800-282-4582 to order brochures
www.discoverhongkong.com/usa

Hungary

Hungary National Tourist Board
150 E. 58th St. 33rd flr.
New York, NY 10155
212-355-0240

Like beautiful picture postcards, the color illustrations in this package will take you for a tour of the sights and attractions of Hungary. Ask for the Hungary travel package which includes a map of the country.
www.go2hungary.com

India

Information Service of India
Embassy of India
2107 Massachusetts Ave. NW
Washington, DC 20008
202-939-7000

Dozens of scenic color photos of India are included in the free India tour kit.

Indonesia

Consulate General of Indonesia
Information Section
Five E. 68th St.
New York, NY 10021
212-879-0600

For facts on the Indonesia archipelago including its history, geography, culture, maps and more, send a card requesting the information package.
www.indony.org

Ireland

Irish Tourist Board
345 Park Ave., 17th flr.
New York, NY 10154
800-SHAMROCK, 800-223-6470
www.ireland.travel.ie

Israel

Israel Government Tourist Office
800 Second Ave., 16th flr.
New York, NY 10017
212-499-5650, 212-499-5660
www.goisrael.com

Send for the collection of guide books and maps of Israel and the Holy Land.
888-77ISRAEL

Italy

Italian Government Travel Office
630 Fifth Ave., Ste. 1565
New York, NY 10111
212-245-4822/5618

A beautiful armchair tour of Italy is in store for you. Write for a brochure complete with road maps and marvelous full-color guide books.
www.italiantourism.com

Ivory Coast

Ivory Coast Embassy
3421 Massachusetts Ave. NW
Washington, DC 20007
202-797-0337

Learn about the rites of Panther Men and the fascinating culture of the Agri Kingdom. All this and much more is in the Ivory Coast travel kit.

Jamaica

Jamaica Tourist Board
1320 S. Dixie Hwy., Ste. 1101
Coral Gables, FL 33146
305-665-0557, 800-233-4JTB
www.jamaicatravel.com

Soft beaches, jungle waterfalls, hot discos and sailing in the sunshine—it's all in a beautiful full-color book that features 56 great vacations. Ask for the free "Jamaica Vacation Book."

Japan

Japan Travel Bureau
810 Seventh Ave., 34th flr.
New York, NY 10019
212-698-4900
www.jtbusa.com

The Japan tour package is an impressive collection of travel booklets in full color with marvelous illustrations. You'll receive a mini-tour of Japan full of facts about Japan's history, plus travel tips and many fascinating tidbits.

Martinique

Martinique Promotion Bureau
444 Madison Ave., 16th flr.
New York, NY 10022
800-391-4909
www.martinique.org

Mexico

The Magic of Mexico
800-44-MEXICO

Call to receive free color brochures and information on the country of Mexico and each state. You will be sent information on archeological sites, colonial sites, beaches and much more.
www.visitmexico.com

Montserrat

Caribbean Tourism Organization
80 Broad St., 32nd flr.
New York, NY 10004
212-635-9530
www.doitcaribbean.com

Morocco

Royal Air Maroc
55 E. 59th St.
New York, NY 10022
212-750-6071

Exotic Morocco has some of the most magnificent scenery in the world. For a kit of travel information and tour packages to this ancient kingdom, send a card to Royal Air Maroc.

Peru

Explorations, Inc.
27655 Kent Rd.
Bonita Springs, FL 34135
941-992-9660

In this package are colorful maps, charts and pictures of native birds, flowers and animals. You'll also find a listing of national parks and reserves, as well as interesting archaeological and historical highlights.

Portugal

Portuguese National Tourist Office
590 Fifth Ave., 4th flr.
New York, NY 10036
212-220-5772

Discover all the beauty of Portugal—its beaches, entertainment and hotels. It's all in the package of full-color brochures.
www.portugalinsite.pt

Car Rental Tips: Cost of renting...insurance coverage...other charges that may be added...what taxes may be charged...etc.
Source: American Society of Travel Agents, 1101 King St., Ste. 200, Alexandria, VA 22314. 703-739-2782. www.astanet.com

Tips on Tipping:
Whom do you tip?
How much?

Source: American Society
of Travel Agents,
1101 King St., Ste. 200,
Alexandria, VA 22314.
703-739-2782
www.astanet.com

Russia

Embassy of the Russian Federation
2650 Wisconsin Ave. NW
Washington, DC 20007
202-298-5700
www.russianembassy.org

St. Maarten

800-ST-MAARTEN

Ask for the free beautiful travel brochures of the island of St. Maarten.

Scotland

800-343-SCOT

Ask for the set of colorful brochures on Scotland.
www.toscotland.com

Singapore

Embassy of Republic of Singapore
3501 International Pl. NW
Washington, DC 20008

Singapore is the place where all of Asia comes together. Get the beautiful color package of things to do and see, plus a map and even a recipe booklet with delightful meals of Singapore.
202-537-3100 Washington
212-223-3331 New York

South Africa

Embassy of South Africa
3051 Massachusetts Ave. NW
Washington, DC 20008
202-232-4400
http://usaembassy.southafrica.net

Spain

Tourist Office of Spain
666 Fifth Ave., 35th flr.
New York, NY 10103
212-265-8822

Switzerland

Swiss National Tourist Office
608 Fifth Ave., Ste. 202
New York, NY 10020
212-757-5944

For a mini-tour of the Alps, send a postcard for the Swiss tour package. You will receive beautifully illustrated booklets, maps, travel tips, recipes and more. All of this comes to you free.
www.myswitzerland.com

Taiwan

Taiwan Visitors Association
405 Lexington Ave., 37th flr.
New York, NY 10174
212-867-1632
www.tbroc.gov.tw

Thailand

Tourism Authority of Thailand
611 N. Larchmont Blvd., 1st flr.
Los Angeles, CA 90004
1-800-Thailand

Come to Thailand and enjoy its dazzling scenery, incredible shopping bargains and the special joy of sharing the Thai people are known for. Send a postcard to get the travel packet.
www.tourismthailand.org

Zambia

Zambia National Tourist Board
237 E. 52nd St.
New York, NY 10022

Zambia has a big package of travel and tourist information waiting for you. The beautiful color brochures are a mini-safari through the African bush.

Free or
Almost Free
From the
Government

The US Government Toll-Free Helpline

Have you ever tried to find an answer to a simple question about the federal government and ended up on a merry-go-round of referrals? Or you may have had a question that was so difficult you had no idea where to begin. Now there is one toll-free number you can call for assistance. It's called the Federal Information Center and it is a clearinghouse of all government agencies. It is designed to help the average person find information quickly and effortlessly.

The Center will also refer you to the government agency that deals with the type of problem or question you may have. The Information Specialists are extraordinary when it comes to finding the exact place you should contact for help. For example, they can help you with whom to contact for help with Social Security benefits, sales and auctions of seized properties, consumer complaints, veteran's benefits, offices of the aging and virtually all other branches of the government. Their hours of operation are 9 a.m. to 8 p.m. EST.

Call them toll-free at 800-688-9889. (Disabled individuals using text phones [TDD/TTY] may call toll-free from anywhere in the US by dialing 800-326-2996.) If you have access to the Internet you can also find help on all government-related questions by going to www.info.gov.

Do You Know How Much Social Security You Will Get?

If you have ever wondered exactly how much money your Social Security benefits will be once you retire, there is an easy way to find out. Get a Personal Earnings and Benefit Estimate Statement. This will now be sent to you automatically. If you do not receive this statement, call the toll-free phone number and ask for an "earnings estimate request form" to fill out and return.

The Social Security Administration will then do a free search of their records and send you a detailed printout of how much has been contributed each year and how much your benefits will be if you retire at different ages. Find out which disability benefits you qualify for and how the value of your benefits compares with the amount of Social Security taxes you have paid over the years. This statement is yours free from the Social Security Administration.

At the same toll-free number they are also happy to answer any other questions you may have relating to your Social Security. Call 800-772-1213 (TTY: 800-325-0778). You can also access them on the Internet at www.ssa.gov.

Do You Need Extra Money?

Many low-income seniors never realize it, but even if they don't qualify for regular Social Security benefits, they may still qualify for thousands of dollars in extra income.

If you are over 65 and find that you have difficulty meeting your

Greater Wealth.
Find out how much your savings bonds are worth...whether they are earning interest... how to transfer ownership or cash them in. On the web at www.publicdebt.treas.gov.

175

The Future of Social Security. How it works …why it is changing …impact on all generations.
Source: Social Security Administration, Pub. #05-10055. 800-772-1213. www.ssa.gov

normal living expenses, or if you are blind or disabled at any age, you may qualify for a program called Supplemental Security Income (SSI). SSI was established to help seniors over the age of 65 who have too little income to pay for their basic needs and to help those who are not able to work because they are disabled regardless of their age.

To qualify you must meet a maximum asset and monthly income qualification, but studies have shown that as many as half of the seniors who do qualify never receive SSI benefits because they don't realize they are eligible for this extra income. Also, once you do qualify for SSI, you will also automatically qualify for both Medicaid and food stamps.

To find out if you qualify, contact your local Social Security office or call the toll-free helpline at 800-772-1213.

Free Food for Seniors

When you live on a limited budget you learn to cut corners wherever you can. But one of the areas where you should never cut corners is in eating properly. If you are living on a limited budget, even if you are living with someone else, you may qualify for food stamps which can save you thousands of dollars. And as a senior, if you are not able to travel to the social services agency to apply for the food stamps, a representative may visit your home or take the application right over the phone. Check the blue pages of your local phone book for a social services agency in your area. You

can also get the address and phone number by calling the Office of the Aging in your area. (See listings in the next chapter.)

Locating a Missing Person

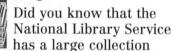

If you are trying to locate a missing relative or friend, a letter to the Social Security Administration may help. When you write, be sure to include as much information as you can about the missing person, including his or her last known address and date of birth. *Write to:*

Public Inquiries
Social Security Administration
6401 Security Blvd., Room 4C5 Annex
Baltimore, MD 21235
800-772-1213
www.ssa.gov

Free Books and Magazines

Did you know that the National Library Service has a large collection of books, magazines, journals and music materials in Braille, large type and recorded format for those who have temporary or permanent vision loss or physical limitations? Special playback equipment is available on a loan basis from the Library of Congress, and cassettes and CDs are available from more than 155 participating libraries. And if you are unable to hold a book or have a serious visual handicap, you can borrow these materials postage-free. They will even pay the postage for returning the materials to them when you are finished. Contact the National Library Service at the address and phone number below or ask your local library to find out what's available to you.

**Handicapped Readers Reference Section
National Library Service for the Blind and Physically Handicapped
Library of Congress
Washington, DC 20542
800-424-9100
www.loc.gov/nls**

Luxury Items at Little or No Cost

Yes, you can really own a boat, luxury car, fancy gems, even a house with all its treasures for just a tiny fraction of its true value. All of these treasures are confiscated from drug raids or other illegal activities. The government has no use for these goods and can't store them all, so they contract with private companies to auction off these goods.

At these auctions you have an excellent chance of getting valuable items for practically nothing. You can get a free copy of the "National Sellers List," which lists the local sellers of the Marshall Services goods. To get that list, you must reach them either by fax, at their Web site or from the Consumer Information Catalog.

Fax: 202-307-9777
www.usdoj.gov/marshals

IRS Auctions Benefit You

The IRS has auctions throughout the country of property of every kind—everything from houses to cars, jewelry and lots more. These things were all seized for nonpayment of taxes. *For a list of sales and auctions of properties seized by the IRS, request the list from:*

**Treasury Sales and Auctions
EG&G Services, Inc.
3702 Pender Dr., Ste. 400
Fairfax, VA 22030
703-273-7373
www.ustreas.gov/auctions**

Striking It Rich

Did you know that the US Government will let you prospect on public lands? If you would like to find out how to strike it rich on government lands, send a card to the Forest Service. Ask for "A Guide to Your National Forests." *Write to:*

**USDA Forest Service
Communications Office—Publications
PO Box 96090
201-14th St., SW
Washington, DC 20090-6090
202-205-1661
www.fs.fed.us**

Free Firewood

Did you know that in most of the 154 national forests, firewood for your own personal use is free? To find out how you can get free firewood and also how to select, purchase and use firewood, ask for the firewood information package. *It's free from:*

**Firewood #559
Forest Service
Communications Office—Publications
201-14th St., SW
Washington, DC 20090-6090
202-205-8333**

Buying US Government Surplus

Every year the federal government buys billions of dollars of every kind of merchandise imaginable.

Hands-On Solutions to Improve Your Profits & Productivity. Energy-saving strategies for small businesses.
Source: US Dept. of Energy, 800-363-3732.

Women and Pensions. What you need to know…and do.
Source: US Dept. of Labor, Pension and Welfare Benefits Administration, 800-998-7542. www.dol.gov/dol/pwba

Much of this is never used and eventually the US Government must sell all this surplus property. Find out how to buy everything from binoculars to automobiles at super-low bargain prices. Call 888-352-9333, or *write to:*

> **Government Liquidation**
> 6263 N. Scottsdale Rd., Ste. 371
> Scottsdale, AZ 85250
> www.drms.com
> www.surplusbid.com

Don't Pay Too Much Income Tax

Wouldn't that be a welcome notice to receive from the IRS? Believe it or not, many seniors really are paying a lot more income tax than they should. The reason is that they just are not aware of all the deductions and exemptions to which they are entitled. To be sure you're not paying more taxes than you should, ask for a free copy of "Protecting Older Americans Against Overpayment of Income Taxes." *Contact:*

> **Special Committee on Aging**
> **US Senate**
> G31 Dirksen Bldg.
> Senate Office
> Washington, DC 20510-6400
> 202-224-5364
> www.senate.gov/~aging

Avoid Paying Too Much Real Estate Tax

Throughout the nation, states and local governments are recognizing that seniors deserve a break when it comes to the real estate taxes they pay on their homes.

After all, by the time they are 65 years old, most seniors no longer have children in public school. And yet they're still paying school taxes on their real estate.

New York State recently instituted what it calls the STAR program. Under this program, seniors aged 65 or older who own a home and who earn less than $60,000 a year are entitled to a generous 45% average reduction in school taxes they normally pay as part of their real estate tax. It is available to all seniors in New York who ask for it. But they will not get the reduction unless they ask. What that means is that you must check with your local town or county tax assessor's office to see if your state offers a senior-citizen tax reduction. Until you find out, you could be paying thousands of dollars too much in real estate tax.

> 518-486-5446
> www.orps.state.ny.us/star/index.cfm

Pension and Retirement Hotline

If you have tax questions dealing with your pension or retirement plans, now you can ask the tax attorneys at the IRS for help. These attorneys specialize in tax law dealing specifically with pension and retirement plans. Get expert tax advice right from the source—for free! Call 877-829-5500.

"You're Too Old…You're Fired"

No, you aren't likely to hear those exact words, but that does not mean you won't be discriminated against because of your age. Just remember that if you are over 40 years old, the law is clear. It is against the law to discriminate against anyone because of their age when it comes to hiring, firing, pay, promotions and other conditions of employment. And to ensure that an employer will not discriminate against you on the basis of your age, sex, race or disability and get away with it, the government has set up the Equal Employment Opportunity Commission (EEOC).

If you feel that you have been a victim of discrimination by an employer (or potential employer), be sure to contact the EEOC. To be connected to the EEOC office nearest you, call 800-669-4000. *Or write to:*

U.S. Equal Employment Opportunity Commission
1801 L St., NW
Washington, DC 20507
www.eeoc.gov

Free Help Getting a New Job

With all the downsizing and early retirements, many older Americans find themselves in a situation where they can't afford to live on just their Social Security checks and yet they are unable to find a new job because of their age or because they need new skills. Now, thanks to government programs aimed specifically at seniors, there is help. This help comes in the form of free job training programs, counseling, as well as financial and tax incentives for companies to hire graduates of these training programs. For more information on

programs available in your area, refer to the listing in the back of this book called "Job Training Programs for Seniors."

Free Money to Fix up Your Home

Is your home in bad need of repair but you just can't afford the money to fix it up? Now there's help in the form of grants of anywhere from $1,000 to as much as $10,000. The money comes from the USDA Rural Housing Service. The Rural Housing Service distributes more than $4 billion in loans and grants annually to improve housing and community facilities in the nation's rural areas.

Right now there are more than 2.5 million substandard homes across the nation. The federal government is helping remedy this situation by giving money to local nonprofit groups who must use this money to make low-interest loans and outright grants that never have to be repaid. This money is for low-income homeowners aged 62 and older who otherwise would have to live in homes that are a safety or health risk.

To apply for a loan or grant, check the blue pages of your phone book under "Federal Government" for your local US Department of Agriculture Rural Development office. If you're unable to find it in the phone book, *you can contact:*

Rural Housing Service National Office
US Department of Agriculture, Room 5037 South Building, 14th St. and Independence Ave. SW
Washington, DC 20250
202-720-4323
www.rurdev.usda.gov

Mortgage Discrimination. Your rights when applying for a home loan. What you can do if you have been a victim of discrimination.
Source: Federal Trade Commission, Consumer Response Center, Washington, DC 20580 or www.ftc.gov.

179

Social Security: What Every Woman Should Know. How it works when you're employed or self-employed...when you retire...more.

Source: Social Security Administration, 800-772-1213. Pub. #05-10127. Free. www.ssa.gov

Free Legal Services

If you have ever needed the services of an attorney, then you already know just how expensive legal help can be. But did you know that you can get legal help worth thousands of dollars? This service is paid for with money from the federal government or from legal services donated by attorneys who volunteer for "pro bono" (free) service to help those who cannot afford legal representation.

See the "Directory of Free Legal Help" in the back of this book, which lists legal-services and pro-bono attorney offices across the country. Find the office nearest you and call them the next time you need the services of an attorney.

Valuable Information from the US Government

The US Government offers thousands of special programs and services which have already been paid for by your tax dollars. But to benefit from them, you must know they are there.

To keep you informed about these programs and to help you with a wide range of problems you may have, the government has hundreds of highly informative booklets that are yours free or practically free. These booklets are distributed through an agency called Consumer Information in Pueblo, Colorado.

All of the publications listed here are either free or are available for a very nominal charge.* You can order up to 25 free pub-

*Each publication's description is followed by an item number for ordering, and the price.

lications by simply enclosing $2 as a processing fee. (See more complete ordering details at the end of this section.)
www.pueblo.gsa.gov
800-FED-INFO
(TTY) 800-326-2996

...Cars

Buying a New Car

Here's a step-by-step guide that can be a helpful tool for bargaining with dealers. 2 pp. #301JJ. 50¢.

Buying a Used Car

Discusses your limited rights when buying from a dealer or private owner. 16 pp. #302JJ. 50¢.

Finding the Best Used Car

Use this step-by-step guide to check out the condition of vehicles you're considering. Covers what to look for on the test drive, warning signs of hidden damage and how to verify the vehicle's history. 10 pp. 605JJ. Free.

How to Find Your Way Under the Hood & Around the Car

Instructions for 14 preventive maintenance services you can perform on your car. 2 pp. #304JJ. 50¢.

How to Get a Great Deal on a New Car

Step-by-step instructions for a proven negotiation technique to save money on your next car. 4 pp. #305JJ. 50¢.

Nine Ways to Lower Your Auto Insurance Costs

Tips on what to do to lower your expenses. Includes a chart to compare discounts. 6 pp. #307JJ. 50¢.

...Children's Learning Activities

Catch the Spirit: A Student's Guide to Community Service

Ideas and information on how young people can help make their community a better place. 15 pp. #501JJ. Free.

Helping Your Child Learn Geography

Teach 5-10-year-old children geography in ways that are challenging and fun. 33 pp. #308JJ. 50¢.

Learning Partners

Activities to help your child learn reading, math, science, history, writing and much more. 30 pp. #310JJ. 50¢.

My History Is America's History

Detailed poster has easy ideas for discovering and preserving your family's history, with useful tips on recording family stories. 2 pp. #360JJ. 50¢.

Timeless Classics

Lists nearly 400 books published before 1960 for children of all ages. Divided into K-12 grade groups. 2 pp. #311HH. 50¢.

...Parenting

Ear Infections and Language Development

Ear infections are a common children's illness. Learn about the symptoms, treatments and the signs of possible hearing damage. Use the language development worksheet to track your child's progress. 11 pp. #370JJ. 50¢.

Fun Play, Safe Play

Use this guide to discover the importance of play in your child's learning and development and how to buy safe toys. 24 pp. #503JJ. Free.

Handbook on Child Support Enforcement

A "how to" guide for getting the payments owed to you and your children. Lists state and federal offices for more information. 61 pp. #505JJ. Free.

Help Yourself to a Healthy Home: Protect Your Children's Health

Find out about potentially harmful products in your home and follow the easy action steps to keep your house healthy, especially if your family has allergies. 24 pp. #506JJ. Free.

Planning For Your Special Needs Child

Learn about setting up a legal guardian and planning for your child's financial, medical and educational needs. 14 pp. #507HH. Free.

Invest Wisely: An Introduction to Mutual Funds. Different types of funds...comparing them by performance and costs. Free. *Source:* US Securities and Exchange Commission, Washington, DC 20549.

Charitable Donations: Give or Take. What to do before donating to make sure your money supports worthwhile causes. Free.

Source: Federal Trade Commission, Consumer Response Center, 877-382-4357. www.ftc.gov

...Education

GED Diploma

Explains what the General Educational Development Diploma tests cover, how to prepare and where to get more information. 16 pp. #509JJ. Free.

Nontraditional Education: Alternative Ways to Earn Your Credentials

Get high school or college credit through the GED program, the National External Diploma program, correspondence and distance study and standardized tests. 13 pp. #101JJ. $2.50.

Planning for College

Strategies to help you plan for tuition and fees along with helpful charts for estimating future costs. 10 pp. #510JJ. Free.

Think College? Me? Now? A Handbook for Students in Middle School and Junior High

Did you know students should start preparing for college in the seventh and eighth grades? Sound too early? Learn about the benefits of planning ahead for college. 24 pp. #102JJ. $1.75.

...Employment

Changing Your Job

Use this guide to assess if your current job is right for you, what to do when you decide to look for a new job and what happens to your benefits when you change jobs. 12 pp. #511JJ. Free.

Employment Interviewing

Follow these preparation tips, including important questions to prepare for and to ask your potential employer. Use the advice on references, job fairs and follow-up letters to get the job. 9 pp. #103JJ. $1.75.

Help Wanted— Finding a Job

Describes both private companies and government agencies that offer help in finding a job. Lists precautions to take when contacting an employment service firm. 8 pp. #316JJ. 50¢.

Here Today, Jobs of Tomorrow: Opportunities in Information Technology

This booklet discusses the high demand for information technology workers and if this field is right for you. 13 pp. #104HH. $2.50.

High Earning Workers Who Don't Have a Bachelor's Degree

Identifies 50 occupations requiring less than a bachelor's degree. 9 pp. #105JJ. $3.00.

Job Outlook in Brief, 1998–2008

Make the most of job trends now and in the future. Here's the forecast on job opportunities and what will be the most sought after skills. 39 pp. #106JJ. $4.75.

Matching Yourself with the World of Work

Don't fall into a job that might not be a perfect fit for you. Find out what to look for in your ideal job with this guide. 19 pp. #107HH. $2.75.

Resumes, Applications and Cover Letters

Use this guide's samples to format a winning cover letter and resume and learn how new technology can help. 15 pp. #108JJ. $2.00.

Tips for Finding the Right Job

How to assess your skills and interests, create a resume, write cover letters and prepare for a job interview. 27 pp. #109JJ. $2.50.

...Federal Programs & Benefits

Choosing a Doctor: A Guide for People with Medicare

Useful information to find the right doctor, with worksheets to help decide what you want in a doctor, questions to ask and more. 31 pp. #517JJ. Free.

Choosing a Hospital: A Guide for People with Medicare

Here are tips on choosing the best possible facility when you or a family member needs hospital care. 19 pp. #518JJ. Free.

Choosing Treatments: A Guide for People with Medicare

Provides advice and worksheets to help you work with your doctor to develop the best treatment plan for any health problem. 31 pp. #519JJ. Free.

Federal Benefits for Veterans and Dependents

Explains disability, pension, health care, education and housing loans and other benefit programs for veterans and their families. 108 pp. #113JJ. $5.00.

Medicare and Home Health Care

Outlines coverage of the Medicare plan, the home health care benefit and who is eligible, how to find an approved home health agency, steps to take if Medicare stops paying for home health care services and more. 21 pp. #521JJ. Free.

Medicare and Other Health Benefits: Your Guide to Who Pays First

Use this guide to help you determine whether Medicare or your other insurance pays first when you receive health care. 37 pp. #522JJ. Free.

Medicare and Your Mental Health Benefits

Your mental health is an important part of your overall well-being. Use this guide to learn what is covered under Medicare. 9 pp. #523JJ. Free.

Medicare Hospice Benefits

Hospice care is a special type of care for terminally ill patients. Tips on how to find a hospice program and where to get more information. 12 pp. #524JJ. Free.

Social Security: Your Number. Protecting your number and records...what the digits mean...etc.
Source: Social Security Administration, 800-772-1213. www.ssa.gov

Tax Benefits for Higher Education. Learn how to claim a tax credit for part or all of tuition paid.
Source: IRS, Publication #970, 800-829-3676.

Medicare Preventive Services...To Help Keep You Healthy

Use this guide to lower your risk of cancer, flu, pneumonia, diabetes and other illnesses. 4 pp. #525JJ. Free.

Medicare Worksheet for Comparing Medicare Health Plans

Health care coverage decisions aren't always easy. Check off these easy-to-follow points and get the best plan for your needs. 9 pp. #526JJ. Free.

Pay It Right! Protecting Medicare from Fraud

Each year, fraudulent claims increase Medicare expenses and premiums. Learn how to spot warning signs of fraud and how to report errors and concerns. 8 pp. #527JJ. Free.

Request for Social Security Statement

A form to complete and return to Social Security to get your earnings history and an estimate of future benefits. 3 pp. #528JJ. Free.

Social Security: Basic Facts

Describes the different kinds of Social Security benefits, who receives them and how they're financed. 17 pp. #529JJ. Free.

Social Security: Understanding the Benefits

Explains retirement, disability, survivor's benefits, Medicare coverage, Supplemental Security Income and more. 41 pp. #530JJ. Free.

Social Security: What Every Woman Should Know

Discusses how a woman's benefits may be affected by disability, divorce, widowhood, retirement or other special situations. 19 pp. #531JJ. Free.

Your Medicare Benefits

It's important to be familiar with what your health care plan covers. Learn about both hospital and medical insurance with this booklet. 19 pp. #532JJ. Free.

...Food

Bulking Up Fiber's Healthful Reputation

Create your own high fiber diet and help reduce your risk of certain cancers, digestive disorders and other ailments. 5 pp. #534HH. Free.

Cooking for Groups: A Volunteer's Guide to Food Safety

Whether it's the family reunion buffet or community cookout, learn how to cook and serve food safely and avoid food-borne illness. 40 pp. #604JJ. Free.

Fruits and Vegetables

This guide helps you to eat 5 a day. Eating fruits and vegetables can reduce the risk of heart disease and cancer. This guide gives you ideas to help you meet the 5 a day goal. 6 pp. #536HH. Free.

Eat Right to Help Lower Your High Blood Pressure

Lists menu ideas and recipes to help you control your weight and high blood pressure. 30 pp. #116JJ. $4.00.

Eating for Life

Tips on how to make healthy, appetizing food choices at home and when eating out. 23 pp. #117HH. $1.50.

Food Guide Pyramid

This easy-to-read guide can help you select the nutrients you need and reduce the fat, cholesterol and sodium in your diet. 29 pp. #118JJ. $1.00.

Growing Older, Eating Better

Good nutrition can lessen the effects of aging and disease and improve the quality of life. Discusses the various causes of poor nutrition and how it can be improved. 5 pp. #537JJ. Free.

Preventing Food-Borne Illness

Describes the bacteria that causes food-borne illness and how to handle food safely. Use the storage guidelines chart to know when to throw away those leftovers. 8 pp. #539JJ. Free.

Recipes and Tips for Healthy, Thrifty Meals

How to create healthy, budget-friendly meals—with tips on planning meals, shopping lists, a sample 2-week menu and 40 great recipes. 76 pp. #119JJ. $6.50.

To Your Health! Food Safety for Seniors

Covers the basic rules of safe food preparation, including a list of foods not recommended for those over 65 and safety tips for delivered meals and meals-to-go. 17 pp. #596HH. Free.

Thermy: Use a Food Thermometer

Don't judge cooked meat by its color—it can make you sick. Get the right thermometer and use this handy temperature chart for safe, delicious food. 4 pp. #541JJ. Free.

Using the Dietary Guidelines for Americans

How to choose a diet that will taste good, be nutritious and reduce chronic disease risks. 8 pp. #321JJ. 50¢.

...Health

Cosmetic Laser Surgery: A High-Tech Weapon in the Fight Against Aging Skin

Lasers can help remove facial wrinkles and lines. This guide explains the procedure, its risks, how to tell if it's right for you and what to look for in a surgeon. 4 pp. #542JJ. Free.

How to Find Medical Information

This book will guide you through a variety of resources—from your local library, to the federal government, to the Internet—to help you get info on an illness or disorder. 24 pp. #544JJ. Free.

Mammography Today

Learn when and how often you should have a mammogram, how to tell if you are getting a high-

Basic Facts About Trademarks. How to register for a product or service—requirements ...fees...application form. Free.

Source: US Dept. of Commerce, Patent and Trademark Office, 800-786-9199...or on the Web at www.uspto.gov.

Poison Lookout Checklist. How to prevent accidental poisonings. Free.
Source: US Consumer Product Safety Commission, Washington, DC 20207. www.cpsc.gov

quality mammogram, what to do if you need to change mammogram facilities and more. 6 pp. #607JJ. Free.

Questions to Ask Your Doctor Before You Have Surgery

Use this booklet to become a better informed and prepared patient. 13 pp. #120JJ. $1.00.

Staying Healthy at 50+

Covers everything from cholesterol levels, various cancers, weight control and checkups, with helpful charts to keep track of your medications, shots and screening test results. 64 pp. #121JJ. $2.75.

Sun, UV and You

 Explains what the UV (ultraviolet radiation) index is and how you can use it to avoid skin cancer, premature aging of the skin and more. 12 pp. #545JJ. Free.

Understanding Breast Changes: A Health Guide for All Women

Describes the various types of breast changes that women experience. Also discusses breast cancer screening, diagnosis, treatment and prevention. 52 pp. #546HH. Free.

Understanding Prostate Changes: A Health Guide for All Men

Learn about prostate enlargement and prostate cancer, including screening and treatment. 38 pp. #547HH. Free.

Water on Tap: A Consumer's Guide to the Nation's Drinking Water

Explains where it comes from and how it's treated, what contaminants are and what to do in case of a problem with either your public or private water supply. 22 pp. #548JJ. Free.

Your Guide to Choosing a Nursing Home

Discusses what to look for in a nursing home and alternatives to nursing homes. Includes an evaluation checklist and a list of helpful resources. 37 pp. #549JJ. Free.

...Drugs & Health Aids

An Aspirin a Day...Just Another Cliché?

You may reach for aspirin when you have a headache, but can aspirin really help reduce the risk of heart attack and stroke? Read about the benefits of aspirin in preventing cardiovascular disease and if taking it is right for you. 4 pp. #550HH. Free.

Basik Lasik

 Find out about Lasik eye surgery, who is a good candidate, how to find a surgeon, possible risks and complications and alternatives to Lasik. 5 pp. #322JJ. 50¢.

Buying Prescription Medicines Online: A Consumer Safety Guide

The Internet now makes it easier than ever to get your prescription medications. Learn how to protect yourself with this guide's helpful list of do's and don'ts when shopping for medications online. 5 pp. #597JJ. Free.

Drug Interactions: What You Should Know

You take a new medication to help you, but some drugs can harm you if taken together. Learn more about protecting yourself and your family from drug and common food interactions. 8 pp. #598JJ. Free.

FDA's Tips for Taking Medicines

Protect yourself from prescription and over-the-counter (OTC) drugs that may react in strange ways to each other, certain foods, alcohol, etc. 4 pp. #608JJ. Free.

Medications and Older Adults

Suggestions on how to prevent dangerous drug combinations, how to make taking medications easier, how to remember medication and how to cut their cost. 4 pp. #554JJ. Free.

Taming Tummy Turmoil

 Describes over-the-counter medications (and their possible side effects) for motion sickness, heartburn, indigestion and overindulgence. 4 pp. #609HH. Free.

To Be or Not to Be—On Hormone Replacement Therapy

Compares the benefits, side effects and long-term health

effects of hormone replacement therapy (HRT). This guide also features quizzes that can help you determine your healthcare preferences and how to weigh the pros and cons of HRT. 34 pp. #599JJ. Free.

...Exercise & Diet

Exercise and Your Heart

 Your heart needs exercise to stay healthy and regular physical activity can lower your risk of heart disease. Learn how to start a new exercise program, how to pace yourself and effective ways to avoid injuries. 37 pp. #145JJ. $2.00.

Fitness and Exercise

Get fit and feel better with daily activities that fit the weather, your lifestyle and your schedule. 12 pp. #610JJ. Free.

Walking for Exercise and Pleasure

Includes illustrated warm-up exercises and advice on how far, how fast and how often to walk for best results. 14 pp. #122JJ. $1.25.

Weight Loss: Finding a Weight Loss Program that Works for You

Use the Body Mass Index (BMI) calculator to determine your BMI and set your weight goal. Then fill in the personal health profile and follow the checklist to compare different weight loss programs. 11 pp. #325JJ. 50¢.

Water on Tap: A Consumer's Guide to the Nation's Drinking Water.
Source: US Environmental Protection Agency, Office of Water Resource Center (RC4100), Washington, DC 20460. www.epa.gov

How to Give Medicine to Your Children. How to give the right dosage ... watch for side effects... avoid choking hazards. Free.

Source: FDA Consumer, 5600 Fishers Ln., Rockville, MD 20857. Pub. #96-3223. 888-463-6332. www.fda.gov

...Medical Problems

Anxiety—Fact Sheet

Describes different types of anxiety disorders and what you can do if you recognize these symptoms in yourself or a loved one. 4 pp. #556JJ. Free.

Arthritis: Timely Treatments for an Ageless Disease

This guide explains the types of arthritis, new treatments available, unproven remedies to guard against and more. 6 pp. #557HH. Free.

Atopic Dermatitis

Individuals with atopic dermatitis, or eczema, suffer from a chronic disease that causes extremely itchy, inflamed skin. Find out more about this disease, its symptoms and treatments. 37 pp. #558JJ. Free.

Boning Up on Osteoporosis

Osteoporosis drains away bone mass over many years without warning to the patient or doctor. Learn more about this dangerous condition and how to prevent it. 7 pp. #611HH. Free.

Breast Cancer: Better Treatments Save More Lives

Every three minutes in the U.S., a woman learns she has breast cancer. Find out about improved diagnostic techniques, the stages of breast cancer and new treatments and drugs that are available. 5 pp. #560JJ. Free.

Cataract in Adults

Cataract is a normal part of aging, but if it makes performing routine tasks too difficult, you may need surgery. Learn more about symptoms and treatments. 13 pp. #123JJ. $1.00.

Controlling Asthma

Discusses what triggers an asthma attack, possible causes and medications to prevent attacks and help relieve symptoms. 5 pp. #600JJ. Free.

Do I Have Arthritis?

Arthritis affects your health, your family, even your financial life. Read about common signs of arthritis and how medications and exercise can help. 28 pp. #561JJ. Free.

Eating Disorders

When should you worry about someone who won't eat or is morbidly thin? Learn the symptoms of different eating diseases, who is most likely to be affected and various treatment options. 8 pp. #612JJ. Free.

Fever Blisters & Canker Sores

Explains causes, treatments and research on these mouth infections. 12 pp. #327JJ. 50¢.

Getting Treatment for Panic Disorder

More than 3 million American adults have episodes of intense, disabling fear. Learn when you need help and what treatment options are available. 5 pp. #562JJ. Free.

Laser Eye Surgery: Is It Worth Looking Into?

Can the new surgical techniques get rid of your glasses and contacts forever? Find out if you're a good candidate and what risks are involved. 4 pp. #566GG. Free.

Lupus

Lupus is a disease in which the immune system attacks the body's healthy cells and tissues. Consult this guide's information charts for warning signs and available treatments. 33 pp. #563JJ. Free.

Noninsulin-Dependent Diabetes

Over 90% of diabetics in the US have noninsulin-dependent diabetes. Use this guide to learn more about this type of diabetes, who is at risk and how it is treated. 35 pp. #328HH. 50¢.

Osteoarthritis

The most common type of arthritis is osteoarthritis, especially among older individuals. This guide discusses its symptoms (pain, swelling and loss of motion) and treatments and also illustrates helpful exercises. 36 pp. #565JJ. Free.

Preventing Stroke

Stroke is the third leading killer in the US and the most common cause of adult-disability. Find out more with this booklet and estimate your risk with its informative stroke-risk chart. 8 pp. #329JJ. 50¢.

Prostate Cancer: No One Answer for Testing or Treatment

Explains how prostate cancer is detected, what the stages are and what you need to know to choose the best treatment option. 6 pp. #613JJ. Free.

Questions & Answers About Arthritis Pain

There are many treatments available depending upon the source of your arthritis pain. Get the facts on available options (conventional and alternative) for short-term relief and long-term pain management. 18 pp. #614JJ. Free.

Rheumatoid Arthritis

Rheumatoid arthritis affects the everyday activities of 2.1 million people in the US This publication discusses diagnosis and treatment and also has a medication chart for drug benefits and side effects. 33 pp. #566JJ. Free.

So You Have High Blood Cholesterol

High blood cholesterol can increase your risk of heart disease. Here are the facts about high cholesterol and what you can do to lower yours. 36 pp. #124JJ. $1.75.

Taking Charge of Menopause

Learn about menopause, its symptoms and health risks associated with it. 5 pp. #567JJ. Free.

Early Childhood: Where Learning Begins—Geography. Ages two to five. *Source:* US Dept. of Education, Ed Pubs, 877-433-7827. ww.ed.gov

Home Playground Safety Tips. Protective surfaces…proper equipment placement… playground maintenance. *Source:* US Consumer Product Safety Commission, Washington, DC 20207…or on the Web at www.cpsc.gov.

Time to Spring Into Action Against Seasonal Allergies

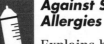

Explains how to treat chronic allergies, including medications, nasal sprays and allergy shots. Covers common FAQs regarding over-the-counter medications. 5 pp. #615HH. Free.

Understanding Acute Low Back Problems

Learn what causes them, what to do if you are experiencing problems, the most effective treatments and how to minimize future back problems. 14 pp. #147JJ. $1.00.

Understanding Treatment Choices for Prostate Cancer

Newly diagnosed prostate cancer patients and their families face many treatment choices. Here's information on how prostate cancer is diagnosed, available treatment options and follow-up care. 44 pp. #568JJ. Free.

Urinary Tract Infections in Adults

Urinary tract infections are a common but serious health problem. Find out more about the causes, symptoms and treatments available. 8 pp. #330JJ. 50¢.

Varicose Vein Treatments

Explains treatments, risks, side effects, what to ask your doctor and more. 2 pp. #331HH. 50¢.

What You Need to Know About Skin Cancer

Taking care now will really pay off in the future. Learn the basic symptoms, how it is diagnosed and treated. Use the step-by-step guide on how to perform regular skin self-exams. 26 pp. #601HH. Free.

…Housing

Buying Your Home: Settlement Costs and Helpful Information

Describes the home buying, financing and settlement (closing) process. Also gives tips on shopping for a loan. 35 pp. #125JJ. $2.00.

Guide to Single-Family Home Mortgage Insurance

Explains FHA mortgage insurance programs, including types available, how to qualify, how to apply, restrictions and more. 14 pp. #332JJ. 50¢.

How to Buy a Home with a Low Down Payment

Describes how to qualify for a low down payment mortgage, determine what you can afford and how mortgage insurance works. 9 pp. #570JJ. Free.

How to Buy a Manufactured (Mobile) Home

Tips on selection and placement, warranties, site preparation, transportation, installation and more. 22 pp. #333JJ. 50¢.

Looking for the Best Mortgage—Shop, Compare, Negotiate

Using these 3 steps can save you thousands of dollars on a home loan or mortgage. Find many useful tips in this booklet. 7 pp. #334JJ. 50¢.

Twelve Ways to Lower Your Homeowners Insurance Costs

Practical tips to help reduce your expenses. Lists phone numbers of state insurance departments for more information. 4 pp. #335JJ. 50¢.

When Your Home Is On the Line: What You Should Know About Home Equity Lines of Credit

Here are questions, terms, tips, a checklist and more—all to help you find the plan that best meets your individual needs and protects your interest. 16 pp. #371JJ. 50¢.

Am I Covered?

 Answers 15 common questions regarding homeowners insurance and explains what is covered in a standard policy. 9 pp. #336JJ. 50¢.

Cooling Your Home Naturally

Ways to save electricity and keep your home cool with landscaping, roof treatments and more. 8 pp. #126JJ. $2.00.

Elements of an Energy-Efficient House

Learn the benefits of having energy-efficient elements in your home—a well-built thermal envelope, controlled ventilation, high-efficiency heating and cooling systems and energy-efficient doors, windows and appliances. 8 pp. #127JJ. $1.50.

Energy Savers: Tips on Saving Energy & Money at Home

A practical guide on reducing your home energy use, with tips on insulation, weatherization, heating and more. 36 pp. #337JJ. 50¢.

...Money & Credit

Consumer Handbook to Credit Protection Laws

Explains how consumer credit laws can help you apply for credit, keep up a good credit standing and complain about an unfair deal. 44 pp. #340JJ. 50¢.

Credit Matters

This guide explains how to qualify for credit, keep a good credit history, get the best deal on a credit card, protect your credit once you have it and how to deal with credit errors. 5 pp. #341JJ. 50¢.

Fair Credit Reporting

Learn what's in your credit report, how you can get a copy and more. 2 pp. #342JJ. 50¢.

Fair Debt Collection

Describes what debt collectors may and may not do if you owe money. How and where to complain if you are harassed, threatened or abused. 2 pp. #343JJ. 50¢.

Childproofing Your Home: 12 Safety Devices to Protect Children.
Source: Consumer Information Center, Dept. 618F, Pueblo, CO 81009. 888-878-3256.

What You Should Know About Space Heaters. Free.
Hazards and safety tips for all types—kerosene …portable electric… wood-burning…etc. Free.
Source: US Consumer Product Safety Commission, Washington, DC 20207. www.cspc.gov

How to Dispute Credit Report Errors

Gives tips on correcting errors, registering a dispute and adding information to your file. 2 pp. #344JJ. 50¢.

ID Theft: When Bad Things Happen to Your Good Name

Protect your banking and credit info with this helpful guide. Includes resources to contact and a sample letter to follow to officially report a dispute. 21 pp. #345JJ. 50¢.

Pretexting: Your Personal Information Revealed

Pretexting is when others get your personal information under false pretenses. Find out about how it happens, the laws against it, how to protect your personal information and what to do if you are a victim. 4 pp. #372JJ. 50¢.

…Investing & Saving

66 Ways to Save Money

Practical ways to cut everyday costs on transportation, insurance, banking, credit, housing, utilities, food and more. 4 pp. #347JJ. 50¢.

Certificates of Deposit: Tips for Investors

CDs aren't just for music. They are savings vehicles that can offer a higher interest rate than a regular savings account. Learn how CDs work, how to purchase them and questions to ask before purchase. 2 pp. #369JJ. 50¢.

Consumer's Almanac

Organize your daily expenses, save and invest for the future and manage your credit with monthly calendars and worksheets. 32 pp. #348JJ. 50¢.

Get the Facts on Saving and Investing

Use this guide's helpful tips and worksheets for calculating net worth, income and expenses. 18 pp. #349JJ. 50¢.

Introduction to Mutual Funds

What they are, how to compare them, what to consider before investing and how to avoid common pitfalls. 15 pp. #351JJ. 50¢.

Investment Swindles: How They Work and How to Avoid Them

Protect yourself against illegal, yet legitimate-sounding, telemarketing and direct mail offers. 22 pp. #577HH. Free.

Investors' Bill of Rights

Here are some tips on what you should know about investments and what information you are entitled to before investing. 7 pp. #578JJ. Free.

Microcap Stock: A Guide for Investors

Microcap stocks are low priced stocks issued by small companies. Here are details on these stocks and how to protect yourself from fraud. 20 pp. #366HH. 50¢.

Planning Financial Security

Here's a step-by-step guide to improving your financial future. It features a worksheet to help track your spending, tips on creating a spending plan and an investor's checklist. 12 pp. #579HH. Free.

Ten Questions to Ask When Choosing a Financial Planner

Covers credentials, costs, services, an interview checklist and resources to contact for more information. 12 pp. #580JJ. Free.

U.S. Savings Bonds

 These bonds offer a safe, convenient way to save money and can be great investments. Learn about the different types of bonds, the state and federal tax benefits and how to purchase savings bonds online. 7 pp. #373JJ. 50¢.

What You Should Know About Financial Planning

Are you planning to buy a house or retire in the near future? This useful guide discusses the benefits of financial planning for these and other life-changing events. 13 pp. #581JJ. Free.

Your Insured Deposit

Explains what is protected and what isn't if your bank should fail, how much of your money is insured, what types of accounts are covered and more. 21 pp. #582JJ. Free.

Your Rights as a Financial Planning Client

When you work with a financial planner, you're putting your financial future in their hands. Here's a checklist of your rights as a client, what to expect from your financial planner and what to do if you have a problem. 5 pp. #595JJ. Free.

...Retirement Planning

401(k) Plans

Covers what these retirement plans are and how they differ from other investment options. Find out what happens when you change employers and what to do if you need the money before retirement. 14 pp. #583JJ. Free.

Annuities

An important tool in planning your retirement could be annuities. Learn the different types of annuities and use this guide's helpful quiz to see if annuities are right for you. 11 pp. #584JJ. Free.

Finding a Lost Pension

Thousands of retired workers in the US are entitled to pensions that they have not claimed. Here's how to find out if you have a lost pension, where to search, documents you'll need and what to do when you find your pension fund. 34 pp. #133HH. $2.00.

General Information Concerning Patents. Free.

Source: US Dept. of Commerce, Patent and Trademark Office, 800-786-9199...or on the Web at www.uspto.gov.

Alcohol-Medication Interactions. How alcohol and various drugs interact...alcohol interactions with antibiotics, antihistamines, anticoagulants and 10 other medication types.

Source: National Institute on Alcohol Abuse and Alcoholism, 6000 Executive Blvd., Willco Building, Bethesda, MD 20892-7003. www.niaaa.nih.gov

Savings Fitness: A Guide to Your Money and Your Financial Future

Get in shape financially. Create your personal savings plan and prepare for retirement with this step-by-step guide. 20 pp. #585JJ. Free.

Top 10 Ways to Beat the Clock and Prepare for Retirement

Gives practical tips to build your retirement savings and lists resources for more information. 2 pp. #586JJ. Free.

Variable Annuities: What You Should Know

Here are the basics on variable annuities—learn what they are, how they work and what you have to pay. This guide also features a checklist of questions to ask before you invest. 20 pp. #367JJ. 50¢.

Women and Retirement Savings

Provides a checklist of questions to ask about retirement benefits, including plan type, eligibility, penalties, spousal benefits and more. 6 pp. #587JJ. Free.

Your Guaranteed Pension

Answers 18 frequently asked questions about the security of private pension plans, including benefits and plan termination. 11 pp. #588JJ. Free.

...Travel

Fly-Rights

Helpful advice for travelers on getting the best fares, what to do with lost tickets and baggage, canceled flights and more. 58 pp. #134HH. $2.00.

Fly Smart

Gives more than 30 steps you can take to help make your flight a safe one. 2 pp. #590JJ. Free.

Lesser Known Areas of the National Park System

Listing by state of more than 170 national parks, their accommodations, locations and historical significance. 49 pp. #135JJ. $3.00.

National Park System Map and Guide

Full color map lists activities at more than 300 parks, monuments and historic sites. #136JJ. $1.25.

National Trails System Map and Guide

Full color map describes eight national scenic trails and nine national historic trails. #137JJ. $1.25.

National Wildlife Refuges: A Visitor's Guide

Use this full color map to plan a visit and learn about hundreds of endangered species and their habitats. #138JJ. $1.75.

Passports: Applying for Them the Easy Way

How, when and where to apply for US passports. Includes information on fees. 2 pp. #355JJ. 50¢.

Travel Smart

Tips on getting info on countries around the world—from health and safety warnings to passport and visa requirements. Also covers what records to copy and where to keep them. 6 pp. #356JJ. 50¢.

Washington: The Nation's Capital

This historic city houses the US government and has many important landmarks. Use this guide to learn more about our country's heritage by exploring Washington D.C. #139JJ. $1.25

...And More

Civil War at a Glance

This full color map illustrates and briefly describes major Civil War battle campaigns. #141JJ. $2.00.

Conserving the Nature of America

Beautiful photos show how the US Fish and Wildlife Service protects the fish, wildlife and plants in more than 500 National Wildlife Refuges. Also provides info on volunteer and recreational opportunities. 24 pp. #591JJ. Free.

2002 Consumer Action Handbook

No consumer should be without this helpful guide. It provides assistance with consumer problems and complaints. Lists consumer contacts at hundreds of companies and trade associations, state and federal government agencies, local and national consumer organizations and much more. #148 pp. #592JJ. Free.

Fishing Is Fun for Everyone

You'll fall for fishing hook, line and sinker. Find out what equipment you'll need, what kind of bait to use, how to cast and tie knots and where to fish for more information. 11 pp. #593JJ. Free.

For the Birds

How to attract different species of birds, feed them and build or buy suitable homes. 50 pp. #357JJ. 50¢.

Internet Auctions: A Guide for Buyers and Sellers

Internet auctions offer a great way to buy or sell all kinds of products. Find out how auctions work, payment options and how to protect yourself. 18 pp. #359JJ. 50¢.

US and the Metric System

Explains how to use metric in everyday life. Includes metric conversion charts and more. 10 pp. #363JJ. 50¢.

The Basics of Foreign Trade and Exchange. Free.
Source: Federal Reserve Bank of New York, Public Information Dept., 33 Liberty St., New York, NY 10045 ...or on the Web at 212-720-6130 www.ny.frb.org/pihome.

Federal Credit Unions. What they are...how to start one for your organization...list of National Credit Union Administration regional offices.
Source: National Credit Union Administration, 1775 Duke St., Alexandria, VA 22314, or on the Web at www.ncua.gov.

Where to Write for Vital Records

This useful guide offers listings for each state on how to obtain birth, death, marriage and divorce certificates. 32 pp. #144JJ. $3.00.

Your Family Disaster Supplies Kit

Lists kinds of food, first aid supplies, tools and other items you should stock for an emergency. 4 pp. #364JJ. 50¢.

Ordering Free Booklets

While there is no charge for individual free publications, there is a $2 service/handling fee to help defray program costs. For $2, you may order as many free booklets as you wish. Payment may be made by check or money order, payable to the "Superintendent of Documents." You can also use a VISA, MasterCard or Discover card. Priority handling is available at an extra charge, explained when you place your order by phone.

Ordering Information

You can order the publications online. There are two types of online orders. One is a totally free special offer and usually includes one or a small number of publications that were advertised in a magazine or newspaper.

The second type of order is when you browse their topic categories and personally select a variety of publications. You can order as many different publications as you wish.

For these larger orders, you pay the sales price noted for any publication you want and there is a flat $2 service fee if you order any of the free publications.

... or

You can place your order via their toll-free telephone order line at: 888-878-3256

... or

Mail your order and payment to:
Consumer Information Center
Dept. WWW
Pueblo, CO 81009

Your State's Office of the Aging

Free Help for Seniors from Your State's Office of The Aging

Every state in the nation has an agency dedicated to providing seniors with a full range of services. These services will vary from state to state but may include:

- Food stamps
- Home-delivered meals
- Transportation to and from medical appointments
- In-home care and assistance, where needed
- Job training programs for older workers wanting to get back into the workforce
- Health insurance counseling and assistance programs to help the elderly get all necessary health care
- Free prescription-drug programs

To find out exactly which services are available to you, contact your state's Office of the Aging directly. Here is a directory of these offices for all 50 states, plus the District of Columbia, Puerto Rico and the Pacific Islands.

National Offices
Administration on Aging, Washington, DC

US Administration on Aging
330 Independence Ave. SW
Washington, DC 20201
800-677-1116
www.aoa.dhhs.gov

National Association of Area Agencies on Aging
927 15th St. NW, 6th flr.
Washington, DC 20005
202-296-8130
www.n4a.org

State Offices

Alabama
Alabama Department of Senior Services
770 Washington Ave., RSA Plaza, Ste. 470
Montgomery, AL 36130
334-242-5743 or 877-425-2243
www.adss.state.al.us

Alaska
Alaska Commission on Aging
PO Box 110209
Juneau, AK 99811-0209
907-465-3250
www.alaskaaging.org

Arizona
Arizona Department of Economic Security Aging and Adult Administration
1789 W. Jefferson, Site Code 950A
Phoenix, AZ 85007
602-542-4446
www.de.state.az.us

Arkansas
Arkansas Division of Aging and Adult Services
Seventh and Main St.
PO Box 1437, Slot S-530
Little Rock, AR 72203-1437
501-682-2441
www.state.ar.us/dhs/aging

California
California Department of Aging
1600 K St.
Sacramento, CA 95814
916-322-3887
www.aging.state.ca.us

Pills, Patches and Shots: Can Hormones Prevent Aging? All about DHEA, human growth hormone, melatonin, testosterone and estrogen.
Source: National Institute on Aging, Public Information Office, Building 31, Room 5C27, 31 Center Dr., MSC 2292, Bethesda, MD 20892. 301-496-1752. www.nia.nih.gov

Choosing a Doctor.
How to choose an internist, family practitioner, specialist. Managed care options.

Source: National Institute on Aging, Public Information Office, Building 31, Room 5C27, 31 Center Dr., MSC 2292, Bethesda, MD 20892. 301-496-1752. www.nia.nih.gov

Colorado

Colorado Division of Aging and Adult Services
1575 Sherman St.
Denver, CO 80203
303-866-2800
www.state.co.us
www.cdhs.state.co.us

Connecticut

Connecticut Dept. of Social Services
25 Sigourney St.
Hartford, CT 06106-5033
800-842-1508
www.dss.state.ct.us

Delaware

Delaware Division of Services for Aging and Adults with Physical Disabilities
1901 N. Dupont Hwy.
New Castle, DE 19720
800-223-9074
www.dsaapd.com

District of Columbia

District of Columbia Office on Aging
441 4th St. NW, Ste. 900
Washington, DC 20001
202-724-5622
www.dcoa.dc.gov

Florida

Florida Department of Elder Affairs
4040 Esplanade Way, Ste. 315
Tallahassee, FL 32399-7000
850-414-2000
http://elderaffairs.state.fl.us/

Georgia

Georgia Division of Aging Services
Two Peachtree St. NW, Ste. 36-385
Atlanta, GA 30303-3142
404-657-5258
www2.state.ga.us/departments/dhr/aging.html

Hawaii

Hawaii Executive Office on Aging
No. 1 Capitol District
250 S. Hotel St., Room 109
Honolulu, HI 96813-2831
808-586-0100
www2.state.hi.us/eoa

Idaho

Idaho Commission on Aging
3380 Americana Terr., Ste. 120
Boise, ID 83720-0007
208-334-3833
www.state.id.us/icoa

Illinois

Illinois Dept. on Aging
421 E. Capitol Ave., Ste. 100
Springfield, IL 62701
217-785-3356; 800-252-8966 (in IL only)
www.state.il.us/aging

Indiana

Indiana Family & Social Services Administration
10 W. Market St., Ste. 600
Indianapolis, IN 46204
317-233-2010
www.ai.org/fssa/elderly/index.html

Iowa

Iowa Department of Elder Affairs
Clemens Building
200 10th St., 3rd flr.
Des Moines, IA 50309-3609
515-242-3333
www.state.ia.us/elderaffairs/

Kansas

Kansas Dept. on Aging
New England Building
503 S. Kansas Ave.
Topeka, KS 66603-3404
785-296-4986; 800-432-3535 (in KS only)
www.k4s.org/kdoa

Kentucky

Kentucky Office of Aging Services
275 E. Main St., SC-D
Frankfort, KY 40621
502-564-6930
www.state.ky.us/aging
http://chs.state.ky.us/

Louisiana

Louisiana Governor's Office of Elderly Affairs
412 N. 4th St.
Baton Rouge, LA 70802
225-342-7100
www.laaging.org

Maine

Maine Bureau of Elder and Adult Services
11 State House Station
35 Anthony Ave.
Augusta, ME 04333
207-624-5335; 800-262-2232
www.state.me.us/dhs/beas

Maryland

Maryland Dept. of Aging
301 W. Preston St., 10th flr.
Baltimore, MD 21201
410-767-1116
www.mdoa.state.md.us

Massachusetts

Massachusetts Executive Office of Elder Affairs
The McCormack Building
One Ashburton Pl., 5th flr.
Boston, MA 02108
617-727-7750; 800-882-2003 (in MA only)
www.state.ma.us/elder

Michigan

Michigan Office of Services to the Aging
Ottawa Building, 3rd flr.
611 W. Ottawa
PO Box 30676
Lansing, MI 48909-8176
517-373-8230
www.miseniors.net

Minnesota

Minnesota Board on Aging
444 Lafayette Rd. North
St. Paul, MN 55155-3843
651-296-2770 or 800-882-6262
www.mnaging.org

Mississippi

Mississippi Division of Aging and Adult Services
750 N. State St.
Jackson, MS 39202
601-359-4925
www.mdhs.state.ms.us

Missouri

Missouri Department of Health and Senior Services
615 Howerton Ct.
PO Box 1337
Jefferson City, MO 65102
573-751-3082
www.dss.state.mo.us/da/da.htm

Safety for Older Consumers: Home Safety Checklist.
Source: US Consumer Product Safety Commission, Washington, DC 20207.
www.cpsc.gov

Helping Children and Teens Understand Alzheimer's Disease.
Parents' guide to questions children may ask about Alzheimer's. Free.
Source: Alzheimer's Association, 800-272-3900.
www.alz.org

Montana

Montana Senior and Long-Term Care Division
111 N. Sanders, Room 210
Helena, MT 59604
406-444-4077
800-332-2272 (in MT only)
www.dphhs.state.mt.us/sltc

Nebraska

Nebraska Division of Aging Services
PO Box 95044
Lincoln, NE 68509-5044
402-471-3121; 800-942-7830 (in NE only)
www.hhs.state.ne.us/ags/agsindex.htm

Nevada

Nevada Division for Aging Services
3100 W. Sahara Ave.
Suite 103
Las Vegas, NV 89102
702-486-3545
www.nvaging.net

New Hampshire

New Hampshire Division of Elderly Services
129 Pleasant St.
Concord, NH 03301
603-271-4688; 800-852-3345 (in NH only)
www.dhhs.state.nh.us

New Jersey

New Jersey Division of Senior Affairs
PO Box 807
Trenton, NJ 08625-0807
609-588-3141; 800-792-8820 (in NJ only)
www.state.nj.us/health/senior/sraffair.htm

New Mexico

New Mexico State Agency on Aging
228 E. Palace Ave.
Santa Fe, NM 87501
505-827-7640; 800-432-2080 (in NM only)
www.nmaging.state.nm.us

New York

New York Office for the Aging
Agency Building #2, Empire State Plaza
Albany, NY 12223
518-474-5731; 800-342-9871 (in NY only)
www.aging.state.ny.us
Elderly Prescription Insurance Coverage
(EPIC) Hotline: 800-332-3742

North Carolina

North Carolina Division of Aging
2101 Mail Service Center
Raleigh, NC 27699-2101
919-733-3983
www.dhhs.state.nc.us/aging

North Dakota

North Dakota Aging Services Division
600 S. 2nd St., Ste. 1C
Bismarck, ND 58504-5729
701-328-8910; 800-451-8693 (in ND only)
http://lnotes.state.nd.us/dhs/dhsweb.nsf/
servicepages/agingservices

Ohio

Ohio Department of Aging
50 W. Broad St., 9th flr.
Columbus, OH 43215-3363
614-466-5500
www.state.oh.us/age

Oklahoma

Oklahoma Aging Services Division
312 N.E. 28th St.
PO Box 25352
Oklahoma City, OK 73125
405-521-2281
www.okdhs.org/aging

Oregon

Oregon Senior & Disabled Services Division
500 Summer St. NE, E02
Salem, OR 97301-1073
503-945-5811; 800-282-8096 (in OR only)
www.sdsd.hr.state.or.us

Pacific Islands-Agana

Guam Division of Senior Citizens
PO Box 2816
Agana, GU 96910
(011) 671-475-0263

Pennsylvania

Pennsylvania Department of Aging
555 Walnut St., 5th flr.
Harrisburg, PA 17101-1919
717-783-1550
www.aging.state.pa.us

Puerto Rico

Governor's Office for Elderly Affairs
Call Box 50063
Old San Juan Station, PR 00902
787-721-4560

Rhode Island

Rhode Island Dept. of Elderly Affairs
160 Pine St.
Providence, RI 02903
401-222-2858
www.dea.state.ri.us

South Carolina

South Carolina Bureau of Aging Services
PO Box 8206
Columbia, SC 29202-8206
803-898-2500
800-868-9095 (in SC only)
www.dhhs.state.sc.us/offices/
long_term_care/ltcindex.htm

South Dakota

Department of Social Services Adult Services & Aging
700 Governor Dr.
Pierre, SD 57501-2291
605-773-3656
www.state.sd.us/social/asa

Tennessee

Tennessee Commission on Aging & Disability
500 Deaderick St., 9th flr.
Nashville, TN 37243-0860
615-741-2056
www.state.tn.us/comaging

Texas

Texas Department on Aging
4900 N. Lamar, 4th flr.
PO Box 12786
Austin, TX 78711
512-424-6840
www.tdoa.state.tx.us

Utah

Utah Division of Aging and Adult Services
120 North 200 West, Room 401
Salt Lake City, UT 84103
801-538-3910
www.hsdaas.state.ut.us

Vermont

Vermont Dept. of Aging and Disabilities
Osgood II Building
103 S. Main St.
Waterbury, VT 05671-2303
802-241-2186
www.dad.state.vt.us

Virginia

Virginia Department for the Aging
1600 Forest Ave., Ste. 102
Richmond, VA 23229
804-662-9333
800-552-3402 (nationwide)
www.aging.state.va.us

For Older Adults.
Playing cards with enlarged numbers...pill alarms...other products.
Source: On the Web at www.maturemart.com.

Don't Let a Fall Be Your Last Trip. How to make your home safe. Medical and personal risk factors.
Source: American Academy of Orthopaedic Surgeons, *Attn:* Falls, PO Box 1998, Des Plaines, IL 60017. Include a business-sized SASE or 800-824-BONES.
www.aos.org

Washington
Washington Aging & Adult Services Administration
PO Box 45600
Olympia, WA 98504-5600
360-725-2300
www.aasa.dshs.wa.gov

West Virginia
West Virginia Bureau of Senior Services
Holly Grove-Bldg. #10
1900 Kanawha Blvd. E
Charleston, WV 25305-0160
304-558-3317
www.state.wv.us/seniorservices

Wisconsin
Wisconsin Bureau of Aging
One W. Wilson St., Room 450
Madison, WI 53707
608-266-2536
www.dhfs.state.wi.us/aging

Wyoming
Wyoming Department of Health Division on Aging
6101 Yellowstone Rd.
Rm. 259B
Cheyenne, WY 82002
307-777-7986; 800-442-2766 (in WY only)
www.wyaging@state.wy.us

State
Pharmaceutical
Programs

State Pharmaceutical Programs

If you are a senior living on a fixed income in one of the following 11 states and you do not have Medicare or private insurance, you could be getting all of your prescription drugs free or for as little as a dollar or two. All you do is make a phone call to your state's office at the number listed. If you live in a state not listed here, check with your state's Office of the Aging (listed in the previous chapter). Also check out the "Directory of Free Prescription-Drug Programs," which follows this section.

Connecticut

CONN PACE Program
PO Box 5011
Hartford, CT 06102
860-832-9265; 800-423-5026 (in CT only)

• Must be state resident for at least six months.

• Must be 65 or older, or receive Social Security Disability.

• Income must not exceed $15,100 (single) or $18,100 (married).

• No Medicaid or private insurance that covers medications.

• Participants pay an annual fee of $25 to register, and $12 for each prescription. Generic drugs must be used wherever available unless physician indicates "brand drug only."

Delaware

Wilmington County
Nemours Health Clinic Program
1801 Rockland Rd.
Wilmington, DE 19803
302-651-4400; 800-292-9538 (in DE only)

In Kent and Sussex Counties:

Nemours Health Clinic Program
915 N. Dupont Blvd., Ste. 104
Milford, DE 19963
302-424-5420; 800-763-9326 (in DE only)

• Must be Delaware resident.

• Must be 65 or older.

• Cannot earn more than $12,500 if single, $17,125 if married.

This privately funded program covers four areas of health needs: dental, eye, hearing and medicines. In the Kent and Sussex offices, the coverage is for eye and hearing problems only.

Illinois

Illinois Department of Revenue Pharmaceutical Assistance Program
PO Box 19022
Springfield, IL 62794
217-524-0084, ext. 32347
www.iltax.com

• Must be a resident of Illinois.

• Must be 65 or older, or must be over 16 and totally disabled, or must be a widow or widower who turned 63 before spouse's death.

• Income of $21,218 for one-person household; $28,480 for two-person household; $35,740 for three-person household.

• Must purchase a Pharmaceutical Assistance card which costs either $5 or $25 a year, depending on income.

• Must use a generic brand drug where available unless willing to pay the difference.

• Covers medications for heart, blood pressure, diabetes and arthritis.

• Web site for up-to-date information: www.revenue.state.il.us, then click on "Circuit Breaker."

Taking a Closer Look at Antioxidants.
Free.
Source: American Institute for Cancer Research, 800-843-8114. www.aicr.org

207

Maine

Maine Revenue & Services
24 State House Station
Augusta, ME 04333
207-626-8475
www.state.me.us/revenue

• Must be a Maine resident.

• Must be 62 or older, or if disabled, 19 or older.

• Income must not exceed $15,448 for an individual.

• Must not be eligible for Medicaid or private insurance benefits.

• Drug will cost $2 or 20% of the price allowed by the Department of Human Services, whichever is greater.

Maryland

Maryland Pharmacy Assistance Program
PO Box 386
Baltimore, MD 21203
410-767-5397; 800-492-1974 (in MD only)

• Must be a Maryland resident.

• Program is for anyone in the state who cannot afford his or her medications.

• Call for income requirements.

Michigan

Elder Prescription Insurance Coverage (EPIC)
PO Box 27586
Richmond, VA 23261
866-747-5844
www.miepic.com

• Must be a resident of Michigan.

• Must be 65 or older.

• Must earn no more than 150% of the federal poverty guidelines.

• Must spend 10% or more of monthly income on drugs, or 8%

if married.

Other programs for Michigan residents:

Medicare and Medicaid Assistance Program: 800-803-7174

Michigan Legal Hotline for Seniors: 800-347-5297

Michigan Dental Association dental program for seniors: 800-255-7543

New Jersey

Pharmaceutical Assistance to the Aged and Disabled (PAAD)
Special Benefit Programs
PO Box 715
Trenton, NJ 08625
609-588-7049; 800-792-9745 (in NJ only)

• Must be New Jersey resident and purchase the medications in the state.

• Must be 65 or older; if on Social Security disability, may be as young as 18.

• Must earn no more than $19,238 if single, or $23,589 if married.

• Copay of $5 per prescription. PAAD will collect payments on your behalf from any insurance or other program you may have that covers prescription drugs.

• Senior Gold program benefits for those who earn up to $10,000 over the income limit. Call for details.

New York

New York State Elderly Pharmaceutical Insurance Coverage (EPIC)
PO Box 15018
Albany, NY 12212
518-452-3773; 800-332-3742
www.health.state.ny.us/nysdoh/epic/faq.htm

• Must be New York State resident.

• Must be 65 or older.

• Income must not exceed $35,000 if single, or $50,000 if married.

• Must not be eligible for Medicaid benefits.

• There are two EPIC plans. Applicants qualify right away by paying an annual fee that will range from $8 to $300, depending on income. There is also the EPIC Deductible Plan, where participant pays no fee but pays full price for the medications until deductible amount starting at $530 to $650 is reached. As income increases, so does deductible, up to $1,715.

Pennsylvania

Pennsylvania Department of Aging Pharmaceutical Assistance Contract for the Elderly (PACE)
555 Walnut St., 5th flr.
Harrisburg, PA 17101-1919
717-787-7313; 800-225-7223 (in PA only)
www.aging.state.pa.us

• Must be a state resident for at least 90 days and purchase the medications in the state.

• Must be 65 or older.

• Income cannot exceed $14,000 if single, or $17,200 if married.

• Copayment $15; or $8 for generic drugs.

• There is also the PACE NET program which allows you to earn more and still qualify. With that program there is a $500 prescription deductible each year.

Rhode Island

Rhode Island Pharmaceutical Assistance to the Elderly (RIPAE)
Rhode Island Department of Elderly Affairs
160 Pine St.
Providence, RI 02903
401-222-2880
www.dea.state.ri.us

• Must be a Rhode Island resident.

• Must be 65 or older.

• Must have no other prescription drug coverage.

• Income must not exceed $35,000 if single, or $40,000 if married.

• Copay 60%, 30% or 15%, depending on income level.

• Program covers drugs needed for the following illnesses: high blood pressure, heart disease, cholesterol, asthma, cancer, Parkinson's, glaucoma, diabetes, Alzheimer's, circulatory insufficiency, chronic respiratory disease, urinary incontinence and depression.

Vermont

**VSCRIPT Program
State Pharmaceutical Assistance Program for Elderly & Disabled**
103 S. Main St.
Waterbury, VT 05671
802-241-2880; 800-250-8427 (in VT only)
www.dsw.state.vt.us

• Must be a Vermont resident.

• Must be 65 or older.

• Income cannot exceed $1,253 per month if single.

• Must not be in a health insurance plan that pays all or part of your prescription drugs.

• Copay of $1 for drugs costing up to $30, and $2 for drugs costing over $30.

• Call for details on other programs.

First Aid Health & Wellness Direct: Catalog of first-aid supplies...biosafety training and kits... eyewear/hearing protection.
Source: Lab Safety Supply, Inc., PO Box 1368, Janesville, WI 53547. 800-356-0783. www.labsafety.com

Directory of Free Prescription-Drug Programs

Free Prescription-Drug Programs

It is a little known fact that the pharmaceutical industry has had a long tradition of providing prescription medicines free of charge to people who might not otherwise be able to afford the medicines they need. This directory lists the drug companies with programs that provide prescription medicine for such people. The programs are listed alphabetically by company. Check with the individual manufacturer for the specific requirements to qualify for their free prescription-drug program.

Common Questions

Q. I need medication but cannot afford to pay for it. Why hasn't my doctor told me about these programs?

A. Believe it or not, even many doctors themselves don't know about these programs until they are brought to the doctor's attention.

Q. What are the steps I should take if I need a medication and can't afford it?

A. First, find out from your doctor the name of the drug you need and the manufacturer. Next, go through this directory and find the listing for the manufacturer. If the medication you need is listed as one that the company offers free for needy patients, have your physician contact the company and request the forms necessary to enroll you in the program. As a general rule, the application for free medication must be filled out and submitted by your doctor.

Q. Who determines whether a medication is covered?

A. The individual pharmaceutical company determines which drugs are covered.

Q. Who is eligible for the program?

A. Once again, each company makes the determination as to who is eligible for its program. Often the company will rely on the doctor's opinion as to whether you are needy enough to qualify for free medication.

If you do not see a particular drug company listed here, that does not mean the company doesn't have a program that covers the medicine you need. For telephone numbers of companies not listed here, ask your doctor to consult a *Physician's Desk Reference* (PDR).

Abbott Laboratories

Contact:
Patient Assistance Program
Abbott Laboratories
200 Abbott Park Rd., D31C, J23
Abbott Park, IL 60064
800-222-6885, Option 1

Products Covered by Program: Isoptin® SR, Mavik, Rythmol®, Synthroid® Tablets, Tarka.

Other Information: Physician must submit documentation proving patient's indigence to the company. A maximum of three-month's supply will be shipped on any one request.

Alza Pharmaceuticals

Contact:

Indigent Patient Assistance Program
c/o Documedics
1250 Bayhill Dr., Ste. 300
San Bruno, CA 94066
800-577-3788

Products Covered by Program: Bicitra, Concerta, Ditropan, Ditropan XL, Elmiron, Flexeril, Mycelex, Neutra-Phos, Neutra-

Polycystic Kidney Disease. Explains this hereditary illness in which cysts form in the body's organs, particularly the kidneys. Symptoms… treatments.
Source: National Kidney Foundation, 30 E. 33rd St., New York, NY 10016. 800-622-9010. www.kidney.org

Understanding Acute Low Back Problems. When to see a doctor… medication, spinal manipulation, massage and other treatments… bed rest versus exercise. *Source:* Agency for Healthcare Research and Quality. Publication online at www.ahrq.gov

Phos-K, OlyCitra Crystal, PolyCitra, PolyCitra Crystal, PolyCitra-K, PolyCitra LC, Progestasert, Testoderm, Urispas.

Other Information: Eligibility is based on patient's income level and insurance status. Physician must request the application from Alza.

American Pharmaceutical Partners

Contact:
NebuPent® Indigent Patient Program
American Pharmaceutical Partners
1101 Perimeter Dr., Ste. 300
Schaumberg, IL 60173
888-391-6300

Product Covered by Program: NebuPent®.

Other Information: This program is designed to provide NebuPent® to AIDS patients who would not otherwise be able to afford this treatment. All questions can be directed to the Indigent Patient Coordinator at the toll-free number above.

Amgen, Inc.
Amgen SAFETY NET Program for EPOGEN®

Contact:
PO Box 13185
La Jolla, CA 92039
800-272-9376. www.amgen.com

Product Covered by Program: EPOGEN®.

 Other Information: This program is for dialysis patients who are uninsured or underinsured and is based on patient's income level. Phone-in or written applications are acceptable. A patient needs a doctor or other medical sponsor.

Amgen SAFETY NET® Program for Neupogen®

Contact:
800-272-9376

Product Covered by Program: Neupogen® (Filgrastim).

Other Information: For medically indigent patients with cancer or HIV. To enroll a patient, provider should call the number listed here.

Astra U.S.A., Inc.
Foscavir® Assistance and Information on Reimbursement (F.A.I.R.)

Contact:
 Parexel
5870 Trinity Pkwy., Ste. 600
Centreville, VA 20120
800-488-FAIR (or 800-488-3247)
703-310-2526 (fax)

Product Covered by Program: Foscavir® Injection.

Other Information: If the patient is not covered by private insurance or public coverage and has an income below a level selected by the company, medication will be provided. Patient does not have to be poor, but would suffer financial hardship if purchased the drug at retail cost. The company determines eligibility based on income information provided by the physician.

AstraZeneca Pharmaceuticals LP

 Contact:
AstraZeneca Foundation
Patient Assistance Program
1800 Concord Pike
PO Box 15437
Wilmington, DE 19850-5437
800-424-3727

Products Covered by Program: Accolate®, Arimidex®, Atacand®, Casodex®, Emla®, Emla Cream®, Lexxel®, Nexium™, Nolvadex®,

Plendil®, Prilosec®, Pulmicort Respules™, Seroquel®, Sorbitrate®, Sular™, Tenoretic®, Tenormin®, Tonocard®, Toprol-XL®, Zestoretic®, Zestril®,Zoladex®, Zomig™.

Other Information: Health care provider must apply on behalf of the patient who has a demonstrated medical need and a financial hardship that would prevent the patient from getting the prescription filled. Physician should make contact. An application will be sent to the physician's office for signature. Once approved, medication will be sent to physician's office in two to four weeks.

Eligibility is determined by the Foundation based on income level/assets and absence of outpatient private insurance, third-party coverage or participation in a public program.

Aventis Pasteur
Indigent Patient Program

Contact:
Customer Account Management
Aventis Pasteur
Discovery Dr.
Swiftwater, PA 18370-0187
800-822-2463; 570-839-0940 (fax)

Products Covered by Program: Imogam® Rabies-HT; Imovax® Rabies, rabies vaccine; Thera-Cys® BCG live intravesical (*Note:* Imovax® and Imogam® Rabies-HT are provided on a post-exposure basis.)

Other Information: Patient must be identified as indigent, uninsured and ineligible for Medicare or Medicaid. Physician must waive all fees and certify that the product will not be sold, traded or used for any other purpose than to treat the patient. Physician needs to specify the quantity of Imogam® Rabies-HT needed for patient (in ml), as well as the number of doses of Imovax® Rabies needed.

Bayer Corporation Pharmaceutical Division

Contact:
Bayer Indigent Patient Program
PO Box 29209
Phoenix, AZ 85038-9209
800-998-9180

Products Covered by Program: Most Bayer pharmaceutical prescription medications used as recommended in prescribing information.

Other Information: Patient must be a US resident, not covered by insurance and have an income below the federal poverty-level guidelines. Physician must monitor medication usage throughout the therapy. Patient/physician can qualify over the phone, with approval or denial given immediately.

Biogen, Inc.
Contact:
The Avonex Support Line℠
800-456-2255

Product Covered by Program: Avonex®.

Other Information: Eligibility is based on patient's insurance status and income.

Boehringer Ingelheim Pharmaceuticals, Inc.

Contact:
Boehringer Ingelheim Pharmaceuticals, Inc. (BIPI) Patient Assistance Program
PO Box 66555
St. Louis, MO 63166
800-556-8317 (for information and form)

Moving Toward a Plant-Based Diet: Menus and Recipes for Cancer Prevention.
Source: American Institute for Cancer Research, Dept. PBD, PO Box 97167, Washington, DC 20090. www.aicr.org

What You Need to Know About Multiple Myeloma— cancer of the white blood cells.
Source: National Cancer Institute, 800-422-6237. www.cancer.gov

Products Covered by Program: Aggrenox®, Atrovent®, Atrovent Nasal, Cafcit, Catapress-TTS, Combivent®, Flomax®, Micardis®, Mobic, Viramune.

Other Information: Patient must be a US citizen who meets established financial criteria and who is ineligible for prescription assistance from public or private sources. A maximum three-month supply of medication will be supplied per request.

Ciba Pharmaceuticals
(See Novartis Pharmaceuticals)

META Pharmaceutical Services LLC
Contact:
Meta Pharmaceutical Services, LLP
The Aricept® Patient Assistance Program
1878 Arena Dr.
Hamilton, NJ 08610
800-226-2072

Product Covered by Program: Aricept®.

Other Information: This program is for US residents with no insurance or other coverage and whose income falls within predetermined guidelines. Patient must have been diagnosed by the physician as having mild or moderate dementia of the Alzheimer's type.

Elan Pharmaceutical
Contact:
Indigent Patient Program
Elan Pharmaceutical
45 Horse Hill Rd.
Cedar Knolls, NJ 07927
973-267-2670

Products Covered by Program: Midrin®, Skelaxin®.

Other Information: To qualify patient must have a net worth of less than $30,000 and no third-party insurance coverage. Physician must provide patient's financial information to the company along with a request for the medication on letterhead. Upon approval, a monthly supply of the medication will be sent to the physician's office.

Fujisawa U.S.A., Inc.
Contact:

Prograf™ Patient Assistance Program
Fujisawa Reimbursement Hotline
PO Box 221644
Chantilly, VA 20153
800-4-PROGRAF (or 800-477-6472)

Product Covered by Program: Prograf™ capsules.

Other Information: Please call the Fujisawa Reimbursement Hotline for an application or for information about eligibility. Once the patient's insurance and financial situation has been described, a member of the program staff can determine whether the patient is likely to qualify.

Genentech, Inc.
Contact:
Uninsured Patient Assistance Program
Genentech, Inc.
460 Pt. San Bruno Blvd.
South San Francisco, CA 94080
800-879-4747
650-225-1366 (fax)

Products Covered by Program: Activase®, Nutropin®, Nutropin AQ™, Protropin®, Rituxan™.

Other Information: An application must be submitted with patient's medical, financial and insurance information. To be eligible, patient must have an annual income of less than $30,000 for Activase®; others based on individual assessment. Patient must not be eligible for public or private insurance reimbursement. Medication will be sent to physician's office.

Weyth Genetics Institute
The Neumega® Access Program
Contact:
888-NEUMEGA, ext. 1 (or 888-638-6342, ext. 1)

Product Covered by Program: Neumega®.

Other Information: This program is for uninsured and underinsured patients with limited financial resources.

Genzyme Therapeutics
Ceredase®/Cerezyme® Access Program (CAP Program)
Contact:
CAP Program
Genzyme Therapeutics
One Kendall Sq.
Cambridge, MA 02139
800-745-4447, ext. 17634

Product Covered by Program: Ceredase®, Cerexyme®.

Other Information: Eligibility is based on financial and medical need. The patient must be uninsured and lack the financial means to purchase the drug. In order to maintain eligibility, patient is expected to continue to explore alternative funding options with the Genzyme Case Management Specialist.

Gilead Sciences, Inc.
Contact:
 Gilead Sciences Reimbursement Support and Assistance Program Services
800-226-2056
(9:00 a.m. to 5:30 p.m. EST)

Product Covered by Program: VISTIDE®, for the treatment of cytomegalovirus (CMV) retinitis in patients with AIDS.

Other Information: To determine eligibility, the patient or physician may request a Patient Assistance Program application and mail or fax the completed application to Gilead Sciences Support Services.

Glaxo Wellcome, Inc.
Contact:
Glaxo Wellcome, Inc.
Patient Assistance Program
PO Box 52185
Phoenix, AZ 85072
800-722-9294
www.glaxowellcome.com/pap

Program materials may also be ordered by health professionals through the Web site.

Products Covered by Program: All marketed Glaxo Wellcome prescription products.

 Other Information: Glaxo Wellcome is dedicated to ensuring that no one is denied access to prescription drugs because of an inability to pay. This program is designed for financially disadvantaged patients who do not qualify for or have drug benefits through private or government-funded programs. Income eligibility is based on multiples of the poverty level, which is then adjusted for household size. The program is available only to patients treated in an outpatient setting.

About Ostomy—the surgical procedure that creates an opening in the abdomen to allow waste to pass through.
Source: United Ostomy Association, 19772 MacArthur Blvd., Ste. 200, Irvine, CA 92612-2405. 800-826-0826. www.uoa.org

217

Digital Disorders and Treatments. Getting help for hammertoes, bone spurs and curled toes. *Source:* American College of Foot and Ankle Surgeons, 515 Busse Hwy., Park Ridge, IL 60068-3150. 888-843-3338. www.acfas.org

Janssen Pharmaceutica

Contact:
Janssen Patient Assistance Program
PO Box 221857
Charlotte, NC 28222
800-652-6227, Option 2

Products Covered by Program: Janssen's medical prescription products including Duragesic®, Nizoral® Tablet, Sporanox®.

Other Information: Medications will be provided free of charge to patients who lack the financial resources and third-party insurance necessary to obtain treatment. Janssen requests that physicians not charge patients beyond insurance coverage for their professional services.

Janssen Cares

Contact:

The Risperdal Patient Assistance Program
PO Box 222098
Charlotte, NC 28222
800-652-6227, Option 1,
Monday through Friday
(9:00 a.m. to 5:00 p.m. EST)
704-357-0036 (fax)

Product Covered by Program: Risperdal®.

Other Information: Reimbursement specialists will determine eligibility based on medical criteria and financial resources. The Risperdal Reimbursement Support Program is designed to answer physicians' and patients' questions and solve problems related to Risperdal reimbursement as efficiently and quickly as possible.

Lederle Laboratories

Lederle PARTNERS IN PATIENT CARE™
Assistance Program
(see Wyeth-Ayerst Laboratories Indigent Patient Program)

Eli Lilly and Company

Contact:
Lilly Cares Patient Assistance Program
Eli Lilly and Company
PO Box 230999
Centreville, VA 20120
800-545-6962

Products Covered by Program: Most Lilly prescription products, such as Axid, Evista, Prozac and insulins (but not controlled substances), are covered by this program. Gemzar® is covered under a separate program (see below).

Other Information: Patients must be US residents. Eligibility is determined on a case-by-case basis based on patient's inability to pay and lack of third-party drug payment assistance. Medications will be provided directly to the physician for dispensing to the patient. Application forms will be provided to the physician to complete and return. Subsequent requests require another prescription and restatement of medical and financial need.

Gemzar® Patient Assistance Program

Contact:
Gemzar® Reimbursement Hotline
888-4-GEMZAR (or 888-443-6927)

Product Covered by Program: Gemzar®.

Other Information: Applications for the program are available by calling the Gemzar Hotline. Applicants will be approved on the basis of low income and not having medical insurance and being ineligible for any programs with a drug benefit including Medicare and Medicaid and third-party coverage.

The Liposome Company, Inc.

Contact:
Reimbursement Program for ABELCET®
750 The City Dr., Ste. 210
Orange, CA 92868
800-345-2252

Product Covered by Program:
Abelcet®.

Other Information:
Eligibility for this program is based on the patient's financial need and lack of coverage by any third-party reimbursement program. The company will determine eligibility based on medical and financial information supplied by the hospital or physician. Application forms must be completed and signed by a physician.

McNeil Consumer Health Care

Contact:
Indigent Patient Program
Ortho-McNeil
PO Box 938
Somerville, NJ 08876
800-962-5357; 800-797-7737

Products Covered by Program:
Imodium®, Vermox®.

Other Information:
Doctor must provide a letter with patient's information with assurance that all other avenues have been explored. Delivery in four to six weeks.

Merck & Company, Inc.

Contact:
The Merck Patient Assistance Program Helpline
800-994-2111: Health care professionals with prescribing privileges may call.

Products Covered by Program:
Most Merck products are covered. Requests for vaccines and injectables are not accepted, with the exception of requests for anti-cancer injectable products.

Other Information: The Merck Patient Assistance Program is designed to provide temporary assistance to patients who truly are unable to afford prescription medications and have no access to any insurance coverage. Eligibility is determined on a case-by-case basis on receipt of a completed application signed by both the physician and the patient and accompanied by a prescription. Once the application is approved, a three-month supply of medication will be sent to the physician for distribution to the patient.

SUPPORT™

Reimbursement Support and Patient Assistance Services for Crixivan®

Contact:
800-850-3430: Health care professionals or patients may call.
www.crixivan.com

Product Covered by Program:
Crixivan®.

Novartis Pharmaceuticals

Contact:
Novartis Pharmaceuticals
Patient Assistance Program
PO Box 8609
Somerville, NJ 08876
800-277-2254, Option 2
www.novartis.com

Products Covered by Program:
Certain single source and/or life-sustaining products. Controlled substances are not included.

Other Information: The Patient Assistance Program provides temporary assistance to patients who are experiencing financial

Your Child and Antibiotics. Bacterial versus viral infections ...how bacteria become drug-resistant...when antibiotics are needed—and when they aren't.
Source: American Academy of Pediatrics, on their Web site at www.aap.org.

The Immune System—How It Works.
Source: National Cancer Institute, Bldg. 31, Room 10A31, Bethesda, MD 20892.
800-4-CANCER (800-422-6237)
www.nci.nih.gov

hardship and have no prescription drug insurance. Patient must complete the application along with the physician and return it for evaluation. Processing takes 4 to 6 weeks.

Ortho Biotech, Inc.
Contact:
Documedics
1250 Bayhill Dr., Ste. 300
San Bruno, CA 94066
800-553-3851
www.procritline.com

Products Covered by Program:
Leustatin® Injection, Procrit® for non-dialysis use.

Other Information: A reimbursement specialist will determine eligibility for a patient who meets specific medical criteria and lacks the financial resources and third-party insurance necessary to obtain treatment. Ortho Biotech requests that physicians not charge FAP patients for professional services.

Ortho Dermatological
Contact:
Ortho-McNeil Patient Assistance Program
PO Box 938
Somerville, NJ 08876
800-797-7737
www.orthomcneil.com

Products Covered by Program:
Prescription products prescribed according to approved labeled indications and dosage regimen.

Other Information: To be eligible for this program, patient should not be eligible for other sources of drug coverage. Patient should also have applied for and been denied coverage

under public-sector programs. Patient's income level should be below poverty level and retail purchase would cause hardship. Health care practitioner should request an application form.

Parke-Davis
Division of Warner-Lambert Company
Contact:
The Parke-Davis Patient Assistance Program
908-725-1247

Products Covered by Program:
Accupril, Accuretic, Dilantin, Estrostet-FE, Femhrt, Lipitor, Loestrin, Neurontin, Zarontin.

Other Information: The physician should request an application from the company's sales representative. Patient must be deemed financially eligible based on company guidelines, the physician's certification and patient's lack of insurance coverage. Up to a three-month supply of medication will be given to the physician for dispensing.

Pfizer, Inc.
Contact:
Pfizer Prescription Assistance
PO Box 230970
Centreville, VA 20120
800-646-4455

Products Covered by Program:
Most Pfizer outpatient products with chronic indications are covered by this program. Diflucan® and Zithromax® are covered by a separate program (see below).

Other Information: Any patient whom a physician is treating as indigent is eligible. Patients musthave incomes below $12,000 (single) or $15,000 (family). Patient must not be eligible for third-party or Medicaid reimbursement for medications. No copayment or cost-sharing is required by the patient.

Specific forms are not required. The physician must write on letterhead to Pfizer, stating that the patient meets the income criteria and is uninsured for prescription drugs. A prescription for the needed medication must also be enclosed. It may take up to four weeks to receive the product.

Diflucan® and Zithromax® Patient Assistance Program

Contact:
800-869-9979

Products Covered by Program: Difucan®, Zithromax®.

Other Information: Patient must not have insurance or other third-party coverage including Medicaid and must not be eligible for a state's AIDS drug-assistance program. Patient must have an annual income of less than $25,000 without dependents or less than $40,000 with dependents. Physician should call the program and explain the patient's situation to the Patient Assistance Specialist. The specialist will then send a short qualifying form which requests insurance status, income information and the amount of Diflucan® or Zithromax® the patient will need. Upon receipt of the completed form, the specialist will make a determination of eligibility on the same day.

Sharing the Care

Contact:
Pfizer, Inc.
PO Box 6057
East Brunswick, NJ 08816
800-984-1500

Products Covered by Program: Certain Pfizer single-source products.

Other Information: The program, a joint effort of Pfizer, the National Governors' Association and the National Association of Community Health Centers, works solely through community, migrant and homeless health centers funded under Section 330 of the Public Health Service Act and that have an in-house pharmacy. The program includes the participation of more than 340 health centers throughout the US. To be eligible, the patient must be registered at a participating health center, must not be covered by any private insurance or public assistance covering pharmaceuticals, must not be enrolled in Medicaid and must have a family income that is equal to or below the federal poverty level.

A Participant in the Arkansas Health Care Access Program

Contact:

Arkansas Health Care Access Program
P.O. Box 56248
Little Rock, AR 72215
501-221-30335
www.ahcaf@aristotle.net

Products Covered by Program: Most Pfizer prescription products are covered.

Other Information: Must be an Arkansas resident to qualify. Eligible individuals are certified by the Arkansas Local County Department of Human Services as being Arkansas residents below the poverty level who do

Pain Control After Surgery: A Patient's Guide. Risks and benefits of various types of treatments.
Source: Agency for Health Care Research and Quality. Online at www.ahrq.gov.

What You Need to Know About Balance and Falls. Exercises… making your home safer. Free.

Source: American Physical Therapy Association, 1111 N. Fairfax St., Alexandria, VA 22314. Include a business-sized SASE. Or call 800-999-2782. www.apta.org

not have third-party insurance coverage for medications, including Medicaid and Medicare. No copayment is required. Physician must waive fee for the initial visit. This program does not apply to individuals during hospital inpatient stays.

A Participant in the Kentucky Physicians Care Program

Contact:
Health Kentucky, Inc.
12700 Shelbyville Rd., Ste. 1000
Louisville, KY 40243
502-254-4214, 502-254-5117 (fax)

Products Covered by Program:
Most Pfizer, Abbott, Johnson & Johnson, Novo Nordisk, Parke-Davis and Pfizer prescription products are covered.

Other Information: Must be a Kentucky resident to qualify. Patient must be certified by the Kentucky Cabinet for Human Resources as Kentuckians below the federal poverty standards without third-party health insurance coverage. No copayment is required from the patient.

A Participant in Commun-I-Care

Contact:
Commun-I-Care
PO Box 186
Columbia, SC 29202
803-933-9183, 803-254-0892 (fax)
www.commun-i-care.org

Products Covered by Program:
Most Pfizer and many other prescription products are covered.

Other Information: Eligible individuals must be South Carolina residents. Patients are first certified by Commun-I-

Care as below the federal poverty line and not covered by any government entitlement programs. No copayment is required from the patient. Physician must waive fee.

Proctor & Gamble Pharmaceuticals, Inc.

Contact:
Proctor & Gamble Pharmaceuticals, Inc.
Patient Assistance Program
800-830-9049

Products Covered by Program:
Actonel, Asacol, Dantrium Capsules, Didronel, Macrobid, Macrodantin.

Other Information: The company relies on the physician's assessment of patient's need to determine eligibility. To qualify, patients should not have insurance coverage for prescription medicines or Medicaid reimbursement. The program is intended for patients who fall below the federal poverty level and have no other means of health care coverage. The amount of product supplied depends on the diagnosis and need, but generally a one-month supply is provided for chronic medication. Refills require a new prescription and application form from the physician. Medication is sent to the physician who provides it to the patient.

Roche Laboratories, Inc.
A Division of Hoffman-La Roche, Inc.

Contact:
Roche Medical Needs Program
Roche Laboratories, Inc.
800-285-4484

Products Covered by Program:
Roche product line, except Lariam, Romazicon, Toradol and Versed.

Other Information: This program is designed for patients who are unable to afford the purchase of medication and who have no third-party medication coverage. It is for individual out-patients and is offered through physicians. It is not intended for clinics, hospitals or other institutions. Applications are provided only to licensed practitioners and a new application must be completed for refills. Up to a three-month supply of the medication will be sent directly to the physician within two to three weeks of acceptance to the program.

Roche Medical Needs Program for CellCept®

Contact:
Roche Transplant Reimbursement Hotline
CellCept®
Medical Needs Program
PO Box 230547
Centreville, VA 20120
800-772-5790

Products Covered by Program: CellCept®.

Roche Medical Needs Program for Cytovene®, Cytovene®-IV, Fortovase™, HIVID® and Invirase®.

Contact:
Roche HIV Therapy Assistance Program
800-282-7780

Products Covered by Program: Cytovene®, Cytovene®-IV, Fortovase™, HIVID® and Invirase®. Cytovene products for use with HIV/AIDS patients.

Roche Medical Needs Program for Roferon®-A, Vesanoid®, Xeloda and FUDR

Contact:
Oncoline™/Hepline™ Reimbursement Hotline
800-443-6676

Products Covered by Program: Roferon®-A, Vesanoid®, Xeloda, FUDR.

Boehringer Ingelheim Pharmaceutical Inc.

Contact:
c/o Patient Assistance Program
PO Box 66555
St. Louis, MO 63166
800-274-8651

Products Covered by Program: Oramorph SR® Tablets, Roxanol™, Roxicodone. Only come in one-month supply.

Other Information: Medication will be provided free of charge through the patient's pharmacist, provided the patient is uninsured and meets annual income requirements. The physician should call the toll-free number to discuss the patient's eligibility with a program representative.

Sandoz Synthelabo, Inc.
(See Novartis Pharmaceuticals)

Sanofi Synthelabo, Inc. Pharmaceuticals

Contact:
Sanofi Synthelabo, Inc.
Needy Patient Program
c/o Product Information Department
90 Park Ave.
New York, NY 10016
800-446-6267

Products Covered by Program: Aralen®, Danocrine®, Drisdol®, Hytakerol®, Mytelase®, NegGram®, pHisoHex®, Plaquenil®, Primaquine®, Skelid®, Primacor®.

Schizophrenia Fact Sheet. Symptoms… medications and their side effect…how family and friends can help.
Source: National Alliance for the Mentally Ill, Colonial Place Three, 2107 Wilson Blvd., Ste. 300, Arlington, VA 22201. 800-950-NAMI (6264). www.nami.org

Lyme Disease: The Facts, The Challenge.
Symptoms…diagnosis
…treatment…
prevention.
Source: National Institute
of Allergy and Infectious
Diseases, Bldg. 31,
Rm. 7A50-MS 2520
31 Center Dr.,
Bethesda, MD 20892.
301-496-5717
www. niaid.nih.gov

Other Information: Eligibility determined based on financial need on a case-by-case basis. Physician can obtain an application from the Sanofi Pharmaceuticals Product Information Department. Once the application is approved by the company, a three-month supply of the medication will be sent directly to the physician in approximately four to six weeks. Each physician is allowed to enroll six patients per year.

Schering-Plough Pharmaceuticals
Commitment to Care
1250 Bayhill Dr., Suite 300
San Bruno, CA 94066

Contact:
For Intron A, call: 800-521-7157
For Other Products: Schering Laboratories
Patient Assistance Program
PO Box 52122
Phoenix, AZ 85072
800-656-9485

Products Covered by Program: Most Schering-Plough prescription drugs.

Other Information: This program is designed to help patients who are truly in need, who are not eligible for private or public insurance reimbursement and cannot afford treatment. Physician and patient complete an application form which will be reviewed on a case-by-case basis.

Pharmacia
Contact:
Pharmacia Patients in Need® Program
PO Box 52059
Phoenix, AZ 85072
800-242-7014

Products Covered by Program: Antihypertensives: Arthrote®, Celebrex; Antihypertensive/Anti-Anginal/ Antiarrhythmic: Covera-HS™; Prevention of NSAID-induced gastric ulcers: Cytotec®.

Other Information: The physician is the sole determinant of a patient's eligibility for this program based on the patient's medical and financial need. The guidelines suggest that the patient have a medical need for the Pharmacia Patients In Need® medication, does not qualify for third-party medication coverage and income falls below a suggested level.

Serono Laboratories, Inc.
Serostim® Program
Contact:
NORD Patient Assistance Program
PO Box 8923
New Fairfield, CT 06812
888-628-6673, 203-746-6896 (fax)
Products Covered by Program: Serostim™ for treatment of AIDS.

Sigma-Tau Pharmaceuticals, Inc.
Contact:
NORD/Sigma-Tau Carnitor®, Matulane Drug Assistance (CDA) Program
c/o NORD
PO Box 8923
New Fairfield, CT 06812
800-999-NORD
Products Covered by Program: Carnitor®, Matulane® and others.
Other Information: Usually a patient over the age of 18 may submit his/her own application. If the patient is a minor, a parent or guardian must submit the application. To be eligible, patient must be a US resident with a legal prescription for Carnitor® or

Matulane®. Patient must show financial need above and beyond any third-party insurance or family resources.

SmithKline Beecham Pharmaceuticals

Contact:
SmithKline Beecham
SKB Foundation
Access to Care Program
c/o Express Scripts/SDS
PO Box 2564
Maryland Heights, MD 63043
800-546-0420

Products Covered by Program:

Paxil® and most Smith-Kline Beecham out-patient prescription products are covered. Controlled substances and vaccines are not. Hycamtin is covered under a separate Access to Care program (see listing below).

Other Information: To be eligible, patient's annual household income must be less than $25,000. Patient must not have medical insurance or coverage under any private or government program that covers prescriptions. Physician must submit the application on an original (not photo-copied) SB Access to Care form supplied by the company. The physician and patient must certify that the program guidelines are being observed. Medication will be sent to the physician for dispensing.

The Oncology Access to Care Hotline

Contact:
800-699-3806 for physicians and patients.
Products Covered by Program:
Hycamtin.

3M Pharmaceuticals

Indigent Patient Pharmaceutical Program
Contact:
Drug Surveillance and Information
3M Pharmaceuticals
3M Center
Bldg. 275-6W-13
St. Paul, MN 55144
800-328-0255, 651-733-6068 (fax)
Products Covered by Program:
Most drug products sold by 3M Pharmaceuticals in the US.

Other Information: This program is for patients whose financial and insurance circumstances prevent them from obtaining 3M Pharmaceuticals drug products considered neces-sary by their physicians. Consideration is on a case-by-case basis.

Wyeth-Ayerst Laboratories

Contact:
The Norplant Foundation Supply and Removal Program
PO Box 29240
Phoenix, AZ 85038
800-760-9030

Product Covered by Program:
Norplant® five-year contraceptive system.

Other Information: Eligibility is determined on a case-by-case basis and limited to individuals who cannot afford the product and who are ineligible for cover-age under private and public-sector programs. Enrollment by health care provider only.

Growing Up Healthy: Fat, Cholesterol and More. Strategies for bringing up healthy children through proper nutrition and exercise.
Source: American Academy of Pediatrics, on their Web site at www.aap.org. 847-434-4000.

Managing Headaches.
Learn how you can manage headaches and what you can do to prevent them.
Source: Wellness Councils of America, 402-827-3590. www.welcoa.org

Wyeth-Ayerst
Patient Assistance Program
800-568-9938

Products Covered by Program:

Various products (not including schedule II, III or IV products). Injectibles and controlled products are not covered.

Other Information:

Limited to individuals, on a case-by-case basis, who have been identified by their physicians as indigent, meaning low or no income and not covered by any third-party agency.

A three-month supply of specific products is provided directly to the physician for dispensing to the patient. The patient's signature is required on the application form.

AIDS Drug Assistance Program (ADAP)

The AIDS Drug Assistance Program (ADAP) provides vital medications to low-income, uninsured or underinsured people with HIV and AIDS. Patients must meet eligibility requirements. For contact information for a particular state not listed below, go to www.aidsinfonyc.org/adap/index.html

California

Department of Health Services
PO Box 942732
Sacramento, CA 94234-7320
Office: (916) 323-9460

Colorado

Department of Public Health
4300 Cherry Creek Drive South
Denver, CO 80246
Office: (303) 692-2674

Connecticut

Department of Social Services
25 Sigourney St.
Hartford, CT 06106
Office: (860) 424-5152

District of Columbia

DC Department of Health
717 14th St., NW, Suite 600
Washington, DC 20005
Office: (202) 727-8826

Florida

Department of Health
4052 Bald Cypress Way, Bin A09
Tallahassee, FL 32399-1715
Office: (850) 245-4444, ext. 2544

Illinois

Illinois Department of Public Health
525 W. Jefferson St., 1st Floor
Springfield, IL 62761
Office: (217) 524-5983

Massachusetts

Department of Public Health
250 Washington St., 3rd Floor
Boston, MA 02108-4619
Office: (617) 624-5328

New Jersey

New Jersey Department of Health
PO Box 363
50 East State St.
Trenton, NJ 08625
Office: (609) 984-6328

New York

New York State Department of Health/ADAP
PO Box 2052, Empire Station
Albany, NY 12220
Office: (518) 459-1641

North Carolina

HIV/STD Prevention and Care Division of Epidemiology
PO Box 29601
Raleigh, NC 27626-0601
Office: (919) 715-3118

Ohio

Ohio Department of Health
246 N. High St., 6th Floor
Columbus, OH 43215
Office: (614) 728-6494

Pennsylvania

Department of Public Welfare
Room 119
PO Box 8021
Harrisburg, PA 17105
Office: (717) 772-6057

Texas

Department of Health
11200 West 49th St.
Austin, TX 78756
Office: (512) 490-2510

Virginia

Virginia Department of Health
PO Box 2448, Room 112
Richmond, VA 23218-2448
Office: (804) 225-4844

Managing Your Pain.
Exercise, heat, cold, massage, more.
Source: Arthritis Foundation, Box 7669, Atlanta 30357-0669. 800-283-7800. www.arthritis.org

Free Legal Services

Legal Services for You

If you have a legal problem and can't afford exorbitant attorney fees, you can get free legal assistance thanks to funding from the US government. To help you get the kind of legal help you need but cannot afford, Congress has given close to $300 million to The Legal Services Corporation. They in turn provide funds for 262 local legal services offices throughout the US. The funding is used to help more than 4 million low-income individuals in civil cases. To find out about the free legal services in your area, check the listings below or contact Legal Services Corporation directly.

Legal Services Corporation
750 First St. NE, 10th flr.
Washington, DC 20002
202-336-8800
www.lsc.gov

You can also get the information you need about local legal services programs in your area by visiting the Web site at www.lsc.gov.

In addition to the legal services funded by the federal government, there are hundreds of pro bono (in other words, free) programs staffed by attorneys who volunteer their time and services to ensure that you get the legal representation you deserve. The following is a listing of such programs. Simply call the program closest to your home for legal assistance.

Alabama

Alabama State Bar Volunteer Lawyers Program
PO Box 671
Montgomery, AL 36101
334-269-1515

Legal Services Corporation of Alabama
207 Montgomery St., Ste. 500
Montgomery, AL 36104
334-264-1471
www.alabamalegalservices.com

Legal Services of Metro Birmingham
1820 Seventh Ave. N
Birmingham, AL 35201
205-328-3540
www.lsmbi.com

Legal Services of North-Central Alabama
2000-C Vernon Dr.
Huntsville, AL 35805
256-536-9645
www.lsnca.org

Pro Bono Program
Mobile Bar Association
103 Dauphin St., Ste.712
Mobile, AL 36602-3221
334-438-1102; fax: 334-434-2479
e-mail: probono@mobilebar.com

Alaska

Alaska Legal Services Corporation
1016 W. Sixth Ave., Ste. 200
Anchorage, AK 99501-6206
907-276-6282
www.ptialaska.net/~aklegal

Arizona

Affordable Housing Law Program
Arizona Community Service Legal Assistance
111 W. Monroe, Ste. 1800
Phoenix, AZ 85003
602-340-7356

Arizona Center for Disability Law
3839 N. Third. St., Ste. 209
Phoenix, AZ 85012
602-274-6287
www.acdl.com

Community Legal Services
PO Box 21538
Phoenix, AZ 85036
602-258-3434; 800-852-9075

Financial Planner Interview: Checklist to help choose the right planner...tough questions to ask...types of services provided...etc.
Source: The National Association of Personal Financial Advisors, 888-333-6659.

How to Spot a Con Artist: Investing scams and how to avoid being a victim.

Source: North American Securities Administrators Association, Inc., 10 G St. NE, Ste. 710, Washington, DC 20002. 202-737-0900.

DNA-People's Legal Services
PO Box 306
Window Rock, AZ 86515
928-871-4151

 Papago Legal Services
PO Box 298
Sells, AZ 85634
520-383-2420

Southern Arizona Legal Aid
64 E. Broadway
Tucson, AZ 85701
520-623-9465

Arkansas

Arkansas Volunteer Lawyers for the Elderly (AVEL)
2020 W. Third St., Ste. 620
Little Rock, AR 72205
501-376-9263

Center for Arkansas Legal Services
303 W. Capitol Ave., Ste. 200
Little Rock, AR 72201
501-376-3423; 800-950-5817

Legal Aid of Arkansas
2126 E. Broadway
West Memphis, AR 72301
870-732-6370

Legal Aid of Arkansas
4083 N. Shiloh Dr., Ste. 3,
Fayetteville, AR 72703
501-442-0600

Western Arkansas Legal Services
901 S. 21st St.
Fort Smith, AR 72901
501-785-5211; 800-364-1134

California

Bay Area Legal Aid
2 W. Santa Clara St., 8th flr.
San Jose, CA 95113
408-283-3700
www.baylegal.org

California Indian Legal Services
510 16St., 4th Flr.
Oakland, CA 94612
510-835-0284
www.calindian.org

California Rural Legal Assistance
631 Howard St., Ste. 300
San Francisco, CA 94105
415-777-2752
www.crla.org

Central California Legal Services
In Fresno: 559-570-1200
In Merced: 209-723-5466
In Visalia: 559-733-8770
www.las.org

Contra Costa Legal Services Foundation
1017 MacDonald Ave.
PO Box 2289
Richmond, CA 94802-2289
510-233-9954

 Disability Rights Education and Defense Fund
2212 Sixth St.
Berkeley, CA 94710
510-644-2555
www.dredf.org

Greater Bakersfield Legal Assistance
615 California Ave.
Bakersfield, CA 93304
661-325-5943
www.gbla@lightspeed.net

Inland Counties Legal Services
1737 Atlanta Ave., Ste. H-2
Riverside, CA 92507
909-683-2555; 888-455-4257

Legal Aid Foundation of Long Beach
110 Pine Ave., Ste. 420
Long Beach, CA 90802
562-435-3501
www.lafla.org

Legal Aid Foundation of Los Angeles
1550 W. Eighth St.
Los Angeles, CA 90019
213-487-3320

Legal Aid of the North Bay
30 N. San Pedro Rd., Ste. 140
San Rafael, CA 94903
415-492-0230

Legal Aid Society of Alameda County
510 16 St., 4th flr.
Oakland, CA 94612
510-451-9261

Legal Aid Society of San Diego
110 S. Euclid Ave.
San Diego, CA 92114
619-262-5557

Legal Aid Society of San Mateo County
521 E. 5th Ave.
San Mateo, CA 94402
650-365-8411; 800-381-8898 (In CA)
www.legalaidsmc.org

Legal Services of Northern California, Inc.
515 12th St.
Sacramento, CA 95814
916-551-2150
www.lsnc.net

Legal Services Program for Pasedena and San Gabriel-Pomona Valley
243 E. Mission Blvd.
Pomona, CA 91766
909-620-5547

San Fernando Valley Neighborhood Legal Services
13327 Van Nuys Blvd.
Pacoima, CA 91331
818-896-5211

Colorado
Colorado Legal Services
1905 Sherman, Ste. 400
Denver, CO 80203
303-837-1313

Connecticut
Connecticut Bar Association Law Works for People
30 Bank St.
PO Box 350
New Britain, CT 06050
860-223-4400
www.ctbar.org

Greater Hartford Legal Assistance
80 Jefferson St.
Hartford, CT 06106
860-541-5000
www.ghla.org

New Haven Legal Assistance Association, Inc.
426 State St.,
New Haven, CT 06510-2018
203-946-4811; fax: 203-498-9271
e-mail: mail@nhlegal.org

Statewide Legal Services of Connecticut
425 Main St.
Middletown, CT 06457

Delaware
Delaware Volunteer Legal Services
PO Box 7306
Wilmington, DE 19803
302-478-8680
www.dvls.org

Legal Services Corporation of Delaware
100 W. 10th St., Ste. 203
Wilmington, DE 19801
302-575-0408

District of Columbia
American Association of Retired Persons
601 E St. NW
Building A, 4th flr.
Washington, DC 20049
202-434-2120
www.aarp.org

Archdiocesan Legal Network
Catholic Charities of Washington, DC
1221 Massachusetts Ave. NW
Washington, DC 20005
202-772-4398

DC Bar Public Services Activities Corporation
1250 H St. NW, 6th flr.
Washington, DC 20005
202-737-4700
www.dcbar.org

Decisions: The Wise Use of Credit. Guidelines to help you avoid financial problems with your credit cards.
Source: Consumer Credit Counseling Services of Michigan, 38505 Country Club Dr., Farmington Hills, MI 48331. 800-547-5005.

The Consumer's Independent Guide to Homeowner's Insurance.

Source: Independent Insurance Agents of America, PO Box 1528, Waldorf, MD 20604. 800-261-4422. www.iiaa.org.

Immigrant & Refugee Rights Project of Washington Lawyers' Committee for Civil Rights & Urban Affairs
11 Dupont Circle NW, Ste. 400
Washington, DC 20036
202-319-1000

Neighborhood Legal Services Program of the District of Columbia
701 Fourth St. NW
Washington, DC 20001

Florida

Bay Area Legal Services
Riverbrook Professional Center, 2nd flr.
829 W. Martin Luther King Jr. Blvd.
Tampa, FL 33603
813-232-1343
www.bals.org

Central Florida Legal Services
128-A Orange Ave.
Daytona Beach, FL 32114
904-255-6573
www.cfls.org

Florida Association for Community Action
6212 NW 43rd St., Ste. A
Gainesville, FL 32653
352-378-6517
www.facq.org

Florida Rural Legal Services
963 E. Memorial Blvd.
Lakeland, FL 33802
863-688-7376; 800-277-7680
www.frls.com

Greater Orlando Area Legal Services
1036 W. Amelia St.
Orlando, FL 32805
407-841-7777

Gulfcoast Legal Services
641 First St. S
St. Petersburg, FL 33701
727-821-0726; 800-230-5920

Jacksonville Area Legal Aid
126 W. Adams St.
Jacksonville, FL 32202
904-356-8371

Legal Aid Service of Broward County
609 SW First Ave.
Fort Lauderdale, FL 33301
954-765-8950

Legal Services of Greater Miami
3000 Biscayne Blvd., Ste. 500
Miami, FL 33137
305-576-0080

Legal Services of North Florida
2119 Delta Blvd.
Tallahassee, FL 32303
850-385-9007
www.lsnf.org

Northwest Florida Legal Services
PO Box 1551
Pensacola, FL 32591
850-432-2336

Seminole County Bar Association Legal Aid
115 Boston Ave., Ste. 2100
Altamonte Springs, FL 32701
407-834-1660

Three Rivers Legal Services
214 W. University Ave.
Gainesville, FL 32601
352-372-0519
www.trls.org

Withlacoochee Area Legal Services
222 SW Broadway St.
Ocala, FL 34474
352-629-0105

Georgia

Atlanta Legal Aid Society
151 Spring St. NW
Atlanta, GA 30303
404-524-5811

Georgia Legal Services Program
1100 Spring St., Ste. 200-A
Atlanta, GA 30309
404-206-5175; 800-498-9469
www.glsp.org

The Pro Bono Project of the State Bar of Georgia
The Hurt Building
50 Hurt Plaza
Atlanta, GA 30303
404-527-8762

Guam

Guam Legal Services Corporation
113 Bradley Pl.
Agana, GU 96910
011-671-477-9811

Hawaii

Legal Aid Society of Hawaii
924 Bethel St.
Honolulu, HI 96813
808-536-4302

Native Hawaiian Legal Corporation
1164 Bishop St., Ste. 1205
Honolulu, HI 96813
808-521-2302

Volunteer Legal Services
1040 Richards St., Ste. 301
Honolulu, HI 96813
808-528-7046

Idaho

Idaho Legal Aid Services
Contract Program
310 N. Fifth St.
PO Box 913
Boise, ID 83701
208-336-8980

Idaho Volunteer Lawyers Program
PO Box 895
Boise, ID 83701
208-334-4510

Illinois

Land of Lincoln Legal Assistance Foundation
2420 Bloomer Dr.
Alton, IL 62002
618-462-0036

Lawyers for the Creative Arts
213 W. Institute Pl., Ste. 401
Chicago, IL 60610
312-649-4111

Legal Assistance Foundation of Chicago
111 W. Jackson Blvd., 3rd flr.
Chicago, IL 60604
312-341-1070
www.lafchicago.org

Prairie State Legal Services
975 N. Main St.
Rockford, IL 61103
815-965-2134
www.pslegal.org

Indiana

Legal Services of Maumee Valley
203 W. Wayne St., Ste. 410
Fort Wayne, IN 46802
219-422-8070; 800-552-4884 (in IN)

Legal Services of Northwest Indiana
504 Broadway, Ste. 301
Gary, IN 46402
219-886-3161

Legal Services Organization of Indiana
Market Square Center, 18th flr.
151 N. Delaware St.
Indianapolis, IN 46204
317-631-9410; 800-869-0212

Legal Services Program of Northern Indiana
105 E. Jefferson Blvd., Ste. 600
South Bend, IN 46601
219-234-8121; 800-288-8121

Iowa

Iowa State Bar Association
Volunteer Lawyers Project
521 E. Locust, Ste. 302
Des Moines, IA 50309
515-244-8617

Legal Aid Society of Polk County
1111 Ninth St., Ste. 380
Des Moines, IA 50314
515-243-1193

Legal Services Corporation of Iowa
1111 Ninth St., Ste. 230
Des Moines, IA 50314
515-243-2151; 800-532-1275

Basic Questions About Credit Reports and Credit Reporting. Free.
Source: Experian Consumer Education, PO Box 1239, Allen, TX 75013.

Home Security Basics. How to prevent burglaries.

Source: Insurance Information Institute, Home Security, 110 William St., New York, NY 10038. Include a business-sized SASE or call 212-346-5500.

Kansas

Kansas Bar Association
PO Box 1037
Topeka, KS 66601
785-234-5696
www.ksbar.org

Kansas Legal Services
712 S. Kansas Ave., Ste. 200
Topeka, KS 66603-3808
785-233-2068
www.kls.org

Kentucky

Access to Justice Foundation
400 Old Vine St., Ste. 203
Lexington, KY 40507
859-255-9913
www.accesstojustice.org

Appalachian Research and Defense Fund of Kentucky
120 N. Front Ave.
Prestonsburg, KY 41653
800-556-3876

Central Kentucky Legal Services
PO Box 12947
Lexington, KY 40583-2947
800-928-4556

Kentucky Legal Aid
PO Box 1776
Bowling Green, KY 42102
866-452-9243
www.ctls.bowlinggreen.net

Legal Aid Society
425 W. Muhammad Ali Blvd.
Louisville, KY 40202
502-584-1254
www.laslou.org

Northern Kentucky Legal Aid Society
302 Greenup St.
Covington, KY 41011
859-431-8200

Louisiana

Arcadiana Legal Services
PO Box 4823
Lafayette, LA 70502
800-256-1175

Capital Area Legal Services
200 Third St.
Baton Rouge, LA 70802
800-256-1900
www.calscla.org

Eighth Coast Guard District Legal Office
Hale Boggs Federal Bldg., Room 1311
501 Magazine St.
New Orleans, LA 70130
504-589-6188

Kisatchie Legal Services
134 St. Denis St.
Natchitoches, LA 71457
800-960-9109
www.cp-tel.net/klsc

Legal Services of North Louisiana
720 Travis St.
Shreveport, LA 71101
800-826-9265

Louisiana Bar Association
Access to Justice Foundation
601 St. Charles Ave.
New Orleans, LA 70130
504-566-1600
www.lsba.org

New Orleans Legal Assistance Corporation
144 Elk Pl., Ste. 1000
New Orleans, LA 70112
504-529-1000
www.nolac.org

Southeast Louisiana Legal Services
PO Drawer 2867
Hammond, LA 70404
985-345-2130; 800-349-0886 (in LA)
www.selegal@charter.net

Maine

Pine Tree Legal Assistance
88 Federal St.
PO Box 547
Portland, ME 04112
207-774-4753
www.ptla.org

Volunteer Lawyers Project
88 Federal St.
Portland, ME 04112
207-774-4348; 800-442-4293

Maryland

Advocates for Children & Youth
School House Legal Services
1800 N. Charles St., Ste. 400
Baltimore, MD 21201
410-727-6352
www.mdlcbalto.org

Legal Aid Bureau
500 E. Lexington St.
Baltimore, MD 21202
410-539-5340

Massachusetts

American Civil Liberties Union of Massachusetts
99 Chauncy St., Ste. 310
Boston, MA 02111
617-482-3170
www.aclu-mass.org

Legal Services for Cape Cod and Islands
460 W. Main St.
Hyannis, MA 02601
508-775-7020; 800-742-4107 (in MA)
www.lscci.org

Massachusetts Justice Project
57 Suffolk St., Ste. 401
Holyoke, MA 01040
413-533-2660; 800-639-1209 (in MA)

Merrimack Valley Legal Services
35 John St., Ste. 302
Lowell, MA 01852
978-458-1465

New Center for Legal Advocacy
257 Union St.
New Bedford, MA 02740
508-996-8576; 800-244-9023

South Middlesex Legal Services
354 Waverly St.
Framingham, MA 01702
508-620-1830; 800-696-1501 (in MA)

Volunteer Lawyers Project of the Boston Bar Association
29 Temple Pl., 3rd flr.
Boston, MA 02111
617-423-0648
www.vlpnet.org

Michigan

Lakeshore Legal Services
Robert A. Verkuilen Bldg.
21885 Dunham Rd., Ste. 4
Clinton Township, MI 48036
810-469-5185

Legal Aid of Central Michigan
300 N. Washington Sq., Ste. 311
Lansing, MI 48933-1223
517-485-5418; 800-968-0044

Legal Services of Eastern Michigan
436 S. Saginaw St.
Flint, MI 48502
810-234-2621

Legal Services of Northern Michigan
446 E. Mitchell St.
Petoskey, MI 49770
616-347-8115

Legal Services of Southeastern Michigan
420 N. Fourth Ave.
Ann Arbor, MI 48104
734-665-6181

Legal Services Organization of Southcentral Michigan
70 E. Michigan Ave., 1st flr.
Battle Creek, MI 49017
616-965-3951; 800-688-3951

Michigan Indian Legal Services
814 S. Garfield Ave., Ste. A
Traverse City, MI 49686
616-947-0122; 800-968-6877
www.mils.org

Oakland Livingston Legal Aid
35 W. Huron St., Ste. 500
Pontiac, MI 48342
248-569-9658; 888-783-8190;

Investment Swindles: How They Work and How to Avoid Them.
Source: National Futures Association, 200 W. Madison St., Ste. 1600, Chicago, IL 60606. 800-621-3570. www.nfa.futures.org

What Everyone Should Know About Title Insurance. Risks covered...title search... what to expect at closing...costs.
Source: Attorneys' Title Guaranty Fund, Inc., 800-252-0402.

State Bar of Michigan
Access to Justice
306 Townsend St.
Lansing, MI 48933
517-372-9030
www.michbar.org

Western Michigan Legal Services
400 Cornerstone Bldg.
89 Ionia Ave. NW
Grand Rapids, MI 49503
616-774-0672; 800-442-2777

Micronesia

Micronesian Legal Services Corporation
PO Box 269
Saipan, MP 96950-0269
011-670-234-6471

Minnesota

Anishinabe Legal Services
PO Box 157
Cass Lake, MN 56633
218-335-2223; 800-422-1335

Central Minnesota Legal Services
430 First Ave. N, Ste. 359
Minneapolis, MN 55401
612-332-8151

Judicare of Anoka County
1201 89th Ave. NE, Ste. 310
Blaine, MN 55434
763-783-4970

Legal Aid Service of Northeastern Minnesota
302 Ordean Bldg.
424 W. Superior St.
Duluth, MN 55802
218-726-4800; 800-622-7266
www.lasnem.org

Legal Services of Northwest Minnesota Corporation
PO Box 838
Moorhead, MN 56560-0838
218-233-8585; 800-450-8585
www.legalaid@lsnmlaw.org

Southern Minnesota Regional Legal Services
700 Minnesota Bldg.
46 E. Fourth St.
St. Paul, MN 55101-1112
651-228-9823

Volunteer Lawyers Network
612-752-6677

Mississippi

Central Southwest Mississippi Legal Services
414 South State St., 3rd flr.
Jackson, MS 39205
601-948-6752; 800-959-6752
www.mslegalservices.org

Mississippi Volunteer Lawyers Project
PO Box 2168
Jackson, MS 39225-2168
601-948-4476

North Mississippi Rural Legal Services
2134 W. Jackson Ave.
PO Box 767
Oxford, MS 38655-0767
662-234-8731

South Mississippi Legal Services Corporation
PO Box 1386
Biloxi, MS 39533
228-374-4160

Southeast Mississippi Legal Services Corporation
111 E. Front St.
Hattiesburg, MS 39401
601-545-2950

Southeast Mississippi Legal Services Corporation
2305 Fifth St., 2nd flr.
Meridian, MS 39302
601-693-5470

Missouri

Legal Aid of Western Missouri
1125 Grand Ave., Ste. 1900
Kansas City, MO 64106
816-474-6750
www.lawmo.org

Legal Services of Eastern Missouri
4232 Forest Park Ave.
St. Louis, MO 63108
314-534-4200; 800-444-0514
www.lsem@lsem.org

Legal Services of Southern Missouri
PO Box 135
Rolla, MO 65402
573-341-3655; 800-999-0249

**Mid-Missouri Legal Services
Corporation**
205 E. Forest Ave.
Columbia, MO 65203
573-442-0116; 800-568-4931

Southeast Missouri Legal Services
PO Box 349
Charleston, MO 63834
573-683-3783; 800-748-7456
www.lsosm.org

Montana

Montana Legal Services Association
801 N. Last Chance Gulch
Helena, MT 59601
406-442-9830; 800-666-6124
www.montanalegalservices.com

**State Bar of Montana Pro Bono
Project**
2442 First Ave. N
Billings, MT 59101
406-252-6351

Nebraska

Nebraska Legal Services
500 S. 18th St., 3rd flr.
Omaha, NE 68102
402-348-1069; 877-250-2016
www.nebls.com

Nebraska State Bar Association
Volunteer Lawyer Project
635 S. 14th St., Ste. 200
Lincoln, NE 68508
402-475-7091
www.nebar.com

Nevada

Nevada Legal Services
701 E. Bridger Ave., Ste. 101
Las Vegas, NV 89101
702-386-1070; 800-522-1070

New Hampshire

Legal Advice and Referral Center
PO Box 4147
Concord, NH 03302
603-224-5723; 800-639-5290 (in NH)

New Jersey

Bergen County Legal Services
61 Kansas St.
Hackensack, NJ 07601
201-487-2166

Cape-Atlantic Legal Services
26 S. Pennsylvania Ave.
Atlantic City, NJ 08401
609-348-4200; 800-870-7547

Essex-Newark Legal Services Project
Five Commerce St., 2nd flr.
Newark, NJ 07102
973-624-4500

**Hudson County Legal Services
Corporation**
574 Summit Ave., 2nd Fl.
Jersey City, NJ 07306
201-792-6363

**Hunterdon County Legal Service
Corporation**
82 Park Ave.
Flemington, NJ 08822
908-782-7979

Legal Aid Society of Mercer County
198 W. State St.
Trenton, NJ 08608
609-695-6249

**Family Talk
About Drinking.**
Sample parent/child
conversations. Free.
Source: Anheuser-Busch
Companies, Inc., 800-359-
8255...On the Web at
www.beeresponsible.com.

239

Helping Your Child Understand Money.
When to begin…setting goals…saving…investment issues…etc. Ask for Item #501. Free.
Source: MetLife Consumer Education Ctr., 800-638-5433.

Legal Aid Society of Morris County
PO Box 900
Morristown, NJ 07960
973-285-6911

Middlesex County Legal Services Corporation
78 New St., 3rd flr.
New Brunswick, NJ 08901-2584
732-249-7600

Ocean-Monmouth Legal Services
9 Robbins St., Ste. 2A
Toms River, NJ 08753
732-341-2727

Passaic County Legal Aid Society
175 Market St., 4th flr.
Paterson, NJ 07505
973-345-7171

Somerset-Sussex Legal Services Corporation
78 Grove St.
Somerville, NJ 08876
908-231-0840

Union County Legal Services Corporation
60 Prince St.
Elizabeth, NJ 07208
908-354-4340

Warren County Legal Services
91 Front St.
PO Box 65
Belvidere, NJ 07823
908-475-2010

New Mexico

Indian Pueblo Legal Services
PO Box 817
Bernalillo, NM 87004
505-867-3391; 800-867-3452

Lawyers Care Pro Bono Project
State Bar of New Mexico
Special Projects
PO Box 25883
Albuquerque, NM 87125
505-797-6066

Legal Aid Society of Albuquerque
PO Box 25486
Albuquerque, NM 87125
505-243-7871

Northern New Mexico Legal Services
805 Early St., Bldg. F
Santa Fe, NM 87502
505-982-2504; 800-373-9881

Southern New Mexico Legal Services
300 N. Downtown Mall
Las Cruces, NM 88001-1216
505-526-4451; 800-376-7665

New York

American Civil Liberties Union
125 Broad St., 18th flr.
New York, NY 10004
212-549-2500
www.aclu.org

Asian-American Legal Defense and Education Fund (AALDEF)
99 Hudson St., 12th flr.
New York, NY 10013
212-966-5932
www.aaldef.org

Chemung County Neighborhood Legal Services
215 E. Church St., Ste. 301
Elmira, NY 14901
607-734-1647

Covenant House
Legal Services Office
460 W. 41st St.
New York, NY 10036
212-613-0300

Legal Aid for Broome and Chenango
30 Fayette St.
Binghamton, NY 13901
607-723-79661
www.hn1325@earthlink.net

Legal Aid of the Chautauqua Region
7 W. Third St., 2nd flr.
Jamestown, NY 14701
716-483-2116

Legal Aid Society of Mid-New York
255 Genesee St., 2nd flr.
Utica, NY 13501
315-732-2131
www.borg.com/~legalaid

Legal Aid Society of Northeastern New York
55 Columbia St.
Albany, NY 12207
518-462-6765; 800-462-2922

Legal Aid Society of Rockland County
2 Congers Rd.
New City, NY 10956
845-634-3627

Legal Services for New York City
212-431-7200

Legal Services of Central New York
472 S. Salina St., Ste. 300
Syracuse, NY 13202
315-475-3127

 Monroe County Legal Assistance Corporation
80 St. Paul St., Ste. 700
Rochester, NY 14604
716-325-2520

Nassau/Suffolk Law Services Committee
One Helen Keller Way, 5th flr.
Hempstead, NY 11550
516-292-8100

Neighborhood Legal Services
Ellicott Square Bldg., Rm. 495
295 Main St.
Buffalo, NY 14203
716-847-0650
www.nls@org.com

NY State Bar Association Department of Pro Bono Affairs
One Elk St.
Albany, NY 12207
518-487-5641
www.nysba.org/public/probono/probono.html

 Niagara County Legal Aid Society
775 Third St.
PO Box 844
Niagara Falls, NY 14302-0844
716-284-8831

North Country Legal Services
100 Court St.
PO Box 989
Plattsburgh, NY 12901-0989
518-563-4022

Southern Tier Legal Services
104 E. Steuben St.
Bath, NY 14810
607-776-4126; 877-776-4126

United States Court of Appeals for the Second Circuit Pro Bono Panel
United States Courthouse
40 Foley Sq., 6th flr.
New York, NY 10007
212-857-8800

Volunteer Lawyers for the Arts
One E. 53rd St., 6th flr.
New York, NY 10022
212-319-2787

Westchester/Putnam Legal Services
4 Cromwell Pl.
White Plains, NY 10601
914-949-1305
www.wpls.org

North Carolina

Land Loss Prevention Project
PO Box 179
Durham, NC 27702
919-682-5969
www.landloss.org

Legal Aid Society of Northwest North Carolina
216 W. Fourth St.
Winston-Salem, NC 27101
336-725-9166; 800-660-6663 (in NC)

Legal Services of North Carolina
224 S. Dawson St.
Raleigh, NC 27601
919-856-2564
www.lsnc.org

A Consumer's Guide to Mortgage Refinancings. Free. *Source:* Federal Reserve Bank of New York, Public Information Dept., 33 Liberty St., New York, NY 10045…or at www.ny.frb.org/pihome.

Mutual Fund Losers.
"Lemon list" of under-performing funds.
Source: On the Web at www.fabian.com.

North Carolina Bar Foundation
Pro Bono Project
PO Box 3688
Cary, NC 27519
919-677-0561

North Central Legal Assistance Program
PO Box 2101
Durham, NC 27702
919-688-6396; 800-331-7594
(in NC)

North Dakota

Legal Assistance of North Dakota
PO Box 1893
Bismarck, ND 58502
701-222-2110; 800-643-5236
www.legalassist.org

North Dakota Legal Services
PO Box 217
New Town, ND 58763
701-627-4719
www.ndak.net/~ndls

North Dakota State Bar Association Lawyer Referral Information Service (LRIS)
PO Box 2136
Bismarck, ND 58502
701-255-1404
www.sband.org

Ohio

Advocates for Basic Legal Equality
Spitzer Bldg.
520 Madison Ave., Ste. 740
Toledo, OH 43604
419-255-0814

Allen County-Blackhoof Area Legal Services Association
311 Bldg., Ste. 307
311 E. Market St.
Lima, OH 45801
419-224-9070

Legal Aid Society of Cleveland
1223 W. Sixth St.,
Cleveland, OH 44113
216-687-1900
www.lasclev.org

Legal Aid Society of Columbus
40 W. Gay St.
Columbus, OH 43215
614-224-8374

Legal Aid Society of Dayton
333 W. First St., Ste. 500
Dayton, OH 45402
937-228-8088

Legal Aid Society of Greater Cincinnati
215 E. Ninth St., Ste. 200
Cincinnati, OH 45202
513-241-9400

Legal Aid Society of Lorain County
538 W. Broad St., Ste. 300
Elyria, OH 44035
440-323-8240; 800-444-7348

Northeast Ohio Legal Services
Metropolitan Tower, 7th flr.
11 Federal Plaza Central
Youngstown, OH 44503
330-744-3196; 800-425-8877
(in OH)

Ohio Legal Assistance Foundation
42 E. Gay St., Ste. 900
Columbus, OH 43215-2914
614-752-8919

Ohio State Legal Services
555 Buttles Ave.
Columbus, OH 43215
614-221-7201; 800-589-5888
www.oslsa.org

Western Legal Services
31 E. High St.
Springfield, OH 45502-1234
937-325-5991; 800-582-0290

Stark County Legal Aid Society
306 Market Ave. N, Ste. 730
Canton, OH 44702
330-456-8361

Community Legal Services
265 S. Main St., 3rd flr.
Akron, OH 44308
330-535-4191

Wooster-Wayne Legal Aid Society
121 W. North St., Ste. 100
Wooster, OH 44691
330-264-9454; 800-998-9454
www.woolegal@neo.bright.net

Oklahoma

Legal Aid of Western Oklahoma
2901 Classen Blvd., Ste. 112
Oklahoma City, OK 73106
405-521-1302

Legal Aid Services of Oklahoma
115 W. Third St., Ste. 700
Tulsa, OK 74103-3403
918-584-3338; 800-299-3338

Oregon

Lane County Legal Aid Service
376 E. 11 Ave.
Eugene, OR 97401-3246
541-342-6056

Marion-Polk Legal Aid Service
1655 State St.
Salem, OR 97301
503-581-5265; 800-359-1845
www.mplas.org

 Legal Aid Services of Oregon
United Carriage Bldg.
700 S.W. Taylor St., Ste. 300
Portland, OR 97205
503-224-4086

Oregon Legal Services Corporation
700 S.W. Taylor St., Ste. 310
Portland, OR 97205
503-224-4094

Oregon State Bar Foundation
Referral and Information Services
5200 SW Meadows Rd.
Lake Oswego, OR 97035
503-684-3763
www.osbar.org

Pennsylvania

Bucks County Legal Aid Society
1290 New Rodgers Rd.
Box 809
Bristol, PA 19007
215-781-1111

 Legal Aid of Southeastern Pennsylvania
410 Welsh St.
Chester, PA 19013
610-874-8421

MidPenn Legal Services
2054 E. College Ave.
State College, PA 16801
814-238-4958; 800-326-9177

 Laurel Legal Services
306 S. Pennsylvania Ave.
Greensburg, PA 15601
724-836-2211; 800-253-9558

Legal Aid of Southeastern Pennsylvania
14 E. Biddle St.
West Chester, PA 19380-2914
610-436-45150; 800-967-9150

Lehigh Valley Legal Services
65 E. Elizabeth Ave., Ste. 903
Bethlehem, PA 18018
610-317-8757
www.lehighlegal.org

Montgomery County Legal Aid Service
317 Swede St.
Norristown, PA 19401
610-275-5400
www.lasp.org

Neighborhood Legal Services Association
928 Penn Ave.
Pittsburgh, PA 15222
412-255-6700

 Northwestern Legal Services
Renaissance Centre, Ste. 1200
1001 State St.
Erie, PA 16501-1833
814-452-6957; 800-665-6957
www.nwls.org

Fraud and Theft Catalog. Manuals and fraud-blocker databases on preventing credit card and check fraud... chargeback problems ...direct-marketing fraud, etc.

Source: Fraud & Theft Information Bureau, Box 400, Boynton Beach, FL 33425. 561-737-8700.

Philadelphia Legal Assistance Center
1424 Chestnut St., 2nd flr.
Philadelphia, PA 19102
215-981-3800

Southwestern Pennsylvania Legal Aid Society
10 W. Cherry Ave.
Washington, PA 15301
724-225-6170; 800-846-0871

Susquehanna Legal Services
329 Market St.
Williamsport, PA 17701
570-323-8741

Puerto Rico

Community Law Office
PO Box 194735
San Juan, PR 00919
787-751-1600

Puerto Rico Legal Services
PO Box 9134
Santurce, PR 00908-9134
787-728-8686
www.servcioslegales.org

Rhode Island

Legal Information & Referral Service for the Elderly
115 Cedar St.
Providence, RI 02903
401-521-5040

Rhode Island Legal Services
56 Pine St., 4th flr.
Providence, RI 02903
401-274-2652; 800-662-5034 (in RI)

South Carolina

Carolina Regional Legal Aid Services Corporation
279 W. Evans St.
Florence, SC 29501
843-667-1896

Legal Services Agency of Western Carolina
One Pendleton St.
Greenville, SC 29601
864-679-3232
www.lsawc.net

Palmetto Legal Services
2109 Bull St.
Columbia, SC 29202
803-799-9668

Piedmont Legal Services
148 E. Main St.
Spartanburg, SC 29306
864-582-0369; 800-922-8176 (in SC)

South Carolina Bar Pro Bono Program
PO Box 608
Columbia, SC 29202-0608
803-799-4015
www.scbar.org

South Dakota

Black Hills Legal Services
528 Kansas City St.
Rapid City, SD 57701
605-342-7171; 800-742-8602 (in SD,ND)

Dakota Plains Legal Services
PO Box 727
Mission, SD 57555-0727
605-856-4444; 800-658-2297 (in SD)

East River Legal Services
335 N. Main Ave., Ste. 300
Sioux Falls, SD 57104
605-336-9230; 800-952-3015 (in SD)

Tennessee

Legal Aid of East Tennessee
502 S. Gay St., Ste. 404
Knoxville, TN 37902
865-637-0484

Legal Aid Society of Middle Tennessee
211 Union St., Ste. 800
Nashville, TN 37201
615-244-6610

Legal Services of Upper East Tennessee
311 W. Walnut St.
PO Drawer 360
Johnson City, TN 37605-0360
423-928-8311

Memphis Area Legal Services
Claridge House, 2nd flr.
109 N. Main St.
Memphis, TN 38103
901-523-8822

Southeast Tennessee Legal Services
414 McCallie Ave.
Chattanooga, TN 37402
423-756-0128

West Tennessee Legal Services
PO Box 2066
Jackson, TN 38302
731-423-0616
www.wtls@wtls.org

Texas

AIDS Legal Resource Project
Texas Human Rights Foundation
803 Hawthorne
Houston, TX 77006
713-522-0636

Bexar County Legal Aid Association
434 S. Main Ave., Ste. 300
San Antonio, TX 78204
210-227-0111

Coastal Bend Legal Services
Pueblo Bldg.
102 Pueblo St.
Corpus Christi, TX 78405
361-883-3623; 800-840-3379 (in TX)

East Texas Legal Services
408 E. Pillar St.
Nacogdoches, TX 75961
936-560-1455

El Paso Legal Assistance Society
1301 N. Oregon
El Paso, TX 79902
915-544-3022

Legal Aid Society of the East Region of Texas
1415 Fannin Ave., 3rd flr.
Houston, TX 77002
713-652-0077; 800-733-8394

Legal Aid of Central Texas
2201 Post Rd., Ste. 104
Austin, TX 78704
512-447-7707; 800-369-9270
www.lact.org

Legal Services of North Texas
1515 Main St.
Dallas, TX 75201
214-748-1234
www.lsnt.org

Pro BAR
301 E. Madison Ave.
Harlingen, TX 78550
956-425-9231

Texas Rural Legal Aid
300 S. Texas Blvd.
Weslaco, TX 78596
956-968-6574; 800-369-0574
www.trla.com

West Texas Legal Services
600 E. Weatherford St.
Fort Worth, TX 76108
817-336-3943; 800-955-3959

Women's Advocacy Project
PO Box 833
Austin, TX 78767
512-476-5377
www.women-law.org

Utah

Utah Legal Services
254 West 400 South, 2nd flr.
Salt Lake City, UT 84101
801-328-8891; 800-662-4245 (in UT)

Utah State Bar Association
Pro Bono Project
645 South 200 East
Salt Lake City, UT 84111
801-531-9077

Vermont

Vermont Legal Aid
PO Box 1367
Burlington, VT 05402
800-889-2047

Insuring Your Home Business. Guidelines to help owners properly insure against loss due to fire or theft, as well as help with liability, car and health coverage.
Source: Insurance Information Institute, 110 William St., New York, NY 10038. 212-669-9200; 800-331-9146

Guide to Management Level Pre-Employment Investigations: How to conduct thorough reviews from high school to the present...credit review...court research, etc.
Source: Research Associates, Inc., 27999 Clemens Rd., Westlake, OH 44145. 800-255-9693.

Virgin Islands

Legal Services of the Virgin Islands
3017 Estate Orange Grove
Christiansted, St. Croix, VI 00820-4375
340-773-2626

Virginia

Blue Ridge Legal Services
PO Box 551
Harrisonburg, VA 22803
540-433-1830; 800-237-0141
www.brls.org

Central Virginia Legal Aid Society
101 W. Broad St., Ste. 101
Richmond, VA 23220
804-648-1012; 800-868-1012

Client Centered Legal Services of Southwest Virginia
PO Box 147
Castlewood, VA 24224
540-762-5501; 800-234-2257

Legal Aid Society of Roanoke Valley
416 Campbell Ave. SW
Roanoke, VA 24016
540-344-2088

Legal Services of Northern Virginia
6400 Arlington Blvd., Ste. 630
Falls Church, VA 22042
703-534-4343

Legal Services of Eastern Virginia
2017 Cunningham Dr., Ste. 300
Hampton, VA 23666
757-827-5078

Rappahannock Legal Services
910 Princess Anne St., Ste. 216
Fredericksburg, VA 22401
540-371-1105

Southwest Virginia Legal Aid Society
227 W. Cherry St.
Marion, VA 24354
540-783-8300; 800-277-6754

Virginia Legal Aid Society
513 Church St.
PO Box 6058
Lynchburg, VA 24505
434-846-1326; 800-552-7676 (in VA)

Washington

Northwest Justice Project
401 Second Ave. S, Ste. 407
Seattle, WA 98104
206-464-1519
www.nwjustice.org

West Virginia

Legal Aid of West Virginia
922 Quarrier St., 4th Fl.
Charleston, WV 25301
304-344-9687; 800-834-0598 (in WV)

Wisconsin

Legal Action of Wisconsin
230 W. Wells St., Room 800
Milwaukee, WI 53203
414-278-7722
www.legalaction.org

Legal Services of Northeastern Wisconsin
201 W. Walnut St., Ste. 203
Green Bay, WI 54303
920-432-4645; 800-236-1127

Western Wisconsin Legal Services
202 N. Main
PO Box 327
Dodgeville, WI 53533-0327
608-935-2741; 800-873-0928

Wisconsin Judicare
PO Box 6100
Wausau, WI 54402
715-842-1681; 800-472-1638 (in WI)
www.judicare.org

Wyoming

Wyoming Legal Services
PO Box 1160
Lander, WY 82520
307-332-6626; 800-442-6170
www.wyoming-legal-services.com

Benefits of being 60+...
Legal Hotlines

There are many legal hotlines that allow individuals over age 60 to speak with an attorney about their legal questions and concerns. Where available, this service can be a helpful source of advice, but not actual representation. The service is generally free of charge, except where specially noted.

Arizona

Arizona Elder Law Hotline
Southern Arizona Legal Aid, Inc.
64 E. Broadway Blvd.
Tucson, AZ 85701
520-623-5137
800-231-5441

California

Senior Legal Hotline
Legal Services of Northern California
515 12th St.
Sacramento, CA 95814
800-222-1753
916-551-2140
http://www.seniorlegalhotline.org

Washington, D.C.

Legal Hotline for the Elderly
Legal Counsel for the Elderly,
AARP Foundation
601 E St. NW
Washington, DC 20049
202-434-2170

Georgia

Georgia Senior Legal Hotline
Atlanta Legal Aid Society
2 Peachtree St., Ste. 3600
Atlanta, GA 30303
888-257-9519
404-657-9915

Hawaii

Senior Legal Hotline
Legal Aid Society of Hawaii
1108 Nuuanu Ave.
Honolulu, HI 96817-5119
888-536-0011
http://www.legalaidhawaii.org

Iowa

Legal Hotline for Older Iowans
Legal Services Corporation of Iowa
1111 9th St., Ste. 230
Des Moines, IA 50314
800-992-8161
515-282-8161

Indiana

Legal Services of Indiana
Senior Hotline
242 W. 7th St.
Bloomington, IN 47404
877-323-6260
http://www.indianajustice.org

Kansas

Elder Law Hotline
Kansas Legal Services
200 N. Broadway, Ste. 500
Wichita, KS 67202
888-353-5337
316-265-9681

Kentucky

Legal HelpLine for Older Kentuckians
Access to Justice Foundation
400 Old Vine St., Ste. 203
Lexington, KY 40507-1910
800-200-3633
http://www.seniorlegalhelpline.org

About...Running a Small Business. Helpful advice, from creating a business plan to sales, marketing and finance.
Source: MetLife Consumer Education Center, 800-638-5433, www.metlife.com

Collection Guide for Creditors: How to reduce bad debts... identify potential bad debts...recognize the delinquent debtor... work with a collection agency.

Source: American Collectors Association, Inc., Box 39106, Minneapolis, MN 55439-0106. Include a business-sized SASE.

Maine

Legal Services for the Elderly Hotline
9 Green St.
Augusta, ME 04338
800-750-5353
207-623-1797
http://www.mainelse.org

Maryland

Maryland Senior Legal Hotline
Legal Aid Bureau
500 East Lexington St.
Baltimore, MD 21202
800-999-8904
410-539-5340
http://www.mdlab.org/srhotline.html

Michigan

Legal Hotline for Michigan Seniors
Elder Law Of Michigan, Inc.
115 West Allegan St., Ste. 720
Lansing, MI 48933
800-347-5297
517-372-5959
http://www.mlan.net/lhom

Mississippi

Legal Line for Elder Mississippians
111 Rue Magnolia
PO Box 994
Biloxi, MS 39533-0994
888-660-0008
228-374-4168

New Hampshire

Senior Citizens Law Project
Advice Line
New Hampshire Legal Assistance
1361 Elm St.
Manchester, NH 03101
888-353-9944 (in-state)
603-624-6000

New Mexico

Lawyer Referral for the Elderly Program
State Bar of New Mexico Special Projects, Inc.
PO Box 25883
Albuquerque, NM 87125
800-876-6657
505-797-6005

Ohio

Pro Seniors' Legal Hotline
Pro Seniors, Inc.
105 E. 4th St., Ste. 1715
Cincinnati, OH 45202
800-488-6070
513-345-4160
http://www.proseniors.org

Pennsylvania

Legal Counsel for the Elderly
AARP Foundation (age 50+)
PO Box 23180
Pittsburgh, PA 15222
May be a charge for certain income levels
800-262-5297

Puerto Rico

Islandwide Seniors Legal Hotline
Puerto Rico Legal Services Corporation
Ponce de Leon 1859-Pda. 26
Apartado 9134
San Juan, PR 00908-9134
800-981-9160
800-981-3432
787-728-2323

Tennessee

Tennessee Elder Law Hotline
Southeast Tennessee Legal Services
414 McCallie Ave.
Chattanooga, TN 37402
800-836-0128
423-756-0128
http://www.setnlegalservices.org

Texas

Legal Hotline for Older Texans
Texas Legal Services Center
815 Brazos, Ste. 1100
Austin, TX 78701
800-622-2520
http://tlsc.org/hotline.html

Washington

CLEAR*Sr. – Coordinated Legal
Education, Advice and Referral
for Seniors
Northwest Justice Project
401 Second Ave. South, Ste. 407
Seattle, WA 98104
888-387-7111
http://www.nwjustice.org

West Virginia

West Virginia Senior Legal Aid, Inc.
1988 Listravia Ave.
Morgantown, WV 26505
800-229-5068
304-291-3900
http://www.seniorlegalaid.org

Wyoming

Wyoming Legal Services
PO Box 1160
Lander, WY 82520
800-442-6710
307-332-6626

About...Selling a Home. How to set a fair price...qualify a buyer ...seek legal representation...tax implications.
Source: MetLife Consumer Education Center, 800-638-5433.

Nationwide Directory of Consumer Protection Offices

Check Out a Company Before Doing Business with It

It is always smart before doing business with any company you have questions about to check with your local Better Business Bureau (BBB). They will be able to tell you whether other consumers have reported any problems they have had with the company. Usually you can find the address and phone number of the bureau nearest you in your local phone book, although some BBBs are serviced by bureaus in adjoining states. To locate the one nearest you, you can also check with the US National Headquarters listed below or use the zip code search or state directory on the Web at www.bbb.org.

United States National Headquarters

Council of Better Business Bureaus
4200 Wilson Blvd., Ste. 800
Arlington, VA 22203
703-276-0100
www.bbb.org

Don't Be a Victim of Consumer Fraud

As a general rule, once it is clear that you are not going to get satisfaction directly from the company you are having a dispute with, the first place to call for help with a consumer problem is your local consumer protection office. It is their job to protect you, the consumer, against unfair and illegal business practices.

Listed here are consumer protection offices throughout the country. If you have a complaint, check this directory for your state, city or county and call the office nearest you.

If you are having a problem with a business outside your state, however, contact the consumer office in the state from which you made the purchase.

When you call a consumer protection office or Attorney General's office, simply ask to be connected to the person in charge of consumer complaints.

Nationwide Consumer Protection Offices

Alabama
Consumer Affairs:
800-392-5658 (in AL only)
334-242-7334

Alaska
Consumer Protection Section in the Office of the Attorney General has been closed. Consumers with complaints are being referred to the Better Business Bureaus in Anchorage and Fairbanks, small claims court and private attorneys.

Arizona—State Offices
Phoenix Consumer Protection: 800-352-8431
Tucson Consumer Protection: 520-628-6504

Arizona—County Offices
Gila County: 520-425-3231
Graham County: 928-428-3620
Greenlee County: 928-865-4108
La Paz County: 928-669-6118
Mohave County: 520-753-0719
Navajo County: 520-524-4026
Pinal County: 520-868-6271
Santa Cruz County: 520-761-7800
Yavapai County: 520-771-3344
Yuma County: 520-329-2270

Arizona—City Office
Tucson Consumer Affairs: 520-791-4886

Arkansas—State Office
Consumer Protection: 501-682-2341;
800-482-8982 (in AR only)

Consumer's Resource Handbook. How to make sure you get what you want—and what you paid for. Includes directory of consumer assistance organizations. 148 pages.
Source: Consumer Information Center, Dept. 595E, Pueblo, CO 81009. 888-878-3256. www.pueblo.gsa.gov

Wanted: The Bandit in Your Mailbox.
Pyramid schemes…
bogus credit card offers
…travel scams…
vacation "prizes"…
chain letters…and
other fraudulent mail
solicitations.
Source: Federal Trade
Commission, Consumer
Response Center, 600
Pennsylvania Ave. NW, Rm.
130, Washington, DC 20580.
www.ftc.gov
877-FTC-HELP (382-4357)

California—State Offices
California Consumer Affairs: 916-445-1254
(consumer information); 800-344-9940
(in CA only)
Office of the Attorney General:
916-322-3360; 800-952-5225 (in CA only)

California—City Office
Santa Monica: 310-458-8336

Colorado—State Offices
Consumer and Food Specialist:
303-239-4114
Consumer Protection Unit: 303-866-5189

Colorado—County Offices
Boulder County: 303-441-3700
Denver County: 720-913-9179
(complaints)
El Paso and Teller Counties:
719-520-6002
Weld County: 970-356-4010

Connecticut—State Offices
Antitrust/Consumer Protection: 860-566-2211
Department of Consumer Protection: 860-
713-6125; 800-842-2649 (in CT only)

Connecticut—City Office
Middletown: 860-344-3491

Delaware—State Offices
Division of Consumer Affairs:
800-220-5424 (in DE only)
Office of the Attorney General, Fraud Division:
302-577-8600

District of Columbia
Consumer Affairs: 202-282-3272

Florida—State Offices
Division of Consumer Services: 850-488-
2221; 800-435-7352 (in FL only)
Office of the Attorney General: 954-712-4600

Georgia—State Office
Governors Office of Consumer Affairs:
404-651-8600; 800-869-1123 (in GA only)

Hawaii—State Offices
Hilo Office of Consumer Protection:
808-933-0910
Honolulu Office of Consumer Protection:
808-586-2630

Office of Consumer Protection:
808-933-0910
Wailuku Office of Consumer Protection:
808-984-8244; 800-468-4644
(in HI only)

Idaho—State Office
Consumer Protection Unit: 208-334-2424;
800-432-3545 (in ID only)

Illinois—State Offices
Chicago Consumer Protection:
312-814-3580
Governor's Office of Citizens Assistance:
217-782-0244; 800-342-3112
(in IL only)
Office of the Attorney General:
800-386-5438 (in IL only)
Springfield Consumer Protection:
217-782-9011; 800-243-0618
(in IL only)

Illinois—Regional Offices

Carbondale Regional Office:
618-529-6400
Champaign Regional Office:
217-278-3366 (voice/TDD)
Chicago Northwest: 773-583-9121
Chicago South: 773-488-2600
Metro East: 618-236-8616
Quincy Regional Office: 217-223-2221
(voice/TDD)
Rockford Regional Office: 815-484-8100

Illinois—County Office
Cook County: 312-603-8700

Illinois—City Offices
Chicago Department of Consumer Services:
312-744-4006
Des Plaines Consumer Protection:
847-391-5006

Indiana—State Office
Consumer Protection: 317-232-6330;
800-382-5516 (in IN only)

Iowa—State Office
Consumer Protection: 515-281-5926

Kansas—State Office
Consumer Protection: 785-296-3751;
800-432-2310 (in KS only)

Kentucky—State Offices
Consumer Protection: 502-696-5389;
    888-432-9257 (in KY only)
Louisville Consumer Protection:
    502-425-4825

Louisiana—State Office
Consumer Protection: 225-342-9638

Maine—State Offices
Consumer Credit Protection:
    207-624-8527; 800-332-8529
    (in ME only)
Office of the Attorney General:
    207-626-8849

Maryland—State Offices
Consumer Affairs Specialist, Office of the
    Attorney General: 410-576-6300
Consumer Protection: 410-528-8662
Motor Vehicle Administration:
    301-729-4550; 800-950-1682
    (in MD only)
Western Maryland: 301-791-4780

Massachusetts—State Offices
Consumer Protection: 617-727-8400
Executive Office of Consumer Affairs:
    617-727-7780

Massachusetts—County Offices
Franklin County: 413-774-5102
Worcester County: 508-754-1176

Massachusetts—City Offices
Boston Mayor's Office of Consumer Affairs:
    617-635-4165
Springfield Mayor's Office of Consumer
    Information: 413-787-6437 (Hampden
    and Hampshire counties)

Michigan—State Offices
Consumer Protection: 517-373-1140
Bureau of Automotive Regulation:
    517-373-4777; 800-292-4204
    (in MI only)

Minnesota—State Office
Office of Consumer Services: 651-296-3353

Mississippi—State Offices
Consumer Protection: 601-359-4230;
    800-281-4418 (in MS only)
Department of Agriculture & Commerce:
    601-359-1111

Missouri—State Office
Office of the Attorney General, Trade
    Offense Division: 314-340-6815;
    800-392-8222 (in MO only)

Montana—State Office
Consumer Affairs: 406-444-4312

Nebraska—State Office
Consumer Protection: 402-471-2682

Nevada—State Offices

Las Vegas Commissioner of Consumer
    Affairs: 702-486-7355;
    800-992-0900 (in NV only)
Reno Consumer Affairs:
    775-688-1800;
    800-992-0900 (in NV only)

New Hampshire—State Office
Consumer Protection: 603-271-3641

New Jersey—State Offices
Consumer Affairs: 973-504-6200;
    800-242-5846 (in NJ only)
New Jersey Division of Law: 973-648-2500

New Mexico—State Office
Consumer Protection: 505-827-6060;
    800-678-1508 (in NM only)

New York—State Offices
New York State Consumer Protection:
    518-474-8583
Bureau of Consumer Frauds & Protection:
    518-474-5481
Bureau of Consumer Frauds & Protection:
    212-416-8345; 800-771-7755 (in NY only)

New York—Regional Offices
Binghamton Regional Office:
    607-721-8779
Buffalo Regional Office:
    716-853-8404
Plattsburgh Regional Office:
518-562-3282
Poughkeepsie Regional Office:
914-485-3900
Rochester Regional Office: 716-546-7430
Suffolk Regional Office: 631-231-2400
Syracuse Regional Office: 315-448-4848
Utica Regional Office: 315-793-2225

How to Plan for the Unexpected: Preventing Child Drownings. Rules for pools...installing barriers—gates, alarms, safety covers, etc.
Source: US Consumer Product Safety Commission, Washington, DC 20207...or on the Web at www.cpsc.gov.

What You Should Know About Using Paint Strippers.
Types of strippers...
safety precautions.
Source: US Consumer Product Safety Commission, Washington, DC 20207...or on the Web at www.cpsc.gov. Item #CPSC-423.

North Carolina—State Office
Consumer Protection: 919-716-6000

North Dakota—State Office
Office of the Attorney General: 701-328-3404; 800-472-2600 (in ND only)

North Dakota—County Office
Red River Valley Community Action:
701-746-5431

Ohio—State Offices
Consumer Frauds and Crimes Section:
614-466-4986 (complaints);
800-282-0515 (in OH only)
Office of Consumers' Counsel:
614-466-9467 (voice/TDD);
800-282-9448 (in OH only)

Oklahoma—State Offices
Attorney General: 405-521-4274
Department of Consumer Credit:
405-521-3653

Oregon—State Offices
Consumer Protection: 503-229-5725
Financial Fraud: 503-378-4732

Pennsylvania—State Offices
Consumer Advocate (utilities only):
717-783-5048
Consumer Protection: 717-787-9707;
800-441-2555 (in PA only)
Pennsylvania Public Utility Commission:
717-783-1740; 800-782-1110
(in PA only)

Rhode Island—State Office
Consumer Protection: 401-274-4400;
800-852-7776 (in RI only)

South Carolina—State Offices
Consumer Protection Office:
803-734-4200; 800-922-1594 (in SC only)
Fraud Hotline: 800-521-4493 (in SC only)
Office of the Attorney General:
803-734-3970
State Ombudsman: 803-734-0457

South Dakota—State Office
Consumer Affairs: 605-773-4400;
800-300-1986 (in SD only)

Tennessee—State Offices
Consumer Affairs: 615-741-4737;
800-342-8385 (in TN only)
Consumer Protection: 615-741-3491

Texas—State Offices

Austin Consumer Protection:
512-463-2070
Dallas Consumer Protection:
214-969-5310
El Paso Consumer Protection:
915-834-5800
Houston Consumer Protection:
713-223-5886
Lubbock Consumer Protection:
806-747-5238
McAllen Consumer Protection:
956-682-4547
San Antonio Consumer Protection:
210-225-4191

Utah—State Offices
Consumer Protection: 801-530-6601;
800-721-7233 (in UT only)
Office of the Attorney General:
801-366-0310

Vermont—State Offices
Office of the Attorney General:
802-828-3171
Consumer Assurance: 802-828-2436

Virginia—State Offices
Office of the Attorney General:
804-786-2116; 800-451-1525
(in VA only)
Richmond Branch of Consumer Affairs:
804-786-2042; 800-552-9963 (in VA only)

Washington—State Offices
Seattle Consumer Services: 206-464-6684;
800-551-4636 (in WA only)
Spokane Office of the Attorney General:
509-456-3123
Tacoma Office of the Attorney General:
253-593-2904

Washington—City Offices
Seattle Department of Licenses & Consumer Affairs: 206-684-8484
Seattle Prosecuting Attorney, Fraud Division:
206-296-9010

West Virginia—State Offices
Consumer Protection: 304-558-8986;
  800-368-8808 (in WV only)
Division of Weights and Measures:
  304-722-0602

Wisconsin—State Offices
Altoona Consumer Protection: 715-839-3848;
  800-422-7128 (in WI only)
Green Bay Consumer Protection:
  920-448-5110; 800-422-7128 (in WI only)
Madison Consumer Protection: 608-224-4949;
  800-422-7128 (in WI only)
Madison Department of Justice:
  608-266-1852

Wisconsin—County Office
Milwaukee County: 414-278-4585

Wyoming—State Office
Office of the Attorney General:
  307-777-7874

American Samoa
Consumer Protection: 011-684-633-4163/64

Puerto Rico
Department of Justice: 787-721-2900
Secretary of Consumer Affairs:
  787-721-0940

Virgin Islands
Commissioner & Consumer Affairs:
  340-774-3130

Avoiding Credit and Charge Card Fraud

Credit and charge card fraud costs cardholders and issuers hundreds of millions of dollars each year. While theft is the most obvious form of fraud, it can occur in other ways. For example, someone may use your card number without your knowledge.

It's not always possible to prevent credit or charge card fraud from happening. But there are a few steps you can take to make it more difficult for a crook to capture your card or card numbers and minimize the possibility.

Guarding Against Fraud

Here are some tips to help protect yourself from credit and charge card fraud.

Do:

• Sign your cards as soon as they arrive.

• Carry your cards separately from your wallet, in a zippered compartment, a business card holder or another small pouch.

• Keep a record of your account numbers, their expiration dates and the phone number and address of each company in a secure place.

• Keep an eye on your card during the transaction, and get it back as quickly as possible.

• Void incorrect receipts.

• Destroy carbons.

• Save receipts to compare with billing statements.

• Open bills promptly and reconcile accounts monthly, just as you would your checking account.

• Report any questionable charges promptly and in writing to the card issuer.

• Notify card companies in advance of a change in address.

Don't:

• Lend your card(s) to anyone.

• Leave cards or receipts lying around.

• Sign a blank receipt. When you sign a receipt, draw a line through any blank spaces above the total.

• Write your account number on a postcard or the outside of an envelope.

Energy Savers—Tips for Saving Energy and Money at Home.
Source: US Department of Energy's Energy Efficiency and Renewable Energy Clearinghouse (EREC). Read online at www.eren.doe.gov.

Vegetarian Nutrition Resource List for Consumers. Books, magazines, brochures. *Source:* US Dept. of Agriculture, Food and Nutrition Information Center, National Agricultural Library, 10301 Baltimore Ave., Beltsville, MD 20705…or on the Web at www.nal.usda.gov/fnic.

• Give out your account number over the phone unless you're making the call to a company you know is reputable. If you have questions about a company, check it out with your local consumer protection office or Better Business Bureau.

Reporting Losses and Fraud

If you lose your credit or charge cards or if you realize they've been lost or stolen, immediately call the issuer(s). Many companies have toll-free numbers and 24-hour service to deal with such emergencies. By law, once you report the loss or theft, you have no further responsibility for unauthorized charges. In any event, your maximum liability under federal law is $50 per card.

If you suspect fraud, you may be asked to sign a statement under oath that you did not make the purchase(s) in question.

For More Information

The Federal Trade Commission works for the consumer to prevent fraudulent, deceptive and unfair business practices in the marketplace and to provide information to help consumers spot, stop and avoid them. To file a complaint, or to get free information on any of 150 consumer topics, call toll-free, 1-877-FTC-HELP (1-877-382-4357), or use the complaint form at www.ftc.gov. The FTC enters Internet, telemarketing and other fraud-related complaints into Consumer Sentinel, a secure, online database available to hundreds of civil and criminal law enforcement agencies worldwide.

Toll-Free Telephone Number Scams

Calls to 800 and 888 numbers are almost always free, but there are some exceptions. Companies that provide audio entertainment or information services may charge for calls to 800, 888 and other toll-free numbers, but only if they follow the Federal Trade Commission's 900-Number Rule.

This Rule requires a company to ask you to pay for entertainment or information services with a credit card or to make billing arrangements with you before they provide the service. If you don't use a credit card, the law says companies also must provide you with a security device, such as a personal identification number (PIN), to prevent other people from using your phone to charge calls to these services.

Presubscription Agreements

For a company to charge you for a call to an 800 or 888 entertainment or information service, it must obtain your agreement to the billing arrangement in advance. The company must tell you all relevant information about the arrangement, including the company's name and address, rates and rate changes, and business telephone number.

The company also must use a security device, like a PIN, to prevent unauthorized charges to your telephone. The presubscription agreement must be in place before you reach the entertainment or information provided by the service. If you authorize a company to charge your credit card for an 800- or 888-number call, the company has met the Rule's requirements.

Prohibitions and Unlawful Practices

Certain practices relating to 800 and 888 numbers are prohibited by the 900-Number Rule. For example, a company can't charge you for dialing an 800 or 888 number unless you have entered into a valid presubscription agreement. Also, if you dial an 800 or other toll-free number, the company is prohibited from automatically connecting you to a 900-number service, and from calling you back collect.

However, the law allows a company to promote a 900-number service during the 800-number call, as long as you would have to hang up and dial the 900 number to reach the service.

Some companies break the law by charging improperly for entertainment and information services that you reach by dialing an 800 or 888 number. For example, some services ask you during the course of a call to simply "Press 1" to be charged automatically. Others advertise a service as free but then unlawfully charge for calls placed to that service. Still others may charge for calls you place to 800 or 888 numbers by billing you for calls to a different type of service, such as calls to an international number. Some will charge a monthly club fee on your phone bill after you call an 800 or 888 number. Other services fail to take adequate precautions to prevent the unauthorized use of your telephone to make these calls; they may charge you for 800-number calls you didn't make or approve.

Minimize Your Risk

Here's how to minimize your risk of unauthorized charges:

Remember that dialing a number that begins with 888 is just like dialing an 800 number; both are often toll-free, but not always.

Companies are prohibited from charging you for calls to these numbers unless they set up a valid presubscription agreement with you first.

Recognize that not all numbers beginning with "8" are toll-free. For example, the area code 809 serves the Dominican Republic. If you dial this area code, you'll be charged international long distance rates.

Make sure any 800 or 888 number you call to get entertainment or information that costs money provides security devices, including PINs, before you enter into a presubscription agreement with them.

Check your phone bill for 800, 888 or unfamiliar charges. Calls to 800 and 888 numbers should be identified. Some may be mislabeled as long-distance or calling card calls and are easy to overlook.

Dispute charges on your phone bill for an 800 or 888 number if you don't have a presubscription arrangement. Follow the instructions on your billing statement.

Realize that if the telephone company removes a charge for an 800- or 888-number call, the entertainment or information service provider may try to pursue the charge through a collection agency. If this happens, you may have additional rights under the Fair Debt Collection Practices Act.

Pump Fiction. How to purchase home exercise equipment wisely.
Source: Federal Trade Commission Consumer Response Center, CRC-240, Washington, DC 20580. 202-382-4357. www.ftc.gov

For More Information

The following organizations can provide additional information and help you file a complaint. Your state Attorney General usually has a division that deals with consumer protection issues.

The Federal Communications Commission's National Call Center at 1-888-CALL-FCC (1-888-225-5322). The Center answers consumer inquiries relating to communications law and policy, matters pending before the FCC and any possible violations of FCC law or policy.

Free and Low-Cost Dental Programs

Free and Low-Cost Dental Programs

Throughout the US professional dental care is available at a reduced rate or even absolutely free to senior citizens and others living on a limited budget. This care is offered through a wide variety of programs sponsored by dental clinics, dental colleges and dentists who volunteer their time and service without charge or at a greatly reduced rate. You will get the finest professional dental care from licensed dentists with many years of experience.

To get free or low-cost dental care, check the listing below for your state. Call the phone number listed and explain that you are a senior citizen looking for a low-cost dental program. In some instances you will be referred to an agency in your area that will assist you in getting the dental care you need. If the organization you call does not have the particular type of care you need, always ask for a referral to another organization that does provide the care.

In addition to the listings below, check with your state's Office of the Aging (page 195). Often they will have access to special programs not available anywhere else.

Alabama

Alabama Dental Association
836 Washington Ave.
Montgomery, AL 36104
334-265-1684; 800-489-2532

**University of Alabama
School of Dentistry**
1919 Seventh Ave. S
Birmingham, AL 35294
205-934-2700

Alaska

Alaska Dental Society
9170 Jewel Lake Rd., Ste. 203
Anchorage, AK 99502
907-563-3003

Anchorage Neighborhood Health Center
1217 East 10th Ave.
Anchorage, AK 99503
907-257-4600

**Senior Citizen Discounts
Anchorage Dental Society**
3400 Spenard Rd., Ste. 10
Anchorage, AK 99503
907-279-9144

Arizona

Arizona Dental Association
4131 N. 36th St.
Phoenix, AZ 85018
602-957-4777; 800-866-2732

**Department of Health Services
Office of Oral Health**
1740 West Adams St., Rm. 10
Phoenix, AZ 85007
602-542-1866

Arkansas

Arkansas State Dental Association
2501 Crestwood Dr., Ste. 205
North Little Rock, AR 72116
501-771-7650

California

**Loma Linda University
School of Dentistry**
11092 Anderson St.
Loma Linda, CA 92350
909-558-4621

**Senior Dent Program
California Dental Association**
PO Box 13749
Sacramento, CA 95853
916-443-0505

Snack Smart for Healthy Teeth. A parent's guide on how to prevent tooth decay... harmful effects of sugary foods...list of healthy snacks...etc.
Source: National Institute of Dental and Craniofacial Research, National Institutes of Health, Bethesda, MD 20892-2190. Also online at www.nidcr.nih.gov. Then click on "Information," and "Health Care and Patient Information."

Nutrition and Oral Health: Making the Connection. How eating habits affect your teeth—including baby-bottle tooth decay. Free.
Source: International Food Information Council Foundation, 1100 Connecticut Ave. NW, Ste. 430, Washington, DC 20036. Include a business-sized SASE. More brochures available on their Web site at www.ific.org.

University of California at Los Angeles School of Dentistry
10833 LeConte Ave.
PO Box 951668
Los Angeles, CA 90095-1668
310-206-3904

University of California School of Dentistry
505 Parnassus Ave.
San Francisco, CA 94143
415-476-1891

University of the Pacific School of Dentistry
2155 Webster St.
San Francisco, CA 94115
415-929-6400

University of Southern California School of Dentistry
925 W. 34th St.
Los Angeles, CA 90089-0641
213-740-2800

Colorado

Colorado Dental Association
3690 S. Yosemite, Ste. 100
Denver, CO 80237
303-740-6900; 800-343-3010 (for members only)

State Health Dept. Oral Health Department
4300 Cherry Creek Dr. S
Denver, CO 80243
303-692-2360

University of Colorado Medical School of Dentistry
4200 East Ninth Ave.
PO Box C284
Denver, CO 80262
303-315-8754

Connecticut

Connecticut State Dental Association
62 Russ St.
Hartford, CT 06106
860-278-5550

University of Connecticut School of Dental Medicine
263 Farmington Ave.
Farmington, CT 06030
860-679-2000

Delaware

Delaware State Dental Society
1925 Lovering Ave.
Wilmington, DE 19806
302-654-4335

Division of Public Health Department of Dentistry
501 W. 14th St.
Wilmington, DE 19801
302-428-4850

Ministry of Caring Dental Program
1410 N. Claymont St.
Wilmington, DE 19802
302-594-9476

Nemours Health Clinic
1801 Rockland Rd.
Wilmington, DE 19801
800-292-9538; 302-651-4400

District of Columbia

District of Columbia Dental Society
502 C St. NE
Washington, DC 20002
202-547-7613

Howard University College of Dentistry
600 W St. NW
Washington, DC 20059
202-806-0008

Florida

Department of Health & Rehabilitative Services Public Health Dental Program
4052 Bald Cypress Way, Bin #A14
Tallahassee, FL 32399-1724
850-245-4333
Ask for referral to a clinic near you.

Florida Dental Association
1111 E. Tennessee St.
Tallahassee, FL 32308
850-681-3629; 800-877-9922

Nova Southeastern University
College of Dental Medicine
3200 S. University Dr.
Davie, FL 33328
954-262-7500

University of Florida
College of Dentistry
PO Box 100425
1600 SW Archer Rd.
Gainesville, FL 32610
352-392-4261

Georgia

Ben Massell Dental Clinic
18 Seventh St. NE
Atlanta, GA 30308
404-881-1858

Georgia Dental Association
7000 Peachtree Dunwoody Rd.
Ste. 200, Bldg. 17
Atlanta, GA 30328
404-636-7553; 800-432-4357 (in GA only)

Medical College of Georgia
School of Dentistry
1459 Laney Walker Blvd.
Augusta, GA 30912
706-721-2696

South Side Medical Center
1039 Ridge Ave. SW
Atlanta, GA 30315
404-688-1350

West End Medical Center
868 York Ave.
Atlanta, GA 30310
404-752-1443

Hawaii

Department of Health
Dental Health Division
1700 Lanakila Ave., Room 203
Honolulu, HI 96817
808-832-5710

Hawaii Dental Association
1345 S. Beretania St., Ste. 301
Honolulu, HI 96814
808-593-7956

Idaho

Idaho State Dental Association
1220 W. Hays St.
Boise, ID 83702
208-343-7543; 800-932-8153 (in ID only)
Ask for a referral to your local Community
Health Center.

Senior Care Program
Boise City/Ada County
3010 W. State St.
Boise, ID 83703
208-345-7783

Illinois

Illinois State Dental Society
PO Box 376
Springfield, IL 62705
217-525-1406

Northwestern University
Dental School
240 E. Huron St.
Chicago, IL 60611
312-503-6837

Southern Illinois University
School of Dentistry
Bldg. 263
2800 College Ave.
Alton, IL 62002
618-474-7000

University of Illinois at Chicago
College of Dentistry
801 South Paulina St.
Chicago, IL 60612
312-996-7558

Indiana

Indiana University
School of Dentistry
1121 W. Michigan St.
Indianapolis, IN 46202
317-274-7433

Senior Smile Dental Care Program
Indiana Dental Association
401 W. Michigan St.
PO Box 2467
Indianapolis, IN 46206
317-634-2610; 800-562-5646

Seal Out Dental Decay.
What are dental sealants…who should get them. Free.
Source: National Institute of Dental and Craniofacial Research, National Institutes of Health, Bethesda, MD 20892-2190. Online at www.nidcr.nih.gov.

What Consumers Need to Know About Private Long Term Care Insurance. What is covered…at what age to buy… selecting a good policy. Free.

Source: American Health Care Association, 1201 L St. NW, Washington, DC 20005. Also on the Web at www.ahca.org/info/informat.htm

Iowa

Iowa Dental Association
505 5th Ave., Ste. 333
Des Moines, IA 50309
515-282-7250; 800-828-2181

**University of Iowa
College of Dentistry**
322 Dental Sciences Bldg.
Iowa City, IA 52242
319-335-7499

Kansas

**Senior Access Program
Kansas Dental Association**
5200 SW Huntoon St.
Topeka, KS 66604
785-272-7360; 800-432-3583

Kentucky

**Jefferson County Dental
Park Duval Community Health Facility**
1817 S. 34th St.
Louisville, KY 40211
502-774-4401

Kentucky Dental Association
1940 Princeton Dr.
Louisville, KY 40205
502-459-5373; 800-292-1855

**University of Kentucky
College of Dentistry**
800 Rose St.
Lexington, KY 40536-0084
859-323-6525

**University of Louisville
School of Dentistry**
Health Sciences Center
501 S. Preston St.
Louisville, KY 40292
502-852-5096

Louisiana

Louisiana Dental Association
7833 Office Park Blvd.
Baton Rouge, LA 70809
225-926-1986

**Louisiana State University
School of Dentistry**
1100 Florida Ave.
New Orleans, LA 70119
504-619-8770

Maine

**Senior Dent Program
Maine Dental Association**
PO Box 99
Manchester, ME 04351
207-622-7900; 800-369-8217

Maryland

Maryland State Dental Association
6410 Dobbin Road, Ste. F
Columbia, MD 21045
410-964-2880; 800-766-2880 (in MD only)

**University of Maryland
Dental School**
666 W. Baltimore St.
Baltimore, MD 21201
410-706-7102

Massachusetts

**Boston University
Goldman School of Dental Medicine**
100 E. Newton St.
Boston, MA 02118
617-638-4787

Harvard Dental Center
188 Longwood Ave.
Boston, MA 02115
617-432-1423

Massachusetts Dental Society
2 Willow St., Ste. 200
Southborough, MA 01745
508-480-9797; 800-342-8747

**Tufts University
School of Dental Medicine**
One Kneeland St.
Boston, MA 02111
617-636-6828

Michigan

Michigan Dental Association
230 N. Washington Sq., Ste. 208
Lansing, MI 48933
517-372-9070

University of Detroit Mercy
School of Dentistry
8200 W. Outer Dr.
Detroit, MI 48213
313-494-6700

University of Michigan
School of Dentistry
PO Box 44285
Detroit, MI 42844
734-763-6933

Minnesota

"First Call For Help"
651-224-1133
Minnesota Dental Association
2236 Marshall Ave.
St. Paul, MN 55104
651-646-7454; 800-950-3368

Neighborhood Health Care Network
651-489-2273

Senior Linkage Line
800-333-2433

University of Minnesota
School of Dentistry
515 S.E. Delaware St.
Minneapolis, MN 55455
612-624-8400

Mississippi

Mississippi Dental Association
2630 Ridgewood Rd.
Jackson, MS 39216
601-982-0442

University of Mississippi
School of Dentistry, Medical Ctr.
2500 N. State St.
Jackson, MS 39216
601-984-6155

Missouri

Missouri Dental Association
230 W. McCarty St.
Jefferson City, MO 65102
573-634-3436; 800-688-1907

University of Missouri
School of Dentistry
650 E. 25 St.
Kansas City, MO 64108
816-235-2111

Montana

Cooperative Health Dental Clinic
1930 Ninth Ave.
Helena, MT 59601
406-443-2584

Donated Dental Services
PO Box 1154
Helena, MT 59624
406-449-9670

Montana Dental Association
PO Box 1154
Helena, MT 59624
406-443-2061; 800-257-4988 (in MT only)

Nebraska

Senior Dent Program
Creighton University School of Dentistry
2802 Webster St.
Omaha, NE 68131
402-280-2865

Nebraska Dental Association
3120 O St.
Lincoln, NE 68510
402-476-1704; 800-234-3120

University of Nebraska Medical Ctr.
College of Dentistry
40th & Holdrege St.
PO Box 830740
Lincoln, NE 68583-0740
402-472-1333

Nevada

Nevada Dental Association
6889 W. Charleston Blvd., Ste. B
Las Vegas, NV 89117
702-255-4211; 800-962-6710

Welcome to the Beef Kitchen.
Shopping…handling…
storing…serving…left-
overs. Everything on the
Web at www.beef.org.
Source: The National
Cattlemen's Beef Association,
5420 S. Quebec St.,
Greenwood Village, CO 80111.

What You Need to Know About Moles and Dysplastic Nevi (atypical moles).
Free.

Source: National Cancer Institute, Box BL, Bldg. 31 Rm. 10A31, 31 Center Dr., MSC 2580, Bethesda, Maryland 20892-2580.

New Hampshire

New Hampshire Dental Society
PO Box 2229
Concord, NH 03302
603-225-5961; 800-244-5961 (in NH only)

New Jersey

New Jersey Dental Association
One Dental Plaza
PO Box 6020
North Brunswick, NJ 08902-6020
732-821-9400

University of Medicine & Dentistry New Jersey Dental School
110 Bergen St.
Newark, NJ 07103-2425
973-972-4242

New Mexico

New Mexico Dental Association
3736 Eubank Blvd. NE, Ste. D-2
Albuquerque, NM 87111
505-294-1368

New York

Columbia University School of Dental & Oral Surgery
622 W. 168 St.
New York, NY 10032
212-305-6726

New York State Dental Association
121 State St.
Albany, NY 12207
518-465-0044; 800-255-2100

New York University Kriser Dental Center
345 E. 24 St.
New York, NY 10010
212-998-9800

State University of New York School of Dental Medicine
3435 Main St.
Buffalo, NY 14214
716-829-2720

North Carolina

North Carolina Dental Society
PO Box 4099
Cary, NC 27519
919-677-1396

University of North Carolina School of Dentistry
Campus Box 7450
Chapel Hill, NC 27599-7450
919-966-1161

North Dakota

North Dakota Dental Association
Box 1332
Bismarck, ND 58502
701-223-8870; 800-795-8870

Ohio

Case Western Reserve Univ. School of Dentistry
2123 Emergency Dr.
Cleveland, OH 44106-4905
216-368-3200

Ohio Dental Association
1370 Dublin Rd.
Columbus, OH 43215
614-486-2700; 800-697-6453

Ohio State University College of Dentistry
Postle Hall
305 W. 12 Ave.
Columbus, OH 43210
614-292-2751

Options Program
635 W. Seventh St., Ste. 309
Cincinnati, OH 45203
513-621-2517; 888-765-6789

Oral Health Access Coordinator Bureau of Oral Health Services
246 N. High St.
Columbus, OH 43266-0118
614-466-4180

Oklahoma

Senior Dent/Care-Dent Programs
Oklahoma Dental Association
629 N.W. Grand Blvd.
Oklahoma City, OK 73118
405-848-8873; 800-876-8890

University of Oklahoma
Health Science Center
College of Dentistry
PO Box 26901
Oklahoma City, OK 73190-3044
405-271-6056

Oregon

Department of Health
Dental Health Division
Community Access Programs
800 N.E. Oregon St.
Portland, OR 97232
503-731-4098

Donated Dental Services
PO Box 66440
Portland, OR 97290
503-774-3898

Oregon Dental Association
17898 S.W. McEwan Rd.
Portland, OR 97224
503-620-3230; 800-452-5628

Oregon Health Services University
School of Dentistry
Sam Jackson Park
611 S.W. Campus Dr.
Portland, OR 97201
503-494-8867

Pennsylvania

Pennsylvania Dental Association
PO Box 3341
Harrisburg, PA 17105
717-234-5941; 800-692-7256

Temple University
School of Dentistry
3223 N. Broad St.
Philadelphia, PA 19140
215-707-2900

University of Pennsylvania
School of Dental Medicine
4001 Spruce St.
Philadelphia, PA 19104
215-898-8961

University of Pittsburgh
School of Dental Medicine
3501 Terrace St.
Pittsburgh, PA 15261
412-648-8615

Puerto Rico

Colegio de Cirujanos Dentistas
Avenida Domenech #200
Hato Rey, PR 00918
787-764-1969

University of Puerto Rico
School of Dentistry
GPO Box 5067
San Juan, PR 00936
787-758-2525

Rhode Island

Rhode Island Dental Association
200 Centerville Pl.
Warwick, RI 02886
401-732-6833

South Carolina

Medical University of South Carolina
College of Dental Medicine
169 Ashley Ave.
Charleston, SC 29425
843-792-2300

Medicare & You.
Handbook is also available in large type, braille or on audiocassette. Free.
Source: US Department of Health and Human Services, Health Care Financing Administration, 7500 Security Blvd., Baltimore 21244. www. medicare.gov or 800-633-4227.

Ten Guides to Proper Medicine Use. Tips on reading medical labels and other safety tips.

Source: Council on Family Health, 1155 Connecticut Ave. NW, Ste. 400, Washington, DC 20036. Include a business-sized SASE. Or go to www.cfhinfo.org.

Senior Care Dental Program
South Carolina Dental Association
120 Stonemark Lane
Columbia, SC 29210
803-750-2277; 800-327-2598

South Dakota

South Dakota Dental Association
PO Box 1194
711 Wells, #240
Pierre, SD 57501
605-224-9133

Tennessee

Meharry Medical College
School of Dentistry
1005 Dr. D.B. Todd Blvd.
Nashville, TN 37208
615-327-6669

Tennessee Dental Association
PO Box 120188
Nashville, TN 37212
615-383-8962

Tennessee Department of Dentistry
Cordell Hull Bldg.
425 Fifth Ave. N
Nashville, TN 37247-1010
615-532-5073

University of Tennessee
College of Dentistry Clinic
875 Union Ave.
Memphis, TN 38163
901-448-6221

 ## Texas

Texas A&M University System
Baylor College of Dentistry
3302 Gaston Ave.
Dallas, TX 75246
214-828-8100

Texas Dental Association
1946 S. IH-35, Ste. 400
Austin, TX 78704
512-443-3675

University of Texas
Health Science Center
Dental Branch
6516 MD Anderson Blvd.
Houston, TX 77030
713-500-4000

University of Texas
Dental School
7703 Floyd Curl Dr.
San Antonio, TX 78209
210-567-3222; 210-567-3217

 ## Utah

Department of Health
Dental Health Division
1365 W. 1000 N
Salt Lake City, UT 84116
801-328-5756

Utah Dental Association
1151 E. 3900 S, Ste. B160
Salt Lake City, UT 84124
801-261-5315; 800-662-6500

Vermont

Island Pond Health Center
Dental Program
PO Box 425
Island Pond, VT 05846
802-723-4300

Vermont Dental Society
100 Dorset St., Ste. 18
South Burlington, VT 05403
802-864-0115

 ## Virginia

Health Department
Dental Division
1500 E. Main St., Room 136
Richmond, VA 23219
804-786-3556

Virginia Commonwealth Univ.
School of Dentistry Clinic
520 N. 12 St.
Richmond, VA 23286
804-828-9190

Washington

**Elderly and Disabled
Washington State Dental Assn.**
2033 Sixth Ave., Ste. 333
Seattle, WA 98121
206-448-1914

**University of Washington
School of Dentistry**
E318 Health Sciences Center, Box 356370
Seattle, WA 98195
206-543-5830

West Virginia

West Virginia Dental Association
2003 Quarrier St.
Charleston, WV 25311
304-344-5246

**West Virginia University
School of Dentistry**
Health Sciences Center—North
PO Box 9465
Morgantown, WV 26506-9400
304-293-2459

Wisconsin

**Dane County Public Health
  Division
Dental Health Program**
1202 Northport Dr.
Madison, WI 53716
608-242-6510

**Marquette University
School of Dentistry**
604 N. 16 St.
Milwaukee, WI 53233
414-288-6500

Wisconsin Dental Association
111 E. Wisconsin Ave., Ste. 1300
Milwaukee, WI 53202
414-276-4520; 800-364-7646

Wyoming

State Health Department
Dental Program
Hathaway Building, 4th flr.
Cheyenne, WY 82002
307-777-7945

Wyoming Dental Association
502 S. Fourth St.
Laramie, WY 82070
307-755-4009; 800-244-0779

**How to Brush and
Floss.** Illustrated, step-
by-step instructions for
the most effective oral
care. Free.
Source: American Academy of
Periodontology, Suite 800,
737 N. Michigan Ave.,
Chicago 60611-2690. 800-
356-7736. On the Web at
www.perio.org.

271

Job Training Programs For Seniors

Job Training Programs for Seniors

The government offers excellent programs aimed at helping seniors get back into the workforce. Listed below are state offices to contact for information about training programs in your area. When you call, ask about the Senior Community Service Employment Program (Title V) and also Job Training Partnership Act Programs (JTPA). These agencies offer job training, help with job searches and resume writing and more. They also offer financial assistance to companies who hire graduates of these programs.

Alabama
Commission on Aging
334-242-5743

Department of Economic & Community Affairs
334-242-5300

Alaska
Alaskan Commission on Aging
907-465-3250

Department of Labor Employment Security Division
907-465-5545

Arizona
Department of Economic Security
602-542-4446

Arkansas
Division of Aging & Adult Services
501-682-2441

Department of Labor, JTPA
501-682-4500

Workforce Investment
501-371-1020

California
Department of Aging
916-327-0575

Employment Development, JTPA
916-654-7110

Colorado
Department of Labor & Employment
303-620-4200

Connecticut
Social Services/Elderly Services Division
860-424-5293

Delaware
Services for Aging & Adults with Physical Disabilities
302-577-4660

District of Columbia
Office on Aging
202-724-3662

Department of Employment Services Senior Aid Office
202-724-7073

Florida
Department of Elder Affairs
800-96-ELDER

Georgia
Division of Aging Services
404-657-5330

Hawaii
Office on Aging
808-586-0100

Honolulu Community Action Program
808-521-4531

Idaho
Commission on Aging
208-334-3833

Staffing and Temporary Jobs: Making Them Work for You. What you should look for in a temporary job...how to take advantage of different opportunities.
Source: American Staffing Association, 277 S. Washington St., Ste. 200, Alexandria, VA 22314. Go to the Web site at www.natss.org.

Resource Directory for Small Business Management. Useful publications and video-tapes for starting and managing a small business.

Source: US Small Business Administration, Washington, DC. 800-827-5722.

Illinois

Department on Aging
312-814-2630; 800-252-8966 (in IL only)

Department of Commerce & Community Affairs
217-782-7500

Indiana

Disability, Aging & Rehabilitation Services
317-232-7000

Iowa

Department of Elder Affairs
515-281-5187

Kansas

Department on Aging
785-296-4986

Kentucky

Social Services/Aging Services Division
502-564-6930

JTPA Coordinator
502-564-5360

 ## Louisiana

Office of Elderly Affairs
225-342-7100

Maine

Bureau of Elder Services
207-624-5120; 207-474-4950

Bureau of Employment Services, JTPA
207-624-5120; 800-760-1573 (in ME only)

 ## Maryland

Department of Aging
410-767-1102; 800-AGE-DIAL (in MD only)

 ## Massachusetts

Office of Elder Affairs
617-727-7750; 800-882-2003 (in MA only)

Michigan

Office of Services to the Aging
517-373-8230

Department of Career Development
517-241-4000

Minnesota

Board on Aging
800-882-6262
Senior Linkage Line
800-333-2433
Office of Aging and Adult Services
651-296-2544

Mississippi

Division of Aging & Adult Services
800-948-3090

Missouri

Division of Workforce Development
800-877-8698

Montana

Green Thumb Program
406-761-4821

Montana JTPA
406-444-1309

Nebraska

Division of Aging and Disability Services
402-471-2307

Nevada

Nevada Business Services, JTPA
702-647-4929

New Hampshire

AARP
603-224-6095

Workforce Opportunity Council, JTPA
603-228-9500; 800-772-7001 (in NH only)

New Jersey

Department of Labor, JTPA
609-292-5005

New Mexico

State Agency on Aging
505-827-7640; 800-432-2080 (in NM only)

Department of Labor, JTPA
505-827-6827

New York

State Office for the Aging
518-474-4425; 800-342-9871 (in NY only)

North Carolina

Division of Aging
919-733-3983

Division of Employment &
Training, JTPA
919-661-6010

North Dakota

Aging Services Division, JTPA
701-328-8910

Green Thumb Program
701-258-8879

Ohio

Department of Aging
614-466-5500

Employment Services, JTPA
614-466-3817

Oklahoma

Aging Services Division
405-521-2327

Oregon

Department of Human Resources
Seniors and Disabled Services
Division
503-945-6413

Pennsylvania

Department of Aging
717-783-1550

Bureau of Workforce Investment,
JTPA
717-787-3354

Rhode Island

Department of Elderly Affairs
401-222-2858

South Carolina

Office on Aging
803-898-2850

Employment Security Commission,
WIA
803-737-9935

South Dakota

Green Thumb Program
605-332-7991

Tennessee

Commission on Aging
615-741-2056

Department of Labor, WIA Office
615-741-1031; 800-255-5872

Texas

Senior Texans Employment
Program
254-776-7002

**Office Equipment
Etiquette:
Remember Others.**
Seven rules of courtesy
for employees to
practice.
Source: Brody Communications
Ltd. 815 Greenwood Ave.,
Ste. 8, Jenkintown, PA 19046.
Include a business-sized SASE.
Or call 800-726-7936.

**Pick Your Poison:
The Most Common
Self-Defeating
Behaviors in
Business.**
Source: Mark Goulston, MD,
1150 Yale St., Ste. 3, Santa
Monica, CA 90403-4722.
Include a business-sized SASE.

Utah

Division of Aging Services
801-538-3910

**Department of Workforce
Services**
801-524-9011; 801-536-7157

Vermont

Department of Aging & Disabilities
802-241-2400

Vermont Training & Development
802-524-3200

Virginia

**Employment Security Department,
Training Division**
804-662-9333

Washington

**Employment Security Department,
Training Division**
360-438-4611

West Virginia

Bureau of Senior Services
304-558-3317

JTPA Employment Services
304-558-5920

Wisconsin

**Department of Workforce
Development**
608-266-3131

Wyoming

Senior Citizens Office
307-635-1245

Colleges with Special Programs For Seniors

Thinking About School?

If you have been thinking about how great it would be to go back to college either to finish your education or to get it started again, there is something very important you should know. There are colleges throughout the US that offer special free or low-cost tuition programs for seniors. Many colleges let you take the courses for full college credit. At others you can take courses just for the fun of it. But one thing is for sure-you can't beat the price.

The listings below are by no means complete. Because of the increase in the 55+ age group, more and more colleges are adding courses and special programs for seniors. If there is a particular college in your town that you might want to attend, call and ask if there are any programs for seniors.

Alabama

Gadsden State Community College
Admissions
PO Box 227
Gadsden, AL 35902-0227
256-549-8200; 800-226-5563
Web site: www.gadsdenst.cc.al.us

The minimum age is 60 and you must be a state resident.
Tuition: Free.
There will be fees for books, parking, etc. Check with the registrar. Courses can be taken for credit if you have a high school or GED diploma.

Jefferson State Community College
Admissions
Northeast Campus
2601 Carson Rd.

Birmingham, AL 35215
205-853-1200
Scrushy Campus
4600 Valleydale Rd.
Birmingham, AL 35242
205-520-5900
Web site: www.jscc.cc.al.us

The minimum age is 60 and you must be a state resident.
Tuition: Free, plus utilities and technology fee of about $4 each per credit.
Courses can be taken for credit on a space available basis.

Alaska

University of Alaska Southeast
Admissions
11120 Glacier Hwy.
Juneau, AK 99801
907-465-6457
Web site: www.jun.alaska.edu

The minimum age is 60 and you must be a state resident.
Tuition is waived, but you must sign up for class on or after the first day of class.
There are additional fees for student government, lab, General Technology, books and materials. You can take unlimited classes for credit provided there is space.

Arkansas

Arkansas State University
Admissions
PO Box 1630
State University, AR 72467
800-382-3030; 870-972-3024
Web site: www.astate.edu

The minimum age is 60 and you must be a state resident.
The tuition is free and courses can be taken for credit. Other charges related to courses will apply. See Treasurer's office after registering.

What Colleges Don't Tell You. Questions to ask to find out what a school is really like—class sizes...teachers ...activities...financial aid...and personal safety.
Source: Case Western Reserve University, Office of Undergraduate Admission, 10900 Euclid Ave., Cleveland 44106. www.cwru.edu. 216-368-2000

Listen to College-level Courses in Your Home or Car. Catalog of audio and video courses featuring professors from top universities on business, fine arts, history, literature, philosophy, religion, science.

Source: The Teaching Co., 800-832-2412. www.teachco.com

Arkansas State University—Beebe
PO Box 1000
Beebe, AR 72012-1000
501-882-8260; 800-632-9985 (in AR only)
Web site: www.asub.edu

The minimum age is 60.
Tuition: Free.
Courses can be taken for credit.
There are basic fees for books, parking, etc.
Special 60's Club for computer and leisure arts classes. Call 501-882-8232.

California

 California State University, Chico
400 W. First St.
Chico, CA 95929-0722
800-542-4426; 530-898-4636
Web site: www.csuchico.edu

The minimum age is 60 and you must be a state resident.
Tuition: $93.00 per semester. Fees for books and activities are extra.
They also have Elder College where students audit only, which is $45.00 per semester.
Both programs are based on space available.

Colorado

 University of Colorado, Boulder
Senior Auditors Program
CU Boulder Alumni Association
Campus Box 459
Boulder, CO 80309
303-492-1411
Web site: www.colorado.edu

The minimum age is 55.
Tuition: One-time fee of $35.00 ($5 for alumni). Only for Colorado residents.
No classes for credit. On a space available basis.

University of Colorado at Denver
Office of Enrollment and Student Affairs
CU-Denver Bldg.
1250 14th St., Ste. 700
Denver, CO 80217
303-556-4372
Web site: www.cudenver.edu

The minimum age is 60. You must be a state resident.
Tuition: Free, plus books and materials.
No grade or credit is given. No limit on the number if courses, but acceptance in each course on a space availability basis.

Connecticut

 University of Connecticut, Storrs
One Bishop Circle, U-56C
Storrs, CT 06269
860-486-2000
Web site: www.uconn.edu

The minimum age is 62 and you must be a state resident.
Tuition: $15.00 per course.
Fees are waived and courses cannot be taken for credit. Audit card must be signed by instructor ahead of time.

University of Hartford Graduate and Adult Academic Services
200 Bloomfield Ave.
West Hartford, CT 06117
860-768-4371
Web site: www.hartford.edu

The minimum age is 65.
Tuition: Any undergraduate course can be audited free. Parking also free.
Fees for books, activities, etc.

Delaware

Delaware Technical and Community College, Owens Campus
PO Box 610, Route 18
Georgetown, DE 19947
302-856-5400
Web site: www.dtcc.edu

The minimum age is 60, and you must be a resident.

Tuition: Free, but there are some fees.

There is an Adult Plus program with special interest courses for people 50+. Call 302-856-5618.

District of Columbia

American University Institute for Learning and Retirement
4400 Massachusetts Ave. NW
Washington, DC 20016
202-885-1000
Web site: www.american.edu

They offer non-credit, low-cost classes for retired people.

The cost is $190 per semester, or $350 for both semesters. There is also a free summer lecture program.

Florida

Florida Institute of Technology
150 W. University Blvd.
Melbourne, FL 32901
800-888-4348; 321-674-8030
Web site: www.fit.edu

The minimum age is 65.

Tuition: Free for a limited number of courses.

There are academic prerequisites for some classes.

Georgia

Augusta State University
2500 Walton Way
Augusta, GA 30904
706-737-1632; 800-341-4373
Web site: www.aug.edu

Seniors 62 and older can take courses free, providing there is space available. To study for credit, you must apply and be accepted as a regular student.

Piedmont College
PO Box 10
165 Central Ave.
Demorest, GA 30535
706-778-3000; 800-277-7020
Web site: www.piedmont.edu

Seniors can attend classes at discounted prices. They can also register to audit a class as a guest, if they are not enrolled for credit at the same time.

Idaho

Boise State University
1910 University Dr.
Boise, ID 83725
208-426-1011
Web site: www.boisestate.edu

The minimum age is 60 and you must be a state resident.

Tuition: $20 registration fee, and $5 per credit, plus related course fees.

Courses can be taken for credit.

College of Southern Idaho
Admissions
PO Box 1238
315 Falls Ave.
Twin Falls, ID 80000-1238
208-733-9554
800-6800-CSI (in ID only)
Web site: www.csi.cc.id.us

College Video Tours. "Visit" a college without traveling. Choose from more than 330 colleges and universities. $15 per tour—averaging one hour each. Free list. *Source:* Collegiate Choice Walking Tours Videos, 41 Surrey Ln., Tenafly, NJ 07670 ...or www.collegiatechoice.com.

Attention Deficits: Tools for Success. Brochures and other information on special diets and teaching other skills to children with attention deficit disorder.

Source: Feingold Association. Call 800-321-3287, or go to the Web site at www.feingold.org.

The minimum age is 60 and you must be a state resident.

You must get a Gold Card from the Office on Aging to take classes for free. There is a fee for books, activities and supplies.

There is a special program for seniors over 60 called "Getting Fit."

Illinois

Southwestern Illinois College
2500 Carlyle Ave.
Belleville, IL 62221
618-235-2700
Web site: www.southwestern.cc.il.us

The minimum age is 62.
Tuition: $5.00 off per credit hour for credit courses.

Indiana

Ball State University Teachers College
Room 1008
Muncie, IN 47306
765-285-1643; 800-482-4BSU
Web site: www.bsu.edu

The minimum age is 60.
Tuition: Seniors pay half the fee rate, and there is no limit on the number of courses.

Indiana University–Purdue
Office of Admissions
University Fort Wayne
2101 E. Coliseum Blvd.
Fort Wayne, IN 46805
219-481-6824
Web site: www.ipfw.edu

The minimum age is 60 and you must be a state resident who is not employed full time.
Tuition: One-half off the regular state resident fee.

You must register during the final registration (providing there is room). The courses can be taken for credit, up to a maximum of 9 credit hours. The only cost is for books.

University of Southern Indiana
8600 University Blvd.
Evansville, IN 47712-3596
812-464-1765
Web site: www.usi.edu

The minimum age is 60 and you must be a state resident.
Call and speak with the Adult Counselor.

Iowa

Iowa Western Community College
2700 College Rd.
Council Bluffs, IA 51503
712-325-3200; 800-432-5852
Web site: www.iwcc.cc.ia.us

The minimum age is 60 and you must be a state resident.

You can attend classes for credit at a reduced tuition. The reduced rate would be equal to 50% of the regular hourly rate, and you are allowed 3 credit hours per semester.

Kansas

Baker University
PO Box 65
618 Eighth Street
Baldwin City, KS 66006-0065
800-873-4282; 785-594-6451
Web site: www.bakeru.edu

The minimum age is 55 and you must be a state resident.

You can take one non-degree-seeking course at a time on a space available basis. All fees are waived except course supplies.

Kentucky

Kentucky State University
400 E. Main St.
Frankfort, KY 40601
502-597-6000
Web site: www.kysu.edu

The minimum age is 65 and you must be a state resident.

Seniors can take courses for credit on a space available basis. All tuition and fees are waived.

Midway College
512 E. Stephens St.
Midway, KY 40347
859-846-5346
Web site: www.midway.edu

The Lewis and Ann Piper Scholarship Program allows seniors aged 60+ (must be a state resident) to take academic courses with all tuition waived. Women can take courses for credit or audit. Men take courses through the Career Development School.

Courses can be audited or taken for credit.

University of Kentucky
Donovan Scholar Program
Ligon House
Lexington, KY 40506-0042
859-257-9000
Web site: www.uky.edu

The Herman L. Donovan Senior Citizens Fellowship Program offers seniors aged 65 free tuition for credit or noncredit. There are fees for books and supplies.

Another program of free, noncredit courses and activities is available for people 60 and older.

Louisiana

Louisiana State University at Alexandria
8100 Highway 71 S
Alexandria, LA 71302
318-473-6423
Web site: www.lsu.edu

The minimum age for seniors is 65 and you must be a state resident.

Tuition: Free.

You pay for books, application fee and supplies. Courses can be taken for credit or audited.

Louisiana State University at Baton Rouge
110 Thomas Boyd Hall
Baton Rouge, LA 70803
225-578-1175
Web site: www.lsu.edu

The minimum age for seniors is 65 and you must be a state resident.

Tuition: Free.

You pay for books, application fee and supplies.

Maine

University of Maine-Augusta
46 University Dr.
Augusta, ME 04330
207-621-3000
Web site: www.uma.maine.edu

The minimum age for seniors is 65 and you must be a state resident.

Tuition: Free.

Books and supplies are extra. Registration on a space available basis.

University of Maine-Fort Kent
23 University Drive
Fort Kent, ME 04743
888-879-8635
Web site: www.umfk.maine.edu

The minimum age for seniors is 65 and you must be a state resident.

You can apply for a tuition waiver (must show financial need) and can take any course for credit or audit.

Maryland

St. Mary's College of Maryland
18952 E. Fisher Rd.
St. Mary's City, MD 20686-3001
240-895-2000
Web site: www.smcm.edu

The minimum age for seniors is 60 and you cannot have full-time employment.

Tuition: Free.

Summer School for Seniors. Two- to 10-week vacation/education programs at eight world-renowned universities in the US and Canada. Free brochure.

Source: Senior Summer School, Inc., Box 4424, Deerfield Beach, FL 33442-4424. www.seniorsummerschool.com or 800-847-2466.

The Story of the Federal Reserve System. Nontechnical, comic book-style summary of how the Fed works.

Source: Federal Reserve Bank of New York, Public Information Dept., 33 Liberty St., New York 10045...or at www.ny.frb.org/pihome.

Courses can be taken for credit or noncredit on a space available basis. You pay for books, supplies and parking.

Western Maryland College
2 College Hill
Westminster, MD 21157
800-638-5005; 410-848-7000
Web site: www.wmdc.edu

The minimum age for seniors is 54 for undergraduate classes and 60 for graduate classes, and you must be a county resident.

Tuition: $25 per class.

Courses can be taken for noncredit.

Massachusetts

Boston University
Evergreen Program
121 Bay State Road
Boston, MA 02215
617-353-9852
Web site: www.bu.edu

The minimum age for seniors is 60.

Tuition: $35 per course.

No credit for courses.

Michigan

Central Michigan University
Registrar's Office
105 Warriner Hall
Mount Pleasant, MI 48859
989-774-4000
Web site: www.cmich.edu

The minimum age is 60 and you must be a state resident for at least a year.

Tuition: Free, subject to available space.

No credit for the courses. There is a fee for parking, books and supplies.

Spring Arbor University
106 E. Main
Spring Arbor, MI 49283
800-968-9103
Web site: www.arbor.edu

The minimum age is 65.

Tuition: $25 per credit hour, and up to two courses may be taken for credit. Additional fees for specific course materials.

You can take up to 6 hours in any semester.

Minnesota

University of Minnesota
200 Fraser Hall
106 Pleasant St. SE
Minneapolis, MN 55455
612-625-5333
Web site: www.umn.edu

The minimum age is 62.

Tuition: $9 per credit hour, for credit, or free if audit. Register after first class meeting, if space available.

Riverland Community College
1900 Eighth Ave. NW
Austin, MN 55912
507-433-0600; 800-247-5039
Web site: www.riverland.cc.mn.us/

The minimum age is 62.

Tuition: $10 per credit, plus fees. Same price if auditing.

You can take courses for credit, on a space available basis.

Mississippi

Delta State University
Admissions Office
Cleveland, MS 38733
662-846-4655
Web site: www.deltast.edu

The minimum age for seniors is 60 and you must be a state resident.

Tuition: $25 per course for credit.

Mississippi Gulf Coast Community College, Jackson County Campus
Admissions
PO Box 100
Gautier, MS 39553
228-497-7800
Web site: www.mgccc.cc.ms.us

The minimum age is 62. You must be a state resident and retired.

Tuition: Free for regular courses for credit. Pay only for books and activity fees.

Missouri

Crowder College
601 Laclede Ave.
Neosho, MO 64850
417-451-3223
Web site: www.crowder.cc.mo.us

The minimum age is 60 and you must be a state resident in the district.

Tuition: Free, plus $25 registration fee, and books, supplies, etc.

Courses can be taken for credit.

Missouri Western State College
4525 Downs Dr.
St. Joseph, MO 64507
816-271-4200
Web site: www.mwsc.edu

The minimum age is 60 and you must be a state resident.

Tuition: Call for current rates, for credit or noncredit.

Montana

Montana Tech of the University of Montana
11300 West Park St.
Butte, MT 59701
800-445-8324
Web site: www.mtech.edu

The minimum age is 62 and you must be a state resident.

Tuition: Call Registrar's office for current discounted amount per credit.

University of Montana
Missoula, MT 59812
406-243-6266
Web site: www.umt.edu

The minimum age is 62 and you must be a state resident.

They have the Golden College plan for seniors where you attend college for credit or noncredit for greatly reduced tuition (about 20%).

Nebraska

McCook Community College
1205 E. Third St.
McCook, NE 69001
308-345-6303; 800-658-4348
Web site: www.mcc.mccook.cc.ne.us/mcc/index.html

The minimum age is 60 and you must be a state resident.

Tuition: Free, plus fees and books.

Courses are given for noncredit.

Mid-Plains Community College
601 W. State Farm Rd.
North Platte, NE 69101
308-532-8740; 800-658-4308
Web site: www.mccook.cc.ne.us

The minimum age is 60 and you must be a state resident.

Tuition: Free.

The only cost is books, activity fees and supplies.

Nevada

University of Nevada, Las Vegas
4505 Maryland Pkwy.
Las Vegas, NV 89154
702-895-3011
Web site: www.unlv.edu

The minimum age is 62 and you must be a state resident for at least one year in order to take academic courses for credit.

Tuition: Free during the year, and half price in the summer.

There is also a special Learning in Retirement program for retired or semi-retired people,

Home-schooling Catalog. Books on language arts…math …science…history… geography…music… and arts.

Source: The Home School, 800-788-1221.

with no age or residency requirements.

Western Nevada Community College
2201 W. College Pkwy.
Carson City, NV 89703
775-445-3277
Web site: www.wncc.nevada.edu

The minimum age is 62 and you must be a state resident.

Tuition: Free.

You can take courses for credit. Your only cost is books and lab fees.

New Hampshire

New Hampshire Community Technical College, Manchester
1066 Front St.
Manchester, NH 03102
603-668-6706
Web site: www.manch.tcc.nh.us

The minimum age is 65 and you must be a state resident.

Tuition: 50%.

You can take courses for credit.

University of New Hampshire at Manchester
220 Hackett Hill Rd.
Manchester, NH 03102
603-668-0700
Web site: www.unh.edu/unhm

The minimum age is 65 and you must be a state resident.

Tuition: Free.

You can take up to 2 courses per semester (subject to available space). The only cost would be a registration fee, books and supplies. You can take courses for credit or noncredit.

New Jersey

Bloomfield College
1 Park Place
Bloomfield, NJ 07003
973-748-9000
Web site: www.bloomfield.edu

The minimum age is 62 and you must be a state resident.

Tuition: $15 for the course (subject to available space), plus fees.

You can take the course for credit or noncredit and the college sets aside a day just for seniors to register.

Fairleigh Dickinson University
1000 River Rd.
Teaneck, NJ 07666
201-692-2214
285 Madison Ave.
Madison, NJ 07940
973-443-8500
Web site: www.fdu.edu

The minimum age is 65 and you must be a resident to join the Educational Program for Older Persons. For a small fee, members may enroll in graduate or undergraduate courses on a space available basis, either for credit or noncredit.

New Mexico

New Mexico State University at Almogordo
Admissions
2400 N. Scenic Dr.
Almogordo, NM 88310
505-439-3700
Web site: www.alamo.nmsu.edu

The minimum age is 65 and you must be a state resident.

Tuition: $8 per credit hour, plus $15 one-time admission fee.

Seniors can take courses for credit or noncredit.

New York

City University of New York
Hunter College
Admissions
695 Park Ave., room 100N
New York, NY 10021
212-772-4490
Web site: www.hunter.cuny.edu

Colleges with Special Programs for Seniors

The minimum age is 60 and you must be a state resident.

Tuition: $65 per semester or session, plus $5 for services.

A senior can audit any 2 classes.

SUNY Purchase
735 Anderson Hill Rd.
Purchase, NY 10577
914-251-6300, ext. 6500
Web site: www.purchase.edu
E-mail: admisweb@purchase.edu

The minimum age is 60 and you must be a state resident.

Tuition: $50 per class to audit classes, provided there is room.

Registration for seniors is usually after full-tuition paying students have registered for their classes.

Wells College
Route 90
Aurora, NY 13026
800-952-9355
Web site: www.wells.edu

The minimum age is 62. Seniors can audit any course for $20 per class, provided there is room in the class.

North Carolina

Appalachian State University
Boone, NC 28608
828-262-2120
Web site: www.appstate.edu

The minimum age is 65 and you must be a state resident.

Tuition: Free.

You can take one course for credit or noncredit. There are fees for books, supplies and activities.

North Dakota

North Dakota State University
PO Box 5454
Fargo, ND 58105
701-231-8643
Web site: www.ndsu.nodak.edu

Tuition: All fees waived.

They have a "Project 65" program, where seniors aged 65+ can audit classes for free.

Ohio

Bowling Green State University
Dept. of Continuing Education
40 College Park
Bowling Green, OH 43403
877-650-8165 (tool free)
Web site: www.bgsu.edu

They have a program for seniors called the SAGE Program, where seniors aged 60 and over can take any credit courses free (subject to available space). You must be a state resident. You pay only for books, supplies and labs. No credit is given for the courses.

Lake Erie College
391 W. Washington St.
Painesville, OH 44077
800-533-4996
Web site: www.lakeerie.edu

Tuition: Free to audit any course (no credit), plus fees, provided there is room in the class.

Must be a state resident.

Oklahoma

Oklahoma State University
104 Whitehurst
Stillwater, OK 74078
405-744-6858
Web site: www.okstate.edu

The minimum age for seniors is 65.

Tuition: Free to audit any course.

There is a fee for books and other supplies. No credit for audited courses.

Stargazing: Weekly Guide to Visible Stars and Planets.
Source: From the editors of Sky & Telescope. www.skypub.com. Click on Sights.

Smithsonian Study Tours—International and Domestic. Trips to 250 destinations… accompanied by scholars and experts. Free brochure.

Source: Smithsonian Study Tours, 1100 Jefferson Dr. SW, Washington, DC 20560. www.si.edu/tsa/sst or 202-357-4700.

Oregon

Oregon Institute of Technology
3201 Campus Dr.
Klamath Falls, OR 97601
800-422-2017
Web site: www.oit.edu

The minimum age for seniors is 65.

Tuition: Free.

The classes can be only for noncredit, and are on a space available basis. They also run an Elderhostel Program during the summer.

Pennsylvania

University of Pennsylvania
3440 Market St., Suite 100
Philadelphia, PA 19104
215-898-7326
Web site: www.upenn.edu

The minimum age is 65.

Tuition: $50 per class.

No credit. Two classes per semester.

Rhode Island

Rhode Island College
600 Mt. Pleasant Ave.
Providence, RI 02908
401-456-8033
Web site: www.ric.edu

Seniors who are at least 60 and residents of the state are eligible.

Tuition: Free tuition plus lab or other course-specific fees. You must have academic prerequisites, and may have to take the Senior Citizens Means Test. Registration only on last day, and on space available basis.

South Carolina

Clemson University
Registrar's Office
105 Sikes Hall
Clemson, SC 29634-5307
864-656-2171
Web site: www.clemson.edu

The minimum age for seniors is 60 and you must be a state resident. Pick up audit cards and waiver forms at the Registrar's office.

Tuition: Free to audit or take any course (space available).

Books and supplies are additional.

South Dakota

Dakota Wesleyan University
1200 W. University Ave.
Mitchell, SD 57301
800-333-8506; 605-995-2650
Web site: www.dwu.edu

Seniors aged 65 or older can enroll in the Blue and White Club program, which enables them to audit any classes (subject to available space) for free tuition.

Tennessee

Tennessee State University
3500 John Merritt Blvd.
Nashville, TN 37209
615-963-5101
Web site: www.tnstate.edu

The minimum age for seniors is 65 and they must be residents of the state.

Tuition: Call Business office for details.

Texas

University of Houston
Central Campus
Bursar's Office
6 Ezekiel W. Cullen Bldg.
Houston, TX 77204-2160
713-743-1096
Web site: www.uh.edu

The minimum age is 65 and you must be a state resident.
Tuition: Free, for noncredit courses. Other miscellaneous fees apply.

For credit you may take up to 6 hours of courses each semester without tuition payment, on a space available basis.

University of North Texas
PO Box 311277
Denton, TX 76203
940-565-2681; 800-UNT-8211
Web site: www.unt.edu

The minimum age is 65.
Tuition: Free.
No credit for the courses.

Utah

Brigham Young University
BYU Evening Classes
122 Harman Bldg.
Provo, UT 84602
801-378-2872
Web site: www.byu.edu

The minimum age is 55 and must be a state resident.
Tuition: $10.00 per class.
Seniors can take any course, but not for credit.

Utah State University
Registrar
1600 Old Main Hill
Logan, UT 84322-1600
435-797-0425 (summer program for seniors); or 435-797-1101
Web site: www.usu.edu

The minimum age is 62 and must be a resident of the state.
Tuition: $10.00 per semester, but no credit is given.

Vermont

Castleton State College
Business Office
Castleton, VT 05735
802-468-1216
Web site: www.csc.vsc.edu

Any senior 62 or older receiving retirement benefits can attend.
Tuition: Free, plus fees.
Any course can be taken for credit.

Virginia

University of Virginia's College at Wise
Admissions
1 College Ave.
Wise, VA 24293
888-282-9324
Web site: www.wise.virginia.edu

Seniors aged 60+ and residents of Virginia (if taxable income for previous year does not exceed $10,000) can take courses for free.

Any senior regardless of income can audit or take non-credit courses for free.

College of William and Mary
Burser's Office
PO Box 8795
Williamsburg, VA 23187
757-221-1220
Web site: www.wm.edu

Any senior 60 years or older and a state resident can audit classes for noncredit free. If they want to take classes for credit, the tuition will be waived for them if taxable income is under $10,000.

Washington

University of Washington
Access Program
Box 355850
Seattle, WA 98195-5850
206-543-8580
Web site: www.washington.edu

The minimum age for seniors is 60 and must be a state resident.
Tuition: Each quarter $5 fee, plus $4 per credit.

General Information Concerning Patents.
Free.
Source: US Dept. of Commerce, Patent and Trademark Office, 800-786-9199…or at www.uspto.gov on the Web.

West Virginia

West Virginia State College
Cashier's Office
PO Box 368
Institute, WV 25112
800-987-2112; 304-766-3141
Web site: www.wvsc.edu

Seniors aged 65 or older can take classes at half price for credit, providing space is available in the class. Tell Cashier's Office to be sure to get reimbursed.

Wisconsin

University of Wisconsin-Milwaukee-OARSS
PO Box 749
Milwaukee, WI 53201
414-229-6732
Web site: www.uwm.edu

Any residents 60 or older can audit courses for free, so long as they have the prerequisites, if any are required.

Wyoming

University of Wyoming
PO Box 3435
Laramie, WY 82071
307-766-5160
Web site: www.uwyo.edu

The minimum age for seniors is 65 and must be a state resident.

Tuition: Free.

Courses can be taken for credit or noncredit. There is a fee for books, supplies and computers.

Nursing Home Complaints

Help with Long-Term Care

In each state there is a Long-Term-Care Ombudsman who is there to investigate complaints about nursing homes. This person acts on behalf of nursing home residents and mediates disputes between nursing homes and residents or their families. The ombudsman is also ready to help if you need information on the nursing homes in your state.

Alabama
334-242-5743

Alaska
907-334-4480

Arizona
602-542-4446

Arkansas
501-682-8952

California
916-323-6681

Colorado
303-722-0300

Connecticut
860-424-5200

Delaware
302-577-4791

District of Columbia
202-434-2140

Florida
850-488-6190

Georgia
404-657-5319

Hawaii
808-586-0100

Idaho
208-334-3833

Illinois
217-785-3143

Indiana
317-232-7134

Iowa
515-242-3327

Kansas
785-296-3017

Kentucky
502-564-6930

Louisiana
225-342-7100

Maine
207-621-1079

Maryland
410-767-1074

Massachusetts
617-727-7750

Michigan
517-347-7398
800-292-7852 (MI only)

Minnesota
651-296-0382

Mississippi
601-359-4927

Missouri
573-526-0727

Montana
406-444-4077

Nevada
702-486-3545

New Hampshire
603-271-4375

New Jersey
609-943-4026

New Mexico
505-255-0971

New York
518-474-7329

North Carolina
919-733-8395

North Dakota
701-328-8910

Ohio
614-466-1221

Oklahoma
405-521-6734

Prescription Medicines and You.
Source: Agency for Healthcare Research, PO Box 8547, Publications Clearinghouse, Silver Spring, MD 20907-8547.

**Estate-Planning
Basics.** Conserving
family assets for the
long term. Free.
Source: The Vanguard Group,
800-523-7731.

Oregon
503-378-6533

Pennsylvania
717-783-7247

South Carolina
803-898-2850

South Dakota
605-773-3656

Tennessee
615-741-2056

Texas
512-424-6840

Utah
801-538-3910

Vermont
802-863-5620

Virginia
804-644-2923

Washington
253-838-6810

West Virginia
304-558-3317

Wisconsin
608-266-8945
800-815-0015 (nationwide)

Wyoming
307-322-5553

Puerto Rico
787-725-1515

Free Help From Your State Government

Your State Government Can Help

All 50 state governments have a phone number to call if you are having problems or need the assistance of a state agency. For example, if you have a housing problem or a consumer complaint and don't know where to turn, you can call the phone number listed here and you will be referred directly to the state agency in your area where someone can help you solve whatever problem you are having.

Alabama
334-242-8000

Alaska
907-465-2111

Arizona
602-542-4900

Arkansas
501-682-3000

California
Northern
916-322-9900
Southern
213-620-3030

Colorado
303-866-5000; 800-332-1716 (in CO only)

Connecticut
860-566-2211

Delaware
302-856-5011; 800-464-4357 (in DE only)

Florida
850-488-1234

Georgia
404-656-2000

Hawaii
808-586-0222; 800-468-4644 (in outer islands only)

Idaho
208-334-2411

Illinois
217-782-2000

Indiana
317-233-0800; 800-457-8283 (in IN only)

Iowa
515-281-5011

Kansas
785-296-0111

Kentucky
502-564-3130

Louisiana
225-342-6600

Maine
207-624-9494

Maryland
410-974-3901

Massachusetts
617-727-7030; 800-392-6090 (in MA only)

Michigan
517-373-1837

Minnesota
651-296-6013

Mississippi
601-359-1000

Missouri
573-751-2000

Montana
406-444-2511

Nebraska
402-471-2311

Nevada
775-687-5000

New Hampshire
603-271-1110

New Jersey
609-292-2121

New Mexico
800-825-6639

New York
518-474-2121

North Carolina
919-733-1110

Is the Deck Shuffled in Your Favor? How to get credit...types of credit available... terminology.
Source: Call for Action Network Office, 5272 River Rd., Ste. 300, Bethesda, MD 20816. 800-647-1756. Online at www.callforaction.org.

The Story of Inflation.
Comic-book style booklet to explain inflation. Free.

Source: Federal Reserve Bank of New York, Public Information Dept., 33 Liberty St., New York, NY 10045...or at www.ny.frb.org

North Dakota
701-328-2000

Ohio
614-466-2000

Oklahoma
405-521-2011

 Oregon
503-378-6500

Pennsylvania
717-787-2121

Rhode Island
401-222-2000

South Carolina
803-896-0000

South Dakota
605-773-3011

Tennessee
615-741-3011

 Texas
512-463-4630

Utah
801-538-3000

Vermont
802-828-1110

Virginia
804-786-0000

Washington
360-753-5000; 800-321-2808 (in WA only)

West Virginia
304-558-3456

Wisconsin
608-266-2211

Wyoming
307-777-7011

US Government Hotlines

US Government Hotlines

Administration on Aging
202-401-4541

Federal Information Center
800-688-9889

Food and Drug Administration
888-INFO-FDA (463-6332)

**Health Care Fraud Hotline
(Inspector General)**
800-447-8477

**IRS—US Department of the Treasury
Information Line**
800-829-1040

IRS Forms Distribution Center
800-829-3676

IRS Tele-Tax Information Line
800-829-4477

Legal Services Corporation
202-336-8800

Medicare Hotline
800-MEDICARE

TTY/TDD
800-820-1202

Social Security Administration Hotline
800-772-1213

TTY/TDD
800-325-0778

**US Department of Housing
& Urban Development
Public Affairs Office**
202-708-0685

US Department of Veterans Affairs
800-827-1000

**IRS Tele-Tax
Information.**
Recorded answers to
your employer tax
questions using an
automated response unit.
Source: IRS employer tax
information, 800-829-4477,
press # 750.

Nationwide Helplines

Nationwide Helplines

Alliance for Aging Research
202-293-2856

Alliance for Retired Americans
202-974-8222

Alzheimer's Association
800-272-3900

Alzheimer's Disease Education and Referral Center
800-438-4380

American Association of Homes & Services for the Aging
202-783-2242
For publications
800-508-9442

American Association of Retired Persons (AARP)
800-424-3410

American Cancer Society Response Hotline
800-227-2345

American Council of the Blind
800-424-8666

American Diabetes Association
800-342-2383; 800-232-3472

American Dietetic Association
800-366-1655

American Heart Association
800-242-8721

American Institute for Cancer Research
800-843-8114

American Lung Association
800-586-4872

Arthritis Foundation Information Line
800-283-7800

Asthma & Allergy Foundation
800-7-ASTHMA

Cancer Care
212-712-8080

Cancer Information Service
800-4-CANCER

Domestic Violence Hotline
800-799-SAFE (7233)

Eldercare Locator
800-677-1116

Epilepsy Foundation
800-332-1000

Equal Employment Opportunity Commission
800-669-4000

Gray Panthers
800-280-5362

Hill-Burton Hotline
(for help with hospital costs)
800-492-0359

Leukemia and Lymphoma Society
800-955-4572

Lighthouse International Center for Vision and Aging
800-334-5497

Medicare Hotline
800-MEDICARE

National Alliance of Breast Cancer Organizations
888-806-2226

National Alliance for the Mentally Ill
800-950-6264

National Association for Incontinence
800-252-3337

National Breast Cancer Coalition
202-296-7477

National Cancer Institute
800-422-6237

National Center on Elder Abuse
202-898-2586

National Citizens' Coalition for Nursing Home Reform
202-332-2275

National Clearinghouse for Alcohol & Drug Information
800-729-6686

What You Need to Know About Melanoma. Signs and symptoms…early diagnosis…treatment… prevention…how to perform a skin self-exam…resources.
Source: National Cancer Institute, 800-422-6237. www.nci.nih.gov

Exercise and Your Arthritis. Helpful exercises and techniques.
Source: Arthritis Foundation, 800-283-7800. www.arthritis.org

National Committee to Preserve Social Security & Medicare
800-966-1935

National Diabetes Information Clearinghouse
301-654-3327

National Digestive Diseases Information Clearinghouse
301-654-3810

National Eye Care Project Helpline
800-222-3937

National Eye Institute
301-496-5248

National Health Information Center
800-336-4797

National Heart, Lung & Blood Institute
800-575-WELL

National Hospice and Palliative Care Organization
800-658-8898

National Institute on Aging
800-222-2225

National Institute on Deafness & Other Communication Disorders Information Clearinghouse
800-241-1044

National Institutes of Health Clinical Center
800-411-1222

National Institute of Mental Health
800-421-4211

National Institute of Neurological Disorders & Stroke
800-352-9424

National Institutes of Health Clinical Center
800-411-1222

National Insurance Consumer Helpline
800-942-4242

National Kidney & Urologic Diseases Information Clearinghouse
301-654-4415

National Mental Health Association
800-969-6642

National Osteoporosis Foundation
800-223-9994

National STD and AIDS Hotlines
800-342-2437

National Senior Citizens Education & Research Center
301-578-8900

National Women's Health Network Information Clearinghouse
202-628-7814

Parkinson's Foundation
800-457-6676

Skin Cancer Foundation
800-SKIN-490

Stuttering Foundation of America
800-992-9392

Y-ME National Breast Cancer Organization
800-221-2141